Methods of Applied Mathematics

N. M. Queen

Department of Mathematical Physics,
University of Birmingham

Nelson

203265

To Mollie

THOMAS NELSON & SONS LIMITED
Nelson House Mayfield Road
Walton-on-Thames Surrey KT12 5PL

P O Box 18123 Nairobi Kenya

Watson Estate Block A 13 Floor
Watson Road Causeway Bay Hong Kong

116-D JTC Factory Building
Lorong 3 Geylang Square Singapore 14

THOMAS NELSON AUSTRALIA PTY LIMITED
19 – 39 Jeffcott Street West Melbourne Victoria 3003

NELSON CANADA LIMITED
81 Curlew Drive Don Mills Ontario M3A 2R1

THOMAS NELSON (NIGERIA) LIMITED
8 Ilupeju Bypass PMB 21303 Ikeja Lagos

ISBN 0 17 771121 3 (limp)
     0 17 761099 9 (cased)
NCN 5866 41 0 (limp)
     5890 41 0 (cased)

© N M QUEEN 1980

First published 1980

Printed and bound in Hong Kong

Preface

This book grew out of lecture notes for several courses in applied mathematics which I have given at the University of Birmingham during the past 15 years. Although a number of excellent textbooks on applied mathematics and mathematical methods are available, none seemed to be completely appropriate for some of the courses that I have taught in recent years.

The intention here is to provide a concise but self-contained account of those methods of applied mathematics which students of mathematics and the physical sciences at the intermediate undergraduate level are likely to require for their more advanced studies. The emphasis is on applicable methods, rather than on abstract mathematics for its own sake or on specific physical applications. On the other hand, it is hoped that this book will help to bridge the gap between the traditional 'pure' and 'applied' mathematics courses by demonstrating that many of the fundamental concepts of both analysis and linear algebra actually play a vital role in applied mathematics. Special attention is paid to the interrelationships between different methods, none of which are considered in isolation.

It is my conviction that it is just as important to understand the precise conditions under which a particular method is applicable as it is to be familiar with the mechanics of its application in concrete situations. For this reason, the approach is generally honest and rigorous, although certain technical details are relegated to the chapter appendices and several general statements are made without proof in cases when a complete analysis would carry the discussion too far afield.

Much of the content of a textbook such as this must inevitably be fairly traditional. Nevertheless, there is scope for individuality, and to a certain extent the precise choice of topics must reflect the author's taste and personal prejudices.

While variations of some of the major themes recur in different contexts, for the most part the individual chapters are organized so that they can be read independently of one another. Several basic concepts from linear algebra are used throughout the book, and the necessary background material is presented in Chapter 1. Chapters 2 and 3 (on extremal problems) are independent of one another, and either or both can be omitted if desired without loss of continuity. The order in which Chapters 4 to 8 are read is of minor importance, but Chapter 9 (on special functions) contains many references to earlier results.

It is assumed that the reader is already familiar with some of the fundamental concepts and results of real analysis, which are freely quoted when required. In my experience, however, many students unfortunately acquire a working knowledge of complex analysis too late to be able to make effective use of it in a course in applied mathematics at this level. Although there are several instances in this book when a deeper insight will be gained by the reader who has a knowledge of the theory of analytic functions of a complex variable, the material is presented in such a way that this background knowledge is not a strict prerequisite.

To successfully master the subject, it is essential for the student to attempt a reasonable number of problems. A varied collection of exercises is included at the end of each chapter, and answers to the problems, when not already incorporated in the statement of the problem, are provided at the end of the book.

A short bibliography of further reading which the student is likely to find rewarding is also given at the end of the book.

Since the material for this book has been gathered over a period of many years, it would be impossible to adequately acknowledge all the original sources. I am indebted to my many colleagues and students, past and present, from whom I have gained invaluable insights and acquired many illuminating examples. Special thanks are due to my wife Mollie, without whose constant support and encouragement the task of preparing the manuscript would have been immeasurably more difficult.

N.M. Queen

Contents

1 Linear algebra

1.1 Linear vector spaces

The mathematical structure known as a *linear vector space* (or simply *vector space*) is an abstraction and natural generalization of the elementary algebra of ordinary geometrical vectors in three dimensions. This algebra is based on two fundamental operations: the addition of two vectors, and the multiplication of a vector by a scalar (i.e., a number). Taken together, these operations lead to the idea of a *linear combination* of vectors, i.e. a finite sum of scalar multiples of certain vectors.

Loosely speaking, a linear vector space is any mathematical structure in which linear combinations of the elements (vectors) in question can be defined and obey all the familiar rules of elementary vector algebra. The concept of a vector space proves to be one of the most fruitful and versatile abstract algebraic structures.

Following the notation of ordinary vector algebra, we shall denote the elements (vectors) of an abstract vector space by bold-face symbols such as x, y, z.

Scalars will be denoted by symbols such as α, β, γ or x, y, z. Although the scalars may in general be elements of any abstract field, for the purposes of this book the reader who is unfamiliar with the concept of a field in abstract algebra may regard them as being the ordinary real, or sometimes complex, numbers. All that matters for the purpose of defining an abstract vector space is that the scalars obey the usual rules of arithmetic.

Formally, a linear vector space V can be defined as a mathematical structure consisting of a set of *vectors*, a set of *scalars* (assumed to form a field), and the two operations of *vector addition* and *scalar multiplication* satisfying the following axioms:

(i) If x and y are vectors in V, there is a unique vector sum $x + y$, which is also a vector in V.

(ii) If x, y and z are vectors in V, then $x + y = y + x$ (the commutative law) and $(x + y) + z = x + (y + z)$ (the associative law).

(iii) If α is a scalar and x is a vector in V, there is a unique product αx, which is a vector in V.

(iv)   The operation of scalar multiplication satisfies the associative law $\alpha(\beta x) = (\alpha\beta)x$ and the two distributive laws $\alpha(x + y) = \alpha x + \alpha y$ and $(\alpha + \beta)x = \alpha x + \beta x$.

(v)   There is a unique *zero vector*, denoted by **0**, having the property $x + 0 = x$ for any **x** in V.

(vi)   For each **x** in V, there exists a corresponding element of V, denoted by $-x$, such that $x + (-x) = 0$.

(vii)   If 1 denotes the multiplicative unit scalar, i.e. the scalar having the property $1 \cdot \alpha = \alpha$ for any scalar α, then $1 \cdot x = x$ for any vector **x** in V.

A vector space is said to be *real* or *complex* when the field of scalars is the field of real or complex numbers, respectively. These are the only cases which will be considered in this book.

At this point, it is appropriate to list several simple examples of linear vector spaces. The reader may readily verify that these algebraic structures actually satisfy all the axioms for a vector space.

Example 1   The vectors are ordered triplets of real numbers, (x_1, x_2, x_3). Addition of two vectors and multiplication of a vector by a scalar (assumed to be a real number) are defined by the rules

$$(x_1, x_2, x_3) + (y_1, y_2, y_3) = (x_1 + y_1, x_2 + y_2, x_3 + y_3),$$

$$\alpha(x_1, x_2, x_3) = (\alpha x_1, \alpha x_2, \alpha x_3).$$

This vector space is equivalent to that of the geometrical vectors in ordinary 3-dimensional space. Analogous vector spaces can of course be defined more generally in n dimensions by considering instead the set of ordered n-tuples of real numbers.

Example 2   The vectors are ordinary complex numbers, the scalars are ordinary real numbers, and the two operations are ordinary arithmetic addition and multiplication.

Example 3   The vectors are continuous real-valued functions $f(x)$ of a real variable x, and the scalars are real numbers. The vector sum of $f(x)$ and $g(x)$ is defined to be the function $f(x) + g(x)$, and the product of a scalar α and a vector $f(x)$ is defined to be the function $\alpha f(x)$. Linear vector spaces in which the vectors are functions belonging to a specified class are sometimes called *function spaces*.

Example 4   The vectors are polynomials $P(z)$ of arbitrary degree in a complex variable z, with complex-valued coefficients, and the scalars are complex numbers. Vector addition and scalar multiplication are defined as in Example 3.

We now consider some general properties of vectors and vector spaces. As we have already mentioned, a linear combination of n vectors $\{x_1, \ldots, x_n\}$ is a sum of the form

$$x = \sum_{i=1}^{n} \alpha_i \, x_i \, . \tag{1}$$

The axioms for a vector space ensure that the order of the terms in such a sum is immaterial.

We say that a set of vectors $\{x_1, \ldots, x_n\}$ is *linearly dependent* if there exists a set of scalars $\{\alpha_1, \ldots, \alpha_n\}$, not all zero, such that the linear combination (1) is equal to zero; otherwise, the vectors $\{x_1, \ldots, x_n\}$ are said to be *linearly independent*. In other words, the vectors $\{x_1, \ldots, x_n\}$ are linearly independent if the expression (1) vanishes only when all the scalars $\{\alpha_1, \ldots, \alpha_n\}$ are equal to zero.

If the vectors $\{x_1, \ldots, x_n\}$ are linearly dependent, then at least one of them is expressible as a linear combination of the others. For suppose that the combination (1) is equal to zero and that k is a value of the index such that $\alpha_k \neq 0$. Then x_k is expressible in the form

$$x_k = \sum_{i \neq k} \left(-\frac{\alpha_i}{\alpha_k} \right) x_i \, .$$

Conversely, if there exists a relation of the form

$$x_k = \sum_{i \neq k} \beta_i \, x_i$$

for some k, then the expression (1) vanishes for some set of scalars α_i which are not all zero (in particular, $\alpha_k \neq 0$).

If, for some finite set of linearly independent vectors $\{x_1, \ldots, x_n\}$, it is true that every vector x of the vector space V in question can be expressed as a linear combination of the form (1), we say that the vectors $\{x_1, \ldots, x_n\}$ form a *basis* for V and that V is *finite-dimensional*. We shall assume throughout the remainder of this chapter that all the vector spaces under consideration are finite-dimensional.

Vector spaces for which no finite basis exists are said to be *infinite-dimensional*. In such cases, it is necessary to consider the possibility of infinite series instead of finite sums of the form (1), so that questions of convergence arise.

The representation (1) of any vector $\mathbf{x}$ in terms of a given basis set $\{\mathbf{x}_1, \ldots, \mathbf{x}_n\}$ is necessarily *unique*. For if there existed a distinct representation

$$\mathbf{x} = \sum_{i=1}^{n} \beta_i \mathbf{x}_i$$

in addition to (1), we would have

$$0 = \sum_{i=1}^{n} (\alpha_i - \beta_i) \mathbf{x}_i,$$

where the coefficients $(\alpha_i - \beta_i)$ are not all zero, and this would contradict the hypothesis that the basis vectors $\mathbf{x}_i$ are linearly independent.

THEOREM   If a vector space V has a basis consisting of n vectors, then any set of $n + 1$ vectors in V is linearly dependent.

PROOF   Let $X \equiv \{\mathbf{x}_1, \ldots, \mathbf{x}_n\}$ be a basis for V, and suppose that $\{\mathbf{y}_1, \ldots, \mathbf{y}_{n+1}\}$ are linearly independent vectors in V. We shall show that this assumption leads to a contradiction. We do this by showing that the vectors of the set X can be replaced one by one by vectors of the set $Y \equiv \{\mathbf{y}_1, \ldots, \mathbf{y}_n\}$ in such a way that a new basis for V is obtained at each stage; the conclusion that Y is a basis implies that $\mathbf{y}_{n+1}$ can be expressed as a linear combination of the vectors $\{\mathbf{y}_1, \ldots, \mathbf{y}_n\}$, so that the combined set cannot be linearly independent.

To carry out the proof, suppose that the first m vectors of the set X have already been replaced by the first m vectors of the set Y, giving a basis set

$$B_m \equiv \{\mathbf{y}_1, \ldots, \mathbf{y}_m, \mathbf{x}_{m+1}, \ldots, \mathbf{x}_n\}.$$

(The trivial case $m = 0$ corresponds to the basis X which is initially given.) Then $\mathbf{y}_{m+1}$ is certainly expressible as some linear combination of the vectors in B_m. We can exclude the case in which $\mathbf{y}_{m+1}$ is expressible as a linear combination of the set $\{\mathbf{y}_1, \ldots, \mathbf{y}_m\}$ alone, since the theorem would then be proved. Suppose therefore that $\mathbf{y}_{m+1}$ is equal to a linear combination of all the vectors of B_m in which at least one of the vectors in the set $\{\mathbf{x}_{m+1}, \ldots, \mathbf{x}_n\}$ has a non-zero coefficient. Without loss of generality (e.g., by relabelling the vectors $\mathbf{x}_i$), we can assume that $\mathbf{x}_{m+1}$ is such a vector. This means that $\mathbf{x}_{m+1}$ can be expressed as a linear combination of $\mathbf{y}_{m+1}$ and the remaining vectors in the set B_m. Thus any linear combination of the vectors in B_m can also be expressed as a linear combination of the vectors in the set

$$B_{m+1} \equiv \{y_1, \ldots, y_m, y_{m+1}, x_{m+2}, \ldots, x_n\}.$$

In other words, B_{m+1} is a basis for the vector space V. Proceeding by induction, we can therefore assert that $B_n = \{y_1, \ldots, y_n\}$ is a basis. Consequently, y_{n+1} can be expressed as a linear combination of the remaining y_i, and the theorem is proved.

An immediate consequence of this theorem is that if a vector space V has a basis consisting of n vectors, then every other basis for V also has precisely n vectors. For if a basis B_2 contained more vectors than a basis B_1, there would exist a linear relation among the vectors of B_2, and this would contradict the hypothesis that B_2 is a basis.

Thus the number of elements in a basis of a finite-dimensional vector space is the same for every basis. This characteristic number is called the *dimension* of the vector space.

The vector space defined in Example 1 of this section is 3-dimensional, since it is clear that the three vectors $(1, 0, 0)$, $(0, 1, 0)$ and $(0, 0, 1)$ form a basis. The vector space in Example 2 is 2-dimensional, since the vectors 1 and i form a basis. Examples 3 and 4 define infinite-dimensional vector spaces.

1.2 Linear transformations and matrices

Suppose that we have a vector-valued function $x' = T(x)$ which associates a unique vector x' in a given vector space V with every vector x in V. If this function has the property

$$T(\alpha x + \beta y) = \alpha T(x) + \beta T(y) \qquad (1)$$

for any vectors x and y in V and any scalars α and β, then T is said to be a linear transformation. It should be remarked that linear transformations can be defined in the more general situation when the original vector x and the transformed vector x' belong to different vector spaces (possibly having different dimensions), but we shall not consider this case here.

From a mathematical point of view, linear transformations are important because they preserve linear relationships between sets of vectors. By this, we mean the following. Suppose, for example, that three vectors x, y and z satisfy some linear relationship

$$\alpha x + \beta y + \gamma z = 0, \qquad (2)$$

where α, β and γ are given scalars. If we apply a linear transformation T to the vectors $\mathbf{x}$, $\mathbf{y}$ and $\mathbf{z}$, we obtain three new vectors $\mathbf{x}'$, $\mathbf{y}'$ and $\mathbf{z}'$, where $\mathbf{x}' = T(\mathbf{x})$, etc. Then these new vectors satisfy the relation

$$\alpha \mathbf{x}' + \beta \mathbf{y}' + \gamma \mathbf{z}' = \mathbf{0} \tag{3}$$

(with the same coefficients α, β and γ as in (2)). This can be seen by simply applying the transformation T to both sides of (2), using the property (1) (and in particular the fact that $T(\mathbf{0}) = \mathbf{0}$, which follows from (1) with $\alpha = \beta = 0$).

We shall see that linear transformations can be represented by means of matrices. (We are assuming that the elementary algebra of matrices is already known, and no formal definitions will be given here.) For this purpose, we require the notion of the 'components' of a vector with respect to a given basis.

Suppose that a given set of vectors $\{\mathbf{u}_1, \ldots, \mathbf{u}_n\}$ forms a basis for V. Then any vector $\mathbf{x}$ in V has a unique representation of the form

$$\mathbf{x} = \sum_{i=1}^{n} x_i \mathbf{u}_i \tag{4}$$

and we say that the coefficients $x_1, \ldots, x_n$ are the *components* of $\mathbf{x}$ with respect to this basis. This is a generalization of the familiar concept of the components of ordinary geometrical vectors.

We now ask how the components of a vector with respect to a fixed basis transform under a linear transformation T. In other words, how are the components of $\mathbf{x}' = T(\mathbf{x})$ related in general to those of $\mathbf{x}$? Applying the transformation T to (4), we have

$$\mathbf{x}' = \sum_{i=1}^{n} x_i \, T(\mathbf{u}_i) . \tag{5}$$

Now, since the vectors $\mathbf{u}_i$ form a basis, the vectors $T(\mathbf{u}_i)$ in (5) must be expressible in the form

$$T(\mathbf{u}_i) = \sum_{j=1}^{n} T_{ji} \, \mathbf{u}_j ,$$

where T_{ji} are certain coefficients, so that

$$\mathbf{x}' = \sum_{i=1}^{n} \sum_{j=1}^{n} x_i \, T_{ji} \, \mathbf{u}_j = \sum_{j=1}^{n} \left(\sum_{i=1}^{n} T_{ji} \, x_i \right) \mathbf{u}_j .$$

In other words, the components x'_j of the transformed vector $\mathbf{x}' = T(\mathbf{x})$ can be expressed in terms of the components x_i of the original vector $\mathbf{x}$ in the form

$$x'_j = \sum_{i=1}^{n} T_{ji}\, x_i . \qquad (6)$$

If we introduce the column matrices

$$\mathbf{x} = \begin{pmatrix} x_1 \\ x_2 \\ \vdots \\ x_n \end{pmatrix}, \qquad \mathbf{x}' = \begin{pmatrix} x'_1 \\ x'_2 \\ \vdots \\ x'_n \end{pmatrix} \qquad (7)$$

and the $n \times n$ square matrix

$$T = \begin{pmatrix} T_{11} & \cdots & T_{1n} \\ \vdots & & \vdots \\ T_{n1} & \cdots & T_{nn} \end{pmatrix}, \qquad (8)$$

equation (6) can be written in the compact matrix notation

$$\mathbf{x}' = T\mathbf{x} , \qquad (9)$$

where the product is interpreted as a matrix product. Strictly speaking, we should employ different symbols for the abstract vectors $\mathbf{x}$ and $\mathbf{x}'$ and their (basis-dependent) matrix representations given in (7), and likewise different symbols for the linear transformation T and its (basis-dependent) matrix representation given in (8). However, our notation is particularly convenient and is not likely to lead to any ambiguity in practice; in fact, column matrices such as (7) are often called 'vectors' or 'column vectors'.

Thus we have shown that every linear transformation in an n-dimensional vector space can be represented by an $n \times n$ matrix (8) such that the components of a given vector $\mathbf{x}$ transform according to the law (9) under this linear transformation. Conversely, it is easy to see that every matrix equation of the form (9) represents a linear transformation in the vector space.

A closely related problem is to discover how the components of a given fixed vector transform when the basis is changed. As before, suppose that a vector $\mathbf{x}$ has components x_i with respect to a given basis $\{\mathbf{u}_1, \ldots, \mathbf{u}_n\}$, as expressed in (4). Let $\{\mathbf{v}_1, \ldots, \mathbf{v}_n\}$ be a second basis. What are the components $\bar{x}_j$ of the vector $\mathbf{x}$ with respect to this new basis?

Our first step in solving this problem is to specify the relation between the new basis vectors and the original ones. Since any vector can be expanded in terms of a given set of basis vectors, there must certainly exist linear relations of the form

$$\mathbf{v}_i = \sum_{j=1}^{n} M_{ij} \, \mathbf{u}_j \tag{10}$$

for some coefficients M_{ij}. Now (10) can be interpreted as a matrix equation

$$V = MU , \tag{11}$$

where V and U are the column matrices

$$V = \begin{pmatrix} \mathbf{v}_1 \\ \vdots \\ \mathbf{v}_n \end{pmatrix}, \qquad U = \begin{pmatrix} \mathbf{u}_1 \\ \vdots \\ \mathbf{u}_n \end{pmatrix}$$

and M is the $n \times n$ matrix whose elements are M_{ij}.

Conversely, each of the vectors $\mathbf{u}_j$ can be expanded in terms of the basis vectors $\mathbf{v}_i$, so that we are led to a matrix equation of the form

$$U = NV \tag{12}$$

for some matrix N. Substituting (12) into (11), we obtain $V = MNV$. But since $V = IV$, where I is the unit matrix, and since each of the vectors $\mathbf{v}_i$ must have a *unique* representation in terms of the full basis set $\{\mathbf{v}_1, \dots , \mathbf{v}_n\}$, we can make the identification $MN = I$. Consequently, (12) can be written

$$U = M^{-1} V . \tag{13}$$

It might be thought that we could immediately write down (13) as a trivial consequence of (11). This is not so, since (13) follows from (11) only if we know (as we have established by the preceding discussion) that the matrix M actually possesses an inverse M^{-1}.

Equation (13) enables us to express the original basis vectors $\mathbf{u}_i$ in terms of the new basis vectors $\mathbf{v}_j$, since it tells us that

$$\mathbf{u}_i = \sum_{j=1}^{n} (M^{-1})_{ij} \, \mathbf{v}_j . \tag{14}$$

Suppose now that a given vector $\mathbf{x}$ has components x_i with respect to the basis $\{\mathbf{u}_1, \dots , \mathbf{u}_n\}$ and that we wish to find its components with respect to the new basis $\{\mathbf{v}_1, \dots , \mathbf{v}_n\}$. Substituting (14) into (4), we obtain

$$\mathbf{x} = \sum_{j=1}^{n} \left[\sum_{i=1}^{n} (M^{-1})_{ij} x_i \right] \mathbf{v}_j .$$

Thus the components of $\mathbf{x}$ with respect to the new basis are given by

$$\bar{x}_j = \sum_{i=1}^{n} \left[(M^{-1})^{\mathrm{T}} \right]_{ji} x_i , \tag{15}$$

where we have introduced the notation A^{T} for the transpose of a matrix A, i.e. the matrix obtained from A by interchanging its rows and columns. In matrix notation, (15) can be written

$$\bar{\mathbf{x}} = (M^{-1})^{\mathrm{T}} \mathbf{x} . \tag{16}$$

Note that the column matrices $\mathbf{x}$ and $\bar{\mathbf{x}}$ represent the *same* vector in terms of two different bases.

Example 1 Let

$$\mathbf{u}_1 = \begin{pmatrix} 1 \\ 0 \end{pmatrix}, \qquad \mathbf{u}_2 = \begin{pmatrix} 0 \\ 1 \end{pmatrix}, \qquad \mathbf{x} = \begin{pmatrix} 2 \\ 3 \end{pmatrix} .$$

Then if $\mathbf{u}_1$ and $\mathbf{u}_2$ are taken as basis vectors in a two-dimensional vector space, the vector $\mathbf{x}$ has the components $x_1 = 2$ and $x_2 = 3$ with respect to this basis. Employing the same notation as in the preceding discussion, let us define a new basis $\{\mathbf{v}_1, \mathbf{v}_2\}$ by the equation $V = MU$ (cf. (11)), where

$$M = \begin{pmatrix} 0 & 1 \\ 2 & 1 \end{pmatrix} .$$

Thus (10) gives

$$\mathbf{v}_1 = \begin{pmatrix} 0 \\ 1 \end{pmatrix}, \qquad \mathbf{v}_2 = \begin{pmatrix} 2 \\ 1 \end{pmatrix} .$$

It is easy to verify that the inverse of the matrix M is

$$M^{-1} = \begin{pmatrix} -\frac{1}{2} & \frac{1}{2} \\ 1 & 0 \end{pmatrix} .$$

According to (16), the components of the vector $\mathbf{x}$ with respect to the basis $\{\mathbf{v}_1, \mathbf{v}_2\}$ are therefore given by

$$\begin{pmatrix} \bar{x}_1 \\ \bar{x}_2 \end{pmatrix} = \begin{pmatrix} -\frac{1}{2} & 1 \\ \frac{1}{2} & 0 \end{pmatrix} \begin{pmatrix} 2 \\ 3 \end{pmatrix} = \begin{pmatrix} 2 \\ 1 \end{pmatrix} .$$

In other words, $\mathbf{x}$ has the expansion $\mathbf{x} = 2\mathbf{v}_1 + \mathbf{v}_2$.

Since the components of all vectors transform in a definite manner when we change from one basis to another, a change of basis must also entail a change in the matrix describing any particular linear transformation. Our final problem is to deduce the law according to which such matrices transform when we change from a basis $\{u_1, \ldots, u_n\}$ to a basis $\{v_1, \ldots, v_n\}$, the basis vectors being related by (10) as before.

Consider a linear transformation $y = A(x)$ described by a matrix A with respect to the original basis:

$$y = Ax . \tag{17}$$

What matrix $\bar{A}$ describes the same transformation with respect to the new basis? We already know how the components of the vectors transform when the basis is changed according to (10):

$$\bar{y} = (M^{-1})^T y, \quad \bar{x} = (M^{-1})^T x$$

or, equivalently,

$$y = M^T \bar{y}, \quad x = M^T \bar{x} .$$

Substituting these relations into (17) and then multiplying by $(M^{-1})^T$ to the left, we find

$$\bar{y} = (M^{-1})^T A M^T \bar{x} .$$

Consequently, with respect to the new basis the linear transformation is represented by the matrix

$$\bar{A} = (M^{-1})^T A M^T . \tag{18}$$

Example 2   Let the basis vectors $\{u_1, u_2\}$ and $\{v_1, v_2\}$ and the matrix M be the same as in Example 1, and consider the transformation defined by the matrix

$$A = \begin{pmatrix} 0 & 1 \\ 1 & 0 \end{pmatrix}$$

with respect to the basis $\{u_1, u_2\}$. If x is the same vector as in Example 1, we find that

$$y \equiv A x = \begin{pmatrix} 3 \\ 2 \end{pmatrix} .$$

We found in Example 1 that in terms of the basis $\{v_1, v_2\}$ the vector x becomes

$$\bar{x} = \begin{pmatrix} 2 \\ 1 \end{pmatrix} ,$$

and an analogous calculation shows that in the new basis the vector **y** becomes

$$\overline{\mathbf{y}} = (M^{-1})^T \, \mathbf{y} = \begin{pmatrix} -\frac{1}{2} & 1 \\ \frac{1}{2} & 0 \end{pmatrix}\begin{pmatrix} 3 \\ 2 \end{pmatrix} = \begin{pmatrix} \frac{1}{2} \\ \frac{3}{2} \end{pmatrix}.$$

Let us find the form of the matrix $\overline{A}$ which describes the same linear transformation A with respect to the new basis (and which should have the property $\overline{\mathbf{y}} = \overline{A}\overline{\mathbf{x}}$). According to (18),

$$\overline{A} = \begin{pmatrix} -\frac{1}{2} & 1 \\ \frac{1}{2} & 0 \end{pmatrix}\begin{pmatrix} 0 & 1 \\ 1 & 0 \end{pmatrix}\begin{pmatrix} 0 & 2 \\ 1 & 1 \end{pmatrix} = \begin{pmatrix} -\frac{1}{2} & \frac{3}{2} \\ \frac{1}{2} & \frac{1}{2} \end{pmatrix}.$$

As a check, it is easy to verify that $\overline{\mathbf{y}} = \overline{A}\overline{\mathbf{x}}$, as expected.

1.3 Scalar products

The familiar scalar product of two vectors in ordinary 3-dimensional space is an extremely useful operation and has an obvious geometric interpretation. This operation has a natural generalization to an abstract vector space, which also proves to be very useful.

A *scalar product* (*inner product*) of two vectors **x** and **y** in a vector space is defined as any complex-valued operation, denoted by $\langle \mathbf{x}|\mathbf{y}\rangle$, which has the following properties:

$$\langle \mathbf{x}|\mathbf{y}\rangle = \langle \mathbf{y}|\mathbf{x}\rangle^*,$$

$$\langle \mathbf{x}|\, \alpha\mathbf{y} + \beta\mathbf{z}\rangle = \alpha\langle \mathbf{x}|\mathbf{y}\rangle + \beta\langle \mathbf{x}|\mathbf{z}\rangle,$$

$$\langle \mathbf{x}|\mathbf{x}\rangle > 0 \text{ if } \mathbf{x} \neq \mathbf{0}.$$

(1)

Different scalar products can of course be defined in the same vector space. The one which is chosen in any particular situation depends on the application in question.

Note that the property

$$\langle \alpha\mathbf{y} + \beta\mathbf{z}|\mathbf{x}\rangle = \alpha^*\langle \mathbf{y}|\mathbf{x}\rangle + \beta^*\langle \mathbf{z}|\mathbf{x}\rangle$$

(2)

(with complex conjugates of α and β on the right-hand side) is a consequence of the first two defining properties of a scalar product in (1).

Example 1 The class of complex-valued functions $F(x)$ which are continuous on the real interval $a \leqslant x \leqslant b$ form a complex vector space under the familiar operations of addition of two functions and multiplication of a function by a complex number. It is readily verified that if

F and G are two such functions, then the operation

$$\langle F|G \rangle \equiv \int_a^b F^*(x)\, G(x)\, dx$$

is a scalar product.

Two vectors $\mathbf{x}$ and $\mathbf{y}$ are said to be *orthogonal* (with respect to a given scalar product) if their scalar product vanishes: $\langle \mathbf{x}|\mathbf{y} \rangle = 0$. Use is often made of a basis all of whose elements are mutually orthogonal. Any set of vectors having this property is said to be an orthogonal set. If, in addition, each vector $\mathbf{u}$ in the set satisfies $\langle \mathbf{u}|\mathbf{u} \rangle = 1$ (in which case we say that it is *normalized*), then the set is said to be *orthonormal*.

The condition of orthonormality for a set of vectors $\{\mathbf{x}_1, \ldots, \mathbf{x}_m\}$ can be written in the concise form

$$\langle \mathbf{x}_i|\mathbf{x}_j \rangle = \delta_{ij}, \tag{3}$$

where δ_{ij}, the so-called Kronecker delta symbol, is defined by

$$\delta_{ij} = \begin{cases} 1, & i = j, \\ 0, & i \neq j. \end{cases}$$

It should be pointed out that if a set of non-zero vectors $\{\mathbf{x}_1, \ldots, \mathbf{x}_m\}$ is orthogonal, then these vectors are certainly linearly independent. For suppose that the vectors were linearly dependent, so that

$$\sum_{i=1}^m \alpha_i\, \mathbf{x}_i = 0 \tag{4}$$

for some set of scalars α_i, not all zero. Let k be a value of the index for which $\alpha_k \neq 0$. Then taking the scalar product of $\mathbf{x}_k$ with (4), we obtain $\alpha_k \langle \mathbf{x}_k|\mathbf{x}_k \rangle = 0$ by virtue of the orthogonality condition. Since $\alpha_k \neq 0$, we have $\langle \mathbf{x}_k|\mathbf{x}_k \rangle = 0$ and hence $\mathbf{x}_k = 0$, which is a contradiction. Therefore the vectors $\{\mathbf{x}_1, \ldots, \mathbf{x}_m\}$ must be linearly independent.

Let us now see how the scalar product of two vectors $\mathbf{x}$ and $\mathbf{y}$ in an n-dimensional vector space can be expressed in terms of their components with respect to a given basis. Let $\{\mathbf{u}_1, \ldots, \mathbf{u}_n\}$ be the basis and suppose that

$$\mathbf{x} = \sum_{i=1}^n x_i\, \mathbf{u}_i, \qquad \mathbf{y} = \sum_{i=1}^n y_i\, \mathbf{u}_i.$$

Then using the properties (1) and (2) of the scalar product, we find

$$\langle x|y \rangle = \left\langle \sum_{i=1}^{n} x_i\, \mathbf{u}_i \,\middle|\, \sum_{j=1}^{n} y_j\, \mathbf{u}_j \right\rangle$$

$$= \sum_{j=1}^{n} y_j \left\langle \sum_{i=1}^{n} x_i\, \mathbf{u}_i \,\middle|\, \mathbf{u}_j \right\rangle$$

$$= \sum_{j=1}^{n} \sum_{i=1}^{n} x_i^{*}\, y_j\, \langle \mathbf{u}_i|\mathbf{u}_j \rangle .$$

In the special case in which the basis is orthonormal, so that $\langle \mathbf{u}_i|\mathbf{u}_j \rangle = \delta_{ij}$, a major simplification can be made:

$$\langle x|y \rangle = \sum_{i=1}^{n} x_i^{*}\, y_i . \tag{5}$$

Equation (5) is a generalization of the familiar expression for the scalar product of ordinary geometrical vectors in terms of their Cartesian components.

It is obviously advantageous to work with orthonormal bases. Suppose that, for a given vector space, we know a basis which is not orthogonal. Can we construct an orthonormal basis? As we shall now see, it turns out that this can always be achieved by means of a simple algorithmic procedure.

Suppose that $\{\mathbf{u}_1, \ldots, \mathbf{u}_m\}$ is any linearly independent set of m vectors (not necessarily a basis). We shall show how to construct an orthonormal set $\{\mathbf{v}_1, \ldots, \mathbf{v}_m\}$, each of whose elements $\mathbf{v}_j$ is some linear combination of the first j elements of the original set:

$$\mathbf{v}_j = \sum_{i=1}^{j} a_{ji}\, \mathbf{u}_i . \tag{6}$$

We begin by normalizing the first vector $\mathbf{u}_1$; i.e., we define

$$\mathbf{v}_1 = \frac{\mathbf{u}_1}{\sqrt{\langle \mathbf{u}_1|\mathbf{u}_1 \rangle}} ,$$

so that $\langle \mathbf{v}_1|\mathbf{v}_1 \rangle = 1$. We now proceed inductively. Suppose that we have already constructed an orthonormal set $\{\mathbf{v}_1, \ldots, \mathbf{v}_k\}$, where each $\mathbf{v}_j$ is a linear combination of the form (6). We shall construct a vector $\mathbf{V}_{k+1}$ (not necessarily normalized) which is a linear combination of the vectors

$\{\mathbf{u}_1, \ldots, \mathbf{u}_{k+1}\}$ and which satisfies $\left\langle \mathbf{v}_j | \mathbf{V}_{k+1} \right\rangle = 0$ for each $j = 1, \ldots, k$. Let us seek such a vector $\mathbf{V}_{k+1}$ in the form

$$\mathbf{V}_{k+1} = b_1 \mathbf{v}_1 + \ldots + b_k \mathbf{v}_k + \mathbf{u}_{k+1} . \tag{7}$$

By virtue of the relations (6), any vector of the form (7) is certainly a linear combination of the vectors $\{\mathbf{u}_1, \ldots, \mathbf{u}_{k+1}\}$. Imposing the orthogonality condition, we require

$$\left\langle \mathbf{v}_j | \mathbf{V}_{k+1} \right\rangle = b_j + \left\langle \mathbf{v}_j | \mathbf{u}_{k+1} \right\rangle = 0, \quad j = 1, \ldots, k ,$$

so that $b_j = - \left\langle \mathbf{v}_j | \mathbf{u}_{k+1} \right\rangle$; these scalar products are determined in terms of the previously constructed vectors. Thus the vector $\mathbf{V}_{k+1}$ has all the properties which we require for $\mathbf{v}_{k+1}$, except that it is not normalized. The normalization condition is now easy to impose without destroying the orthogonality conditions. We observe that the vector $\mathbf{V}_{k+1}$ cannot vanish, since it is constructed through (7) as a linear combination of the vectors $\{\mathbf{u}_1, \ldots, \mathbf{u}_{k+1}\}$, which are linearly independent by hypothesis. Hence $\left\langle \mathbf{V}_{k+1} | \mathbf{V}_{k+1} \right\rangle > 0$ and we can define the vector

$$\mathbf{v}_{k+1} = \frac{\mathbf{V}_{k+1}}{\sqrt{\left\langle \mathbf{V}_{k+1} | \mathbf{V}_{k+1} \right\rangle}} ,$$

which has all the required properties. By induction, the process can be continued until all the vectors in the original set $\{\mathbf{u}_1, \ldots, \mathbf{u}_m\}$ are exhausted, and the new set $\{\mathbf{v}_1, \ldots, \mathbf{v}_m\}$ obtained in this way is orthonormal.

This process of constructing an orthonormal set $\{\mathbf{v}_1, \ldots, \mathbf{v}_m\}$, each of whose vectors $\mathbf{v}_j$ is a linear combination of the first j vectors of a given set $\{\mathbf{u}_1, \ldots, \mathbf{u}_m\}$ of linearly independent vectors, is called the *Gram-Schmidt process*. The Gram-Schmidt process can actually be carried out in practice in any concrete situation and is of great importance in constructing orthonormal bases.

Note that if the original set of vectors $\{\mathbf{u}_1, \ldots, \mathbf{u}_m\}$ is a basis, then the new orthonormal set $\{\mathbf{v}_1, \ldots, \mathbf{v}_m\}$ constructed in this way is also a basis. For if this were not so, there would exist a vector $\mathbf{V}$ which is not expressible as a linear combination of the vectors $\{\mathbf{v}_1, \ldots, \mathbf{v}_m\}$, so that the set $\{\mathbf{v}_1, \ldots, \mathbf{v}_m, \mathbf{V}\}$ containing $m + 1$ vectors would be linearly independent, and this would contradict the theorem of Sec. 1.1.

Example 2   Let

$$\mathbf{u}_1 = (1, 0, 1), \quad \mathbf{u}_2 = (-1, 1, 2), \quad \mathbf{u}_3 = (2, 3, 0)$$

be vectors in ordinary 3-dimensional space, with the usual (Euclidean) scalar product

$$\langle (x_1, x_2, x_3) | (y_1, y_2, y_3) \rangle = \sum_{i=1}^{3} x_i y_i .$$

Then the Gram-Schmidt process gives, following the same notation as above,

$$v_1 = \frac{1}{\sqrt{2}} (1, 0, 1),$$

$$V_2 = - \langle v_1 | u_2 \rangle \, v_1 + u_2 = -\frac{1}{\sqrt{2}} v_1 + u_2 = \frac{1}{2}(-3, 2, 3),$$

$$v_2 = \frac{1}{2\sqrt{22}} (-3, 2, 3),$$

$$V_3 = - \langle v_1 | u_3 \rangle \, v_1 - \langle v_2 | u_3 \rangle \, v_2 + u_3$$

$$= -\frac{2}{\sqrt{2}} v_1 - (0) v_2 + u_3 = (1, 3, -1),$$

$$v_3 = \frac{1}{\sqrt{11}} (1, 3, -1).$$

The set of vectors $\{v_1, v_2, v_3\}$ is then orthonormal, as can be verified by direct calculation.

1.4 Eigenvalue problems

The eigenvalue problem in a finite-dimensional vector space, which arises in applications in many different contexts, is as follows. We are given a square matrix A, which we can think of as a representation of a linear transformation in the vector space, and we wish to find all vectors x such that Ax is a scalar multiple of x, i.e.

$$Ax = \lambda x . \tag{1}$$

Thus the problem is to solve the equation (1) (known as the *eigenvalue equation* for the matrix A) for all non-zero (or, as we say, non-trivial) vectors x and associated scalars λ satisfying this equation. The zero vector $x = 0$ is of course always a solution of (1) for any value of λ and is therefore of no special interest.

Any vector $\mathbf{x}$ which satisfies the equation (1) is called an *eigenvector* of the matrix A (assuming always that $\mathbf{x}$ is non-zero), and the corresponding value of λ is called the *eigenvalue* associated with this eigenvector. Other names for eigenvectors which are sometimes found in the literature are *characteristic vectors, proper vectors* and *latent vectors*; eigenvalues are also known as *characteristic values, proper values* and *latent roots.*

It should be noted that an eigenvector is never uniquely defined, since if $\mathbf{x}$ is an eigenvector associated with an eigenvalue λ, then any scalar multiple of this vector, say $\mu\mathbf{x}$, is also an eigenvector associated with the same eigenvalue λ.

More generally, if $\mathbf{x}$ and $\mathbf{y}$ are two eigenvectors associated with the same eigenvalue λ, then any linear combination $\alpha\mathbf{x} + \beta\mathbf{y}$ is also an eigenvector associated with the eigenvalue λ, since in that case $A(\alpha\mathbf{x} + \beta\mathbf{y}) = \alpha A\mathbf{x} + \beta A\mathbf{y} = \lambda (\alpha\mathbf{x} + \beta\mathbf{y})$. Thus it is easy to see that the set of all eigenvectors associated with a given eigenvalue always forms a linear vector space (which is a subspace of the original vector space). Such a space of eigenvectors may be of dimension 1 (in which case it consists of eigenvectors which are all scalar multiples of one another) or of any higher dimension, up to the dimension of the full vector space. (An example of this last case is the unit matrix, for which any vector is an eigenvector corresponding to the eigenvalue 1.)

An important property of the eigenvalues of a matrix is that they are an intrinsic characteristic of the linear transformation represented by the matrix and do not depend on the basis with respect to which it is described. In other words, matrices A and $\overline{A}$ which describe the same linear transformation with respect to different bases have the same eigenvalues. To see this, suppose that $A\mathbf{x} = \lambda\mathbf{x}$. We recall that if we change to a new basis, the components of the vector $\mathbf{x}$ and the matrix A transform according to the equations

$$\overline{\mathbf{x}} = N^{-1} \mathbf{x}, \qquad \overline{A} = N^{-1}AN,$$

where N is some matrix (called M^{T} in Sec. 1.2). Conversely,

$$\mathbf{x} = N\overline{\mathbf{x}}, \qquad A = N\overline{A}N^{-1}.$$

Substituting these relations into the original eigenvalue equation $A\mathbf{x} = \lambda\mathbf{x}$ and multiplying by N^{-1} to the left, we see that $\overline{A}\overline{\mathbf{x}} = \lambda\overline{\mathbf{x}}$. This shows that λ is also an eigenvalue of the matrix $\overline{A}$ (with eigenvector $\overline{\mathbf{x}}$). In fact, the eigenvectors $\mathbf{x}$ and $\overline{\mathbf{x}}$ describe the same vector with respect to the two different bases.

Before considering the general properties of eigenvalues and eigenvectors in greater detail, we discuss the computational problem of solving the eigenvalue problem for a given matrix. Equation (1) can be rewritten as

$$(A - \lambda I) \mathbf{x} = \mathbf{0} , \tag{2}$$

where I is the unit matrix. This equation, when written (with respect to a specific basis) in the form

$$\begin{pmatrix} A_{11} - \lambda & A_{12} & \cdots & A_{1n} \\ A_{21} & A_{22} - \lambda & \cdots & A_{2n} \\ \vdots & \vdots & & \vdots \\ A_{n1} & A_{n2} & \cdots & A_{nn} - \lambda \end{pmatrix} \begin{pmatrix} x_1 \\ x_2 \\ \vdots \\ x_n \end{pmatrix} = \begin{pmatrix} 0 \\ 0 \\ \vdots \\ 0 \end{pmatrix} , \tag{3}$$

can be interpreted as a system of n simultaneous linear algebraic equations for the n unknowns $x_1, \ldots, x_n$. It is known from linear algebra that a necessary and sufficient condition for the existence of a non-trivial solution to such a system of homogeneous equations (i.e., equations with zeros on the right-hand sides) is the vanishing of the determinant of the coefficients:

$$\det (A - \lambda I) = \begin{vmatrix} A_{11} - \lambda & A_{12} & \cdots & A_{1n} \\ A_{21} & A_{22} - \lambda & \cdots & A_{2n} \\ \vdots & \vdots & & \vdots \\ A_{n1} & A_{n2} & \cdots & A_{nn} - \lambda \end{vmatrix} = 0 . \tag{4}$$

Equation (4), which is called the *characteristic equation* (or *secular equation*) associated with the matrix A, is clearly a polynomial equation of degree n in λ and therefore possesses precisely n roots (if the roots are counted according to their multiplicity). Thus any $n \times n$ matrix always has n (possibly repeated) eigenvalues. We shall generally be concerned with only real matrices in this book. However, even in this case, the eigenvalues may be complex. Once the eigenvalues have been determined by solving the characteristic equation (4), the associated eigenvectors can be found by returning to the eigenvalue equation in the form (3). We illustrate the method by means of some examples.

Example 1   Let

$$A = \begin{pmatrix} 1 & 1 \\ 0 & 2 \end{pmatrix} .$$

The characteristic equation, $\det(A - \lambda I) = 0$, is

$$\begin{vmatrix} 1 - \lambda & 1 \\ 0 & 2 - \lambda \end{vmatrix} = \lambda^2 - 3\lambda + 2 = 0,$$

so that the eigenvalues are $\lambda = 1, 2$. The eigenvectors are determined by solving the system of simultaneous equations $(A - \lambda I)x = 0$ for each eigenvalue in turn.

For $\lambda = 1$, we have

$$\begin{pmatrix} 0 & 1 \\ 0 & 1 \end{pmatrix} \begin{pmatrix} x_1 \\ x_2 \end{pmatrix} = \begin{pmatrix} 0 \\ 0 \end{pmatrix}.$$

Hence $x_2 = 0$, with no restriction on x_1. In other words, any vector

$$\begin{pmatrix} x_1 \\ x_2 \end{pmatrix} = \begin{pmatrix} \alpha \\ 0 \end{pmatrix} = \alpha \begin{pmatrix} 1 \\ 0 \end{pmatrix}$$

is an eigenvector corresponding to $\lambda = 1$.

For $\lambda = 2$, we have

$$\begin{pmatrix} -1 & 1 \\ 0 & 0 \end{pmatrix} \begin{pmatrix} x_1 \\ x_2 \end{pmatrix} = \begin{pmatrix} 0 \\ 0 \end{pmatrix}.$$

The first equation in this system gives $-x_1 + x_2 = 0$, while the second equation is satisfied by any values of x_1 and x_2. Thus any vector of the form

$$\begin{pmatrix} x_1 \\ x_2 \end{pmatrix} = \beta \begin{pmatrix} 1 \\ 1 \end{pmatrix}$$

is an eigenvector corresponding to $\lambda = 2$.

Example 2   Let

$$A = \begin{pmatrix} 5 & 4 & -2 \\ 4 & 5 & 2 \\ -2 & 2 & 8 \end{pmatrix}.$$

Here the characteristic equation is found to be

$$\begin{vmatrix} 5-\lambda & 4 & -2 \\ 4 & 5-\lambda & 2 \\ -2 & 2 & 8-\lambda \end{vmatrix} = -\lambda^3 + 18\lambda^2 - 81\lambda = 0,$$

and this leads to the eigenvalues $\lambda = 0, 9, 9$; note that $\lambda = 9$ is a double root of the characteristic equation.

For $\lambda = 0$, the eigenvalue equation becomes

$$\begin{pmatrix} 5 & 4 & -2 \\ 4 & 5 & 2 \\ -2 & 2 & 8 \end{pmatrix} \begin{pmatrix} x_1 \\ x_2 \\ x_3 \end{pmatrix} = \begin{pmatrix} 0 \\ 0 \\ 0 \end{pmatrix}$$

and it is readily shown (e.g., by assigning an-arbitrary value to one of the three unknowns and solving any pair of equations for the remaining two) that the corresponding eigenvectors are given by

$$\begin{pmatrix} x_1 \\ x_2 \\ x_3 \end{pmatrix} = \alpha \begin{pmatrix} 2 \\ -2 \\ 1 \end{pmatrix}.$$

For $\lambda = 9$, we have instead

$$\begin{pmatrix} -4 & 4 & -2 \\ 4 & -4 & 2 \\ -2 & 2 & -1 \end{pmatrix} \begin{pmatrix} x_1 \\ x_2 \\ x_3 \end{pmatrix} = \begin{pmatrix} 0 \\ 0 \\ 0 \end{pmatrix}.$$

In this case, all three rows of the matrix are proportional to one another, so that there is only a single linear relation between x_1, x_2 and x_3, namely

$$2x_1 - 2x_2 + x_3 = 0 .$$

We can therefore assign arbitrary values to any two of the variables x_1, x_2 and x_3. If, for example, $x_1 = 1$ and $x_2 = 0$, then the linear relation requires that $x_3 = -2$; alternatively, if $x_1 = 0$ and $x_2 = 1$, then $x_3 = 2$. It is clear that any solution for x_1, x_2 and x_3 (which can be specified by the values of x_1 and x_2) must be given by some linear combination of these two solutions. Therefore all eigenvectors belonging to $\lambda = 9$ are of the form

$$\begin{pmatrix} x_1 \\ x_2 \\ x_3 \end{pmatrix} = \beta \begin{pmatrix} 1 \\ 0 \\ -2 \end{pmatrix} + \gamma \begin{pmatrix} 0 \\ 1 \\ 2 \end{pmatrix}$$

and these eigenvectors form a two-dimensional vector space.

Example 3   Let

$$A = \begin{pmatrix} 0 & 2+i \\ 2-i & 4 \end{pmatrix}.$$

The characteristic equation is

$$\begin{vmatrix} -\lambda & 2+i \\ 2-i & 4-\lambda \end{vmatrix} = \lambda^2 - 4\lambda - 5 = 0$$

and has roots $\lambda = -1, 5$. Putting $\lambda = -1$, we have

$$\begin{pmatrix} 1 & 2+i \\ 2-i & 5 \end{pmatrix} \begin{pmatrix} x_1 \\ x_2 \end{pmatrix} = \begin{pmatrix} 0 \\ 0 \end{pmatrix}$$

and we find the eigenvectors

$$\begin{pmatrix} x_1 \\ x_2 \end{pmatrix} = \alpha \begin{pmatrix} -2-i \\ 1 \end{pmatrix}.$$

For $\lambda = 5$, we have instead

$$\begin{pmatrix} -5 & 2+i \\ 2-i & -1 \end{pmatrix} \begin{pmatrix} x_1 \\ x_2 \end{pmatrix} = \begin{pmatrix} 0 \\ 0 \end{pmatrix},$$

which leads to the eigenvectors

$$\begin{pmatrix} x_1 \\ x_2 \end{pmatrix} = \beta \begin{pmatrix} 1 \\ 2-i \end{pmatrix}.$$

So far we have been concerned with arbitrary square matrices. However, some of the applications considered later in this book involve only real symmetric matrices. As we shall see, the eigenvalues and eigenvectors of a real symmetric matrix have certain special properties. It turns out that the properties which we require also hold for the more general class of *Hermitian matrices*, i.e. matrices A (with complex-valued elements) that have the property $A^\dagger = A$; here $A^\dagger \equiv (A*)^T$ denotes the Hermitian conjugate of A, i.e. the matrix obtained from A by taking in turn both the complex conjugate and the transpose. Since the derivations of the properties which we shall require for real symmetric matrices apply almost verbatim to the more general class of Hermitian matrices, we shall give them for this more general case.

These derivations can be written in a very concise form by introducing the familiar scalar product of two vectors (in terms of their components with respect to an orthogonal basis) by the equation

$$\langle \mathbf{x} | \mathbf{y} \rangle = \sum_{i=1}^{n} x_i^* y_i . \tag{5}$$

It is also convenient to introduce the notation

$$\langle \mathbf{x} | M | \mathbf{y} \rangle \equiv \langle \mathbf{x} | M\mathbf{y} \rangle , \tag{6}$$

where M is an arbitrary square matrix.

It is easy to verify that the quantity (6) has the property

$$\langle \mathbf{x} | M | \mathbf{y} \rangle * = \langle \mathbf{y} | M^\dagger | \mathbf{x} \rangle . \tag{7}$$

To see this, we simply evaluate both sides of (7), using (5) and (6). Thus

$$\langle \mathbf{x} | M\mathbf{y} \rangle = \sum_{i=1}^{n} x_i^* (M\mathbf{y})_i = \sum_{i=1}^{n} x_i^* \sum_{j=1}^{n} M_{ij} y_j ,$$

$$\langle \mathbf{y} | M^\dagger \mathbf{x} \rangle = \sum_{j=1}^{n} y_j^* (M^\dagger \mathbf{x})_j = \sum_{j=1}^{n} y_j^* \sum_{i=1}^{n} M_{ij}^* x_i ,$$

and these two expressions are indeed complex conjugates of each other, as required in (7).

We are now in a position to derive the important special properties of Hermitian matrices.

THEOREM 1   All the eigenvalues of a Hermitian matrix are *real*.

PROOF   Suppose that A is Hermitian and that $A\mathbf{x} = \lambda\mathbf{x}$, where λ and $\mathbf{x}$ (or, more precisely, the components of $\mathbf{x}$) are possibly complex. Then $\langle \mathbf{x}|A|\mathbf{x} \rangle = \lambda \langle \mathbf{x}|\mathbf{x} \rangle$. Since $A^\dagger = A$, the quantity $\langle \mathbf{x}|A|\mathbf{x} \rangle$ is real, and $\langle \mathbf{x}|\mathbf{x} \rangle$ is also real. Therefore λ is real, as required.

THEOREM 2   Eigenvectors belonging to distinct eigenvalues of a Hermitian matrix are mutually orthogonal.

PROOF   Suppose that

$$A\mathbf{x} = \lambda\mathbf{x},$$
$$A\mathbf{y} = \mu\mathbf{y}.$$

Taking the scalar products of the first and second of these equations with $\mathbf{y}$ and $\mathbf{x}$, respectively, we have

$$\langle \mathbf{y}|A|\mathbf{x} \rangle = \lambda \langle \mathbf{y}|\mathbf{x} \rangle,$$
$$\langle \mathbf{x}|A|\mathbf{y} \rangle = \mu \langle \mathbf{x}|\mathbf{y} \rangle.$$

If $A^\dagger = A$, the complex conjugate of the last equation can be written

$$\langle \mathbf{y}|A|\mathbf{x} \rangle = \mu \langle \mathbf{y}|\mathbf{x} \rangle,$$

where we have used the fact that μ is real. Consequently,

$$\lambda \langle \mathbf{y}|\mathbf{x} \rangle = \mu \langle \mathbf{y}|\mathbf{x} \rangle.$$

Thus, if $\lambda \neq \mu$, then $\langle \mathbf{y}|\mathbf{x} \rangle = 0$. In other words, any two eigenvectors $\mathbf{x}$ and $\mathbf{y}$ belonging to distinct eigenvalues λ and μ are mutually orthogonal.

These two theorems are well illustrated by the results of Examples 2 and 3 earlier in this section. The two eigenvalues $\lambda = 0, 9$ in Example 2 are both real, and it can be verified by direct calculation that the eigenvectors associated with $\lambda = 0$ are orthogonal to those associated with $\lambda = 9$ for arbitrary values of the parameters α, β and γ.

1.5 Diagonalization of matrices

In Sec. 1.2 we saw that the same linear transformation is described by different matrices with respect to different bases, and we showed that if

$M \equiv N^{\mathrm{T}}$ is the matrix which generates the new basis from the old one according to the equation

$$\mathbf{v}_i = \sum_{j=1}^{n} M_{ij} \mathbf{u}_j , \qquad (1)$$

then any matrix A transforms according to the law

$$\overline{A} = N^{-1}AN$$

when the basis is changed. This transformation law is called a *similarity transformation*, and two matrices A and $\overline{A}$ which are related in this way are said to be *similar*.

It is a familiar fact that problems of a geometrical character can often be simplified by a judicious choice of a coordinate system. Likewise, the description of a linear transformation can sometimes be greatly simplified by an appropriate choice of a basis.

Under fairly general conditions, a matrix A can be transformed into a *diagonal* matrix $\overline{A}$ by means of a similarity transformation. This process of *diagonalizing* a matrix is of great importance for many applications.

In particular, it can be shown that if a matrix A possesses a set of eigenvectors which form a basis of the vector space, then A is represented by a diagonal matrix $\overline{A}$ with respect to that basis; moreover, the diagonal elements of $\overline{A}$ are then equal to the eigenvalues of A.

To see this, suppose that $\{\mathbf{v}_1, \ldots, \mathbf{v}_n\}$ is a basis of eigenvectors with corresponding eigenvalues $\{\lambda_1, \ldots, \lambda_n\}$. Then $A\mathbf{v}_k = \lambda_k \mathbf{v}_k$ for $k = 1, \ldots, n$. If an arbitrary vector x has the representation

$$\mathbf{x} = \sum_{i=1}^{n} x_i \mathbf{v}_i \qquad (2)$$

with respect to this basis, then

$$A\mathbf{x} = \sum_{i=1}^{n} x_i A \mathbf{v}_i = \sum_{i=1}^{n} \lambda_i x_i \mathbf{v}_i . \qquad (3)$$

Comparing (2) and (3), we see that the linear transformation corresponding to the matrix A, when expressed in terms of the basis $\{\mathbf{v}_1, \ldots, \mathbf{v}_n\}$, is given by the matrix

$$\overline{A} = \begin{pmatrix} \lambda_1 & 0 & \cdots & 0 \\ 0 & \lambda_2 & \cdots & 0 \\ \vdots & \vdots & & \vdots \\ 0 & 0 & \cdots & \lambda_n \end{pmatrix} .$$

As this argument suggests, the problem of diagonalizing a matrix can be solved by first solving the eigenvalue problem for the matrix. Indeed, we shall see how the similarity transformation which diagonalizes a given matrix A can be constructed explicitly, once a basis of eigenvectors of A is known.

Suppose that A is initially specified with respect to a given basis $\{u_1, \ldots, u_n\}$ (whose vectors are not necessarily eigenvectors, so that A is not necessarily diagonal). Suppose also that a basis of eigenvectors $\{v_1, \ldots, v_n\}$ has been found and that these eigenvectors have the representation (1) in terms of the original basis. It is easy to see from (1) that M is the matrix whose row k $(k = 1, \ldots, n)$ contains the components of the eigenvector v_k with respect to the original basis. Equivalently, its transpose $N \equiv M^T$ has columns which consist of these eigenvectors. Now we know that the matrix $\bar{A} = N^{-1}AN$ must be the diagonal matrix whose diagonal elements are the eigenvalues of A. Thus we have an effective procedure for diagonalizing a matrix A if we know a basis of eigenvectors of A.

Example 1   In Example 1 of Sec. 1.4, we found that the matrix

$$A = \begin{pmatrix} 1 & 1 \\ 0 & 2 \end{pmatrix}$$

has the eigenvectors

$$v_1 = \begin{pmatrix} 1 \\ 0 \end{pmatrix}, \qquad v_2 = \begin{pmatrix} 1 \\ 1 \end{pmatrix},$$

corresponding to the eigenvalues $\lambda_1 = 1$ and $\lambda_2 = 2$, respectively, and it is easy to see that these eigenvectors are linearly independent and therefore form a basis. We therefore construct the matrix

$$N = \begin{pmatrix} 1 & 1 \\ 0 & 1 \end{pmatrix}.$$

As is easily verified, the inverse of this matrix is

$$N^{-1} = \begin{pmatrix} 1 & -1 \\ 0 & 1 \end{pmatrix}.$$

Consequently, the similarity transformation which diagonalizes A is

$$\bar{A} = N^{-1}AN = \begin{pmatrix} 1 & 0 \\ 0 & 2 \end{pmatrix},$$

and we see that the diagonal elements of $\bar{A}$ are indeed the eigenvalues of A.

We have seen that it is possible to diagonalize a matrix A by means of a similarity transformation whenever A has a basis of eigenvectors. Not every square matrix has this property, as we can see from a simple counter-example. Consider, for example, the matrix

$$A = \begin{pmatrix} 1 & 0 \\ 1 & 1 \end{pmatrix}.$$

Its characteristic equation is $(1 - \lambda)^2 = 0$, so that the only eigenvalue is $\lambda = 1$. Putting $\lambda = 1$, the equation $(A - \lambda I)x = 0$ becomes

$$\begin{pmatrix} 0 & 0 \\ 1 & 0 \end{pmatrix}\begin{pmatrix} x_1 \\ x_2 \end{pmatrix} = \begin{pmatrix} 0 \\ 0 \end{pmatrix},$$

so that the complete system of eigenvectors is given by

$$\begin{pmatrix} x_1 \\ x_2 \end{pmatrix} = \alpha \begin{pmatrix} 0 \\ 1 \end{pmatrix},$$

where α is an arbitrary constant. Since there is at most only one linearly independent eigenvector, no basis of eigenvectors exists in this case.

However, this situation is exceptional, and it is found that most matrices do possess a basis of eigenvectors. A general class of matrices for which a basis of eigenvectors necessarily exists is the class of matrices for which all the eigenvalues are distinct. We already know that this property holds for Hermitian matrices, since in this case eigenvectors associated with distinct eigenvalues are mutually orthogonal and hence linearly independent; if all n eigenvalues of an $n \times n$ Hermitian matrix are distinct, then their corresponding eigenvectors form a basis. The corresponding property for square matrices in general is a consequence of the following theorem:

THEOREM   If $\{u_1, \ldots, u_m\}$ is a set of (non-zero) eigenvectors corresponding to a set of distinct eigenvalues $\{\lambda_1, \ldots, \lambda_m\}$ (not necessarily the complete set) of a matrix A, then these eigenvectors are linearly independent.

PROOF   We carry out the proof by induction. The theorem is obviously true for $m = 1$, since a single non-zero vector forms a linearly independent set. Let us assume that the theorem is true for $m = k$ and show that this implies its validity for $m = k + 1$. Suppose that the set of eigenvectors $\{u_1, \ldots, u_{k+1}\}$ were linearly dependent but that any subset of k of these vectors were linearly independent. Then u_{k+1} can be written as a linear combination of the other vectors in the form

$$u_{k+1} = \sum_{i=1}^{k} \alpha_i u_i, \qquad (4)$$

where the coefficients α_i are all non-zero. Without loss of generality (relabelling the vectors if necessary), we can assume that the eigenvalue λ_{k+1} corresponding to $\mathbf{u}_{k+1}$ is non-zero. Multiplying both sides of (4) by the matrix A, using the fact that $A\mathbf{u}_i = \lambda_i \mathbf{u}_i$, and dividing by λ_{k+1}, we have

$$\mathbf{u}_{k+1} = \sum_{i=1}^{k} \left(\frac{\alpha_i \lambda_i}{\lambda_{k+1}} \right) \mathbf{u}_i . \tag{5}$$

Now subtracting (4) from (5), we obtain the linear relation

$$\sum_{i=1}^{k} \left(\frac{\alpha_i (\lambda_i - \lambda_{k+1})}{\lambda_{k+1}} \right) \mathbf{u}_i = 0$$

in which the coefficients are non-zero, thus contradicting our hypothesis that the set $\{\mathbf{u}_1, \ldots, \mathbf{u}_k\}$ is linearly independent. This completes the proof.

If a matrix has any repeated eigenvalues, the total number of distinct eigenvalues will be less than the dimension of the matrix, so that we cannot invoke the preceding theorem to argue that there exists a basis of eigenvectors. Nevertheless, for certain important classes of matrices it can be shown that one can always find a basis of eigenvectors, even when the matrix has multiple eigenvalues; in such cases, an eigenvalue of multiplicity m always has m linearly independent eigenvectors. We state here without proof that Hermitian matrices (and, in particular, real symmetric matrices) always have this property. This means that such matrices can always be reduced to diagonal form by a similarity transformation

$$\overline{A} = U^{-1}AU . \tag{6}$$

Let us now consider the nature of the transformation (6) that diagonalizes a Hermitian matrix A (and, in particular, a real symmetric matrix). We recall that U can be constructed in such a way that its columns form a basis of eigenvectors $\mathbf{u}_i$ of the matrix A. Now we know that eigenvectors of a Hermitian matrix belonging to distinct eigenvalues are mutually orthogonal. If any eigenvalue is repeated and has multiplicity k, we shall assume that there exist k linearly independent eigenvectors corresponding to this eigenvalue. Since any linear combination of these eigenvectors is also an eigenvector, we can assume without loss of generality that these k eigenvectors have been chosen to be orthonormal; indeed, such an orthonormal set can be constructed by means of the Gram-Schmidt orthogonalization process.

Thus it is possible to choose a set of n eigenvectors $\{\mathbf{u}_1, \ldots, \mathbf{u}_n\}$ of an $n \times n$ Hermitian matrix so that they form an orthonormal set. This means that the matrix U constructed from these eigenvectors has the property

$$(U^\dagger U)_{ij} = \sum_{k=1}^{n} U_{ki}^* \, U_{kj} = \delta_{ij}, \tag{7}$$

since the vectors which form the columns of U are mutually orthogonal. In matrix notation, the condition (7) reads

$$U^\dagger U = I. \tag{8}$$

This means that

$$U^\dagger = U^{-1}. \tag{9}$$

A matrix U having the property (8) or (9) is said to be *unitary*. The fact that U is unitary means that the transformation (6) which diagonalizes the Hermitian matrix A can be written in the form

$$\overline{A} = U^\dagger A U. \tag{10}$$

Equation (10) is a significant simplification of (6), since it is far easier to evaluate the Hermitian conjugate $U^\dagger$ of a matrix U than to evaluate its inverse U^{-1}.

As we have already mentioned, several problems considered later in this book require the diagonalization of a real symmetric matrix B. In this case, it is clear that the eigenvectors (or, more precisely, their components) can always be chosen to be real, since we know that the eigenvalues are real and the corresponding eigenvectors are determined by the solution of a system of simultaneous equations with purely real coefficients. Thus a real symmetric matrix B can be diagonalized by a transformation of the special form

$$\overline{B} = R^T B R, \tag{11}$$

where R has the property

$$R^T R = I \tag{12}$$

or, equivalently,

$$R^T = R^{-1}. \tag{13}$$

A real matrix R having the property (12) or (13) is called an *orthogonal matrix*. Geometrically, the change of basis corresponding to the transformation (11) can be interpreted as a rotation and/or reflection of a Cartesian coordinate system about the origin. This can readily be seen from the fact that the relation $\overline{x} = Rx$ preserves the 'length' of the vector x:

$$\sum_{i=1}^{n} |\overline{x}_i|^2 = \overline{x}^T \overline{x} = x^T R^T R x = x^T x = \sum_{i=1}^{n} |x_i|^2.$$

We conclude this section with an example of the diagonalization of a real symmetric matrix.

Example 2   Let

$$B = \begin{pmatrix} 5 & 4 & -2 \\ 4 & 5 & 2 \\ -2 & 2 & 8 \end{pmatrix}.$$

The eigenvalue problem for this matrix was solved in Example 2 of Sec. 1.4. However, the two eigenvectors which we constructed there for the double eigenvalue $\lambda = 9$ were not mutually orthogonal. To obtain an *orthogonal* matrix R such that the transformation (11) diagonalizes the matrix B, we must first construct an *orthonormal* basis of eigenvectors. We therefore apply the Gram-Schmidt orthogonalization procedure to the previously determined eigenvectors of the matrix B. This gives the complete orthonormal set of eigenvectors

$$\mathbf{u}_1 = \tfrac{1}{3}\begin{pmatrix} 2 \\ -2 \\ 1 \end{pmatrix}, \quad \mathbf{u}_2 = \tfrac{1}{\sqrt{5}}\begin{pmatrix} 1 \\ 0 \\ -2 \end{pmatrix}, \quad \mathbf{u}_3 = \tfrac{1}{3\sqrt{5}}\begin{pmatrix} 4 \\ 5 \\ 2 \end{pmatrix}.$$

Therefore the transformation which diagonalizes the matrix B is

$$\bar{B} = \begin{pmatrix} \frac{2}{3} & -\frac{2}{3} & \frac{1}{3} \\ \frac{1}{\sqrt{5}} & 0 & -\frac{2}{\sqrt{5}} \\ \frac{4}{3\sqrt{5}} & \frac{5}{3\sqrt{5}} & \frac{2}{3\sqrt{5}} \end{pmatrix} \begin{pmatrix} 5 & 4 & -2 \\ 4 & 5 & 2 \\ -2 & 2 & 8 \end{pmatrix} \begin{pmatrix} \frac{2}{3} & \frac{1}{\sqrt{5}} & \frac{4}{3\sqrt{5}} \\ -\frac{2}{3} & 0 & \frac{5}{3\sqrt{5}} \\ \frac{1}{3} & -\frac{2}{\sqrt{5}} & \frac{2}{3\sqrt{5}} \end{pmatrix},$$

and it can be verified by straightforward calculation that

$$\bar{B} = \begin{pmatrix} 0 & 0 & 0 \\ 0 & 9 & 0 \\ 0 & 0 & 9 \end{pmatrix}.$$

As we expect, the diagonal elements of $\bar{B}$ are the eigenvalues of B.

1.6 Quadratic forms

If A is a given Hermitian matrix and $\mathbf{x}$ is an arbitrary vector with (complex) components $x_1, \ldots, x_n$ with respect to a particular orthonormal basis, the quantity

$$Q(x_1, \ldots, x_n) \equiv \langle \mathbf{x}|A|\mathbf{x} \rangle = \mathbf{x}^{*\mathrm{T}} A \mathbf{x} = \sum_{i=1}^{n} \sum_{j=1}^{n} x_i^* A_{ij} x_j \qquad (1)$$

is called a *Hermitian quadratic form*.

We have seen that if A is Hermitian, then there exists a unitary matrix U such that $\overline{A} = U^\dagger A U$ is diagonal. This means that the change of basis which diagonalizes the matrix A also brings the corresponding Hermitian quadratic form into diagonal form:

$$Q(\overline{x}_1, \ldots, \overline{x}_n) \equiv \langle \overline{\mathbf{x}}|\overline{A}|\overline{\mathbf{x}} \rangle = \overline{\mathbf{x}}^{*\mathrm{T}} \overline{A} \overline{\mathbf{x}} = \sum_{i=1}^{n} \lambda_i |\overline{x}_i|^2, \qquad (2)$$

where the coefficients λ_i (the diagonal elements of $\overline{A}$) are the eigenvalues of the matrix A. The vectors $\mathbf{x}$ in (1) and $\overline{\mathbf{x}}$ in (2) are both arbitrary, but we can think of them as being related by the equation $\overline{\mathbf{x}} = U^\dagger \mathbf{x}$, since we can then make the identification

$$\overline{\mathbf{x}}^{*\mathrm{T}} \overline{A} \overline{\mathbf{x}} = \mathbf{x}^{*\mathrm{T}} U U^\dagger A U U^\dagger \mathbf{x} = \mathbf{x}^{*\mathrm{T}} A \mathbf{x}.$$

In the special case in which all the elements A_{ij} are real, so that we have a real symmetric matrix A, and the vectors $\mathbf{x}$ are restricted to purely real vectors, an expression of the form (1) (in which we can drop the asterisks) is called a *real quadratic form*. In this case, the matrix A can be diagonalized by means of a transformation of the type $\overline{A} = R^\mathrm{T} A R$, where R is a real orthogonal matrix, and the corresponding real quadratic form becomes

$$Q(\overline{x}_1, \ldots, \overline{x}_n) = \sum_{i=1}^{n} \lambda_i \overline{x}_i^2.$$

Here $\overline{\mathbf{x}}$ and $\mathbf{x}$ are related by $\overline{\mathbf{x}} = R^\mathrm{T} \mathbf{x}$.

Example   Let $Q(x, y, z)$ be a function of three real variables defined by

$$Q(x, y, z) = 5x^2 + 5y^2 + 8z^2 + 8xy - 4xz + 4yz.$$

Then $Q(x, y, z)$ is a real quadratic form, which in matrix notation can be written

$$Q(x, y, z) = (x \;\; y \;\; z) \begin{pmatrix} 5 & 4 & -2 \\ 4 & 5 & 2 \\ -2 & 2 & 8 \end{pmatrix} \begin{pmatrix} x \\ y \\ z \end{pmatrix} \equiv \mathbf{x}^\mathrm{T} B \mathbf{x}.$$

Now B can be identified as the matrix considered in Example 2 of the preceding section, where the diagonalization was carried out. Since we know from that example that the eigenvalues of B are $\lambda = 0, 9, 9$, we can say that the corresponding diagonal quadratic form has the structure

$$Q(\bar{x}, \bar{y}, \bar{z}) = 9\bar{y}^2 + 9\bar{z}^2.$$

The matrix R which makes $R^T BR$ diagonal was constructed in the previous example. We can use this matrix to determine the new vector components $\bar{x}, \bar{y}, \bar{z}$ in terms of the original components x, y, z by means of the relation $\bar{x} = R^T x$:

$$\begin{pmatrix} \bar{x} \\ \bar{y} \\ \bar{z} \end{pmatrix} = \begin{pmatrix} \frac{2}{3} & -\frac{2}{3} & \frac{1}{3} \\ \frac{1}{\sqrt{5}} & 0 & -\frac{2}{\sqrt{5}} \\ \frac{4}{3\sqrt{5}} & \frac{5}{3\sqrt{5}} & \frac{2}{3\sqrt{5}} \end{pmatrix} \begin{pmatrix} x \\ y \\ z \end{pmatrix}. \tag{3}$$

Real quadratic forms provide a useful tool in analytic geometry. Suppose, for example, that a surface in ordinary three-dimensional space is specified by means of the equation

$$5x^2 + 5y^2 + 8z^2 + 8xy - 4xz + 4yz = 36,$$

where (x, y, z) are Cartesian coordinates. In this form, the nature of the surface represented by the equation is by no means obvious. However, once we discover (as in the example considered above) that the equation can be transformed to the form

$$9\bar{y}^2 + 9\bar{z}^2 = 36$$

by going over to a new coordinate system, we can immediately recognize that the surface in question is a circular cylinder of radius 2, whose symmetry axis is along the $\bar{x}$-direction.

Let us determine the orientation of this $\bar{x}$-axis with respect to the original system of coordinates (x, y, z). In terms of the new coordinates $(\bar{x}, \bar{y}, \bar{z})$, a unit vector along the $\bar{x}$-axis is given by

$$\bar{u}_1 = \begin{pmatrix} 1 \\ 0 \\ 0 \end{pmatrix}.$$

With respect to the coordinates (x, y, z), the components of this vector are given by

$$u_1 = R\bar{u}_1, \tag{4}$$

where R is the transpose of the matrix used in (3). It is easy to see by examining the matrix product in (4) that the required unit vector u_1 is given by the first column of R (or first row of R^T), namely

$$\mathbf{u}_1 = \begin{pmatrix} \frac{2}{3} \\ -\frac{2}{3} \\ \frac{1}{3} \end{pmatrix}.$$

This is, in fact, the first eigenvector of the matrix B considered above. By a similar argument, vectors along the $\bar{y}$- and $\bar{z}$-directions are given by the second and third eigenvectors.

It should be clear from this example that the nature of a surface in n-space represented by an equation of the type $Q(x_1, \ldots, x_n) = 1$, where $Q(x_1, \ldots, x_n)$ is a real quadratic form in n variables, can be readily understood by diagonalizing the quadratic form. The type of surface represented by such an equation depends on the relative signs of the various terms of the diagonal form, i.e. on the signs of the eigenvalues of the symmetric matrix associated with the quadratic form.

As an example, let us examine the various possibilities in three dimensions. We take first the case in which all three eigenvalues of the associated matrix are positive. Then after diagonalization the equation can be written in the form

$$a^2\bar{x}^2 + b^2\bar{y}^2 + c^2\bar{z}^2 = 1,$$

where the coefficients are the eigenvalues. This equation represents an ellipsoid whose principal axes (symmetry axes) coincide with the axes of

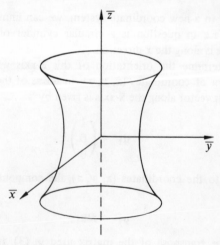

Fig. 1.1

the new coordinate system. As we have seen, these special directions are specified by the eigenvectors of the associated matrix. The lengths of the principal semi-axes (the distances from the origin to the extremities) are $1/a$, $1/b$ and $1/c$ (taking a, b and c to be positive for definiteness).

Suppose next that one eigenvalue is negative and the other two are positive, and for definiteness let the negative eigenvalue be the third one. Then the equation in diagonal form can be written

$$a^2\bar{x}^2 + b^2\bar{y}^2 - c^2\bar{z}^2 = 1.$$

This represents a hyperboloid of one sheet (see Fig. 1.1) with its symmetry axis along the $\bar{z}$-direction.

If the first two eigenvalues are negative and the third is positive, then in diagonal form the equation can be written

$$c^2\bar{z}^2 - a^2\bar{x}^2 - b^2\bar{y}^2 = 1.$$

This represents a hyperboloid of two sheets (Fig. 1.2), and the $\bar{z}$-axis is again the symmetry axis. The gap between the two sheets corresponds to the region $|z| < 1/c$.

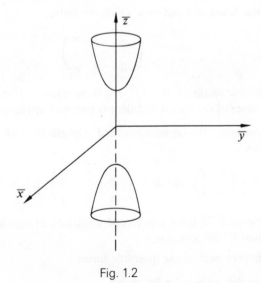

Fig. 1.2

Other special types of surfaces can occur when one or two of the eigenvalues are equal to zero.

Similar analyses can of course be made in different numbers of dimensions.

Problems

1 Using the defining properties of a scalar product, show that $\langle 0|x\rangle =$ $\langle x|0\rangle = 0$ for any vector x.

2 If a scalar product is defined in a vector space, the *norm* of any vector x is the (non-negative) real number $\|x\| \equiv \sqrt{\langle x|x\rangle}$. Using the axioms for a scalar product, show that the norm has the general properties $|\langle x|y\rangle| \leqslant \|x\| \|y\|$ (the Schwarz inequality) and $\|x + y\| \leqslant \|x\| + \|y\|$ (the triangle inequality).

3 The Legendre polynomials $P_n(x)$ ($n = 0, 1, 2, \ldots$) can be defined by the following properties: (i) $P_n(x)$ is a polynomial of degree n in the variable x; (ii) $P_n(1) = 1$; (iii) any two distinct Legendre polynomials $P_m(x)$ and $P_n(x)$ ($m \neq n$) are mutually orthogonal in the sense that

$$\int_{-1}^{1} P_m(x)P_n(x)dx = 0.$$

Use these properties to construct the first four Legendre polynomials $P_0(x)$, $P_1(x)$, $P_2(x)$ and $P_3(x)$.

4 Find the values of b and c for which the matrix

$$\begin{pmatrix} 2 & -1 & 0 \\ -1 & 3 & b \\ 0 & b & c \end{pmatrix}$$

has an eigenvector $(1 \ 0 \ -1)^T$. For these values of b and c, find all the eigenvalues of the matrix and their corresponding eigenvectors.

5 (i) Determine the eigenvalues and eigenvectors of the following matrices:

(a) $M = \begin{pmatrix} 2 & 1 \\ 1 & 2 \end{pmatrix}$, (b) $M = \begin{pmatrix} 3 & -2 & 4 \\ -2 & -2 & 6 \\ 4 & 6 & -1 \end{pmatrix}$, (c) $M = \begin{pmatrix} 0 & 1 & 1 \\ 1 & 0 & 1 \\ 1 & 1 & 0 \end{pmatrix}$.

(ii) For each of these matrices M, construct an orthogonal matrix R such that $R^T M R$ is diagonal.

(iii) Express each of the quadratic forms

(a) $f(x, y) = 2x^2 + 2y^2 + 2xy$,
(b) $g(x, y, z) = 3x^2 - 2y^2 - z^2 - 4xy + 8xz + 12yz$,
(c) $h(x, y, z) = 2xy + 2xz + 2yz$

as a linear combination of squares such as $f(x, y) = a\bar{x}^2 + b\bar{y}^2$, where $(\bar{x}, \bar{y})$ are new coordinates, and find expressions for the new coordinates. Describe the curve $f(x, y) = C$ in the xy-plane and the surfaces $g(x, y, z) = C$ and $h(x, y, z) = C$ in space, where C is a positive constant.

6 Show that if λ is an eigenvalue of a matrix A, then λ^n is an eigenvalue of the matrix A^n. Extend this result to polynomial functions of a matrix.

7 Determine whether the quadratic form

$$Q(x, y, z) = x^2 + 3y^2 + kz^2 + 2xy + 4xz + 2yz$$

is positive definite or negative definite for (i) $k = 4$, (ii) $k = 6$.

8 A matrix A is said to be *skew-Hermitian* if $A^\dagger = -A$. Show that the eigenvalues of a skew-Hermitian matrix are purely imaginary.

9 Show that the eigenvalues of a unitary matrix are of modulus unity.

10 Show that if two Hermitian matrices A and B have the same eigenvalues, then they are related by a similarity transformation of the form $B = U^\dagger A U$, where U is a unitary matrix.

11 Show that the sum of the eigenvalues of any (not necessarily diagonalizable) square matrix is equal to the trace of the matrix (i.e., the sum of its diagonal elements). (This property provides a useful check on calculations of the eigenvalues of matrices.)

12 (i) Show that if $Q(x_1, \ldots, x_n)$ is a Hermitian quadratic form, then Q is real for arbitrary (complex) values of the variables $x_1, \ldots x_n$.

(ii) Show that if A is a positive definite Hermitian matrix, then $\langle x|y \rangle \equiv x^{*T} A y$ defines a scalar product.

13 Prove that if the matrices A and B are both Hermitian and positive definite, then $A + B$ is also Hermitian and positive definite.

14 Show that the curve $5x^2 + 5y^2 + 6xy = 8$ in the xy-plane is an ellipse and determine the directions and lengths of its principal axes.

2 Extrema in several variables

2.1 Taylor's theorem

We begin by introducing some notation which will be useful throughout the remainder of this book. If a real function $f(x)$ is continuous in an interval $a \leqslant x \leqslant b$, we write $f \in C [a, b]$; more generally, if it possesses a continuous derivative $f^{(m)}(x)$ of order m in this interval, we write $f \in C_m [a, b]$. Note that $C_m [a, b]$, the class of functions having continuous derivatives $f^{(m)}(x)$ for $x \in [a, b]$, forms a linear vector space under the usual operations of addition of two functions and multiplication of a function by a real constant.

Taylor's theorem for a function of a single real variable states that if $f(x) \in C_m [a, b]$, then

$$f(b) \equiv f(a + \delta x) = f(a) + \delta x \, f'(a) + \ldots + \frac{1}{(m-1)!} (\delta x)^{m-1} f^{(m-1)}(a) + R_m,$$

(1)

where the remainder term R_m (in Lagrange's form) can be expressed in the form

$$R_m = \frac{1}{m!} (\delta x)^m f^{(m)} (\xi)$$

for some number ξ in the range $a < \xi < a + \delta x$.

For many purposes, what is important is only the fact that R_m contains the factor $(\delta x)^m$. In particular, since $f^{(m)} (x)$ is assumed to be continuous at $x = a$, we have

$$\lim_{\delta x \to 0} \left[\frac{R_m}{(\delta x)^m} \right] = \frac{f^{(m)} (a)}{m!},$$

which is equal to some finite constant (possibly zero). We express the fact that this limit exists and is finite by saying that R_m is of order $(\delta x)^m$ for small δx. Mathematically, this is symbolized by means of the 'big O' notation: $R_m = O [(\delta x)^m]$ as $\delta x \to 0$. More generally, if we have a situation in which

$$\lim_{x \to x_0} \left[\frac{g(x)}{f(x)} \right] = K,$$

where K is some finite constant, we write $g(x) = O[f(x)]$ as $x \to x_0$.

Another related notation is the 'little o' symbol. If

$$\lim_{x \to x_0} \left[\frac{g(x)}{f(x)} \right] = 0,$$

then we say that $g(x)$ is of smaller order than $f(x)$ as x approaches x_0 and we write $g(x) = o[f(x)]$ as $x \to x_0$. This is, of course, a somewhat stronger condition than the previous one.

Returning to Taylor's theorem, we can now write the remainder term in (1) in either of the forms $R_m = O[(\delta x)^m]$ or $R_m = o[(\delta x)^{m-1}]$. The point at which the limit is taken (in this case, $\delta x \to 0$) will often not be written explicitly when it is clear from the context.

Let us now recall the fundamentals of the theory of extrema (minima and maxima) for differentiable functions of a single variable. According to equation (1) with $m = 2$, the variation in the function satisfies the relation

$$\delta f \equiv f(a + \delta x) - f(a) = \delta x \, f'(a) + o(\delta x) \tag{2}$$

(which is often abbreviated in the symbolic 'differential' notation $df = (df/dx)dx$). It follows directly from (2) that $f'(a) = 0$ is a necessary condition for $f(x)$ to have a relative minimum or maximum at $x = a$. To see this, suppose that we had $f'(a) \neq 0$. Then the remainder term $o(\delta x)$ can be made smaller than $\delta x f'(a)$ in magnitude in a sufficiently small neighbourhood $|x - a| < \epsilon$, where $x = a + \delta x$. Since $\delta x f'(a)$ assumes both positive and negative values in any such neighbourhood, then so also does δf. In other words, we cannot have a relative minimum or maximum at $x = a$ if the derivative $f'(a)$ is non-zero.

If $f'(a) = 0$, we say that $f(x)$ has a stationary point at $x = a$ (not necessarily an extremum). By an argument analogous to that given above, it follows at once from Taylor's theorem with the remainder term $R_m = o[(\delta x)^{m-1}]$ that if the first non-vanishing derivative at a stationary point is of even order, then the stationary point is a minimum or maximum according as the value of this derivative is positive or negative; if the first non-vanishing derivative is of odd order, then the stationary point is a point of inflection.

To develop an analogous theory for functions of several variables, we must first obtain the generalization of Taylor's theorem for this case.

Consider a function $f(\mathbf{x})$, where we use the vector notation $\mathbf{x} \equiv (x_1, \ldots, x_n)$ to denote a point in n-space. Suppose that all the partial derivatives of f of order m are continuous in some neighbourhood of the point $\mathbf{x} = \mathbf{a} \equiv (a_1, \ldots, a_n)$. Let $\mathbf{a} + \delta \mathbf{x}$ be any other point in this neighbourhood. As a first step, we define a function of a single variable

$$F(\lambda) \equiv f(\mathbf{a} + \lambda \, \delta \mathbf{x})$$

for fixed $\mathbf{a}$ and $\delta\mathbf{x}$, so that $F(0) = f(\mathbf{a})$, while $F(1) = f(\mathbf{a} + \delta\mathbf{x})$. The function $F(\lambda)$ describes the behaviour of $f(\mathbf{x})$ when $\mathbf{x}$ is restricted to the straight line joining the points $\mathbf{x} = \mathbf{a}$ and $\mathbf{x} = \mathbf{a} + \delta\mathbf{x}$.

Taylor's theorem in one variable tells us that

$$F(1) = F(0) + F'(0) + \ldots + \frac{1}{(m-1)!} F^{(m-1)}(0) + \frac{1}{m!} F^{(m)}(\xi), \qquad (3)$$

where $0 < \xi < 1$. By expressing $F(\lambda)$ and its derivatives in terms of $f(\mathbf{x})$ and its derivatives, we obtain Taylor's theorem in several variables. Putting $\mathbf{x} = \mathbf{a} + \lambda\,\delta\mathbf{x}$, we have, by the chain rule,

$$\frac{dF}{d\lambda} = \sum_{i=1}^{n} \frac{\partial f}{\partial x_i} \frac{dx_i}{d\lambda} = \sum_{i=1}^{n} \delta x_i \frac{\partial f}{\partial x_i} = \left(\sum_{i=1}^{n} \delta x_i \frac{\partial}{\partial x_i} \right) f$$

and, more generally,

$$\frac{d^m F}{d\lambda^m} = \left(\sum_{i=1}^{n} \delta x_i \frac{\partial}{\partial x_i} \right)^m f.$$

Thus, rewriting (3) in terms of the function $f(\mathbf{x})$, we obtain Taylor's theorem in n variables in the form

$$f(a_1 + \delta x_1, \ldots, a_n + \delta x_n) = f(a_1, \ldots, a_n) + \sum_{i=1}^{n} \delta x_i \left[\frac{\partial f}{\partial x_i} \right]_{\mathbf{x} = \mathbf{a}} + \ldots$$

$$+ \frac{1}{(m-1)!} \left[\left(\sum_{i=1}^{n} \delta x_i \frac{\partial}{\partial x_i} \right)^{m-1} f \right]_{\mathbf{x} = \mathbf{a}} + \frac{1}{m!} \left[\left(\sum_{i=1}^{n} \delta x_i \frac{\partial}{\partial x_i} \right)^{m} f \right]_{\mathbf{x} = \mathbf{a} + \xi\,\delta\mathbf{x}}.$$

In particular, for $m = 3$ we have, in conventional vector notation,

$$\delta f \equiv f(\mathbf{a} + \delta\mathbf{x}) - f(\mathbf{a})$$

$$= \delta\mathbf{x} \cdot [\nabla f]_{\mathbf{x} = \mathbf{a}} + \tfrac{1}{2} \sum_{i=1}^{n} \sum_{j=1}^{n} \delta x_i\, \delta x_j \left[\frac{\partial^2 f}{\partial x_i\, \partial x_j} \right]_{\mathbf{x} = \mathbf{a}} + o(|\delta\mathbf{x}|^2),$$

where $\nabla f \equiv (\partial f/\partial x_1, \ldots, \partial f/\partial x_n)$ is the gradient of $f(\mathbf{x})$ in n dimensions, and the scalar product of two vectors $\mathbf{c} \cdot \mathbf{d}$ is defined in the usual way as

$$\mathbf{c} \cdot \mathbf{d} = \sum_{i=1}^{n} c_i d_i.$$

2.2 Stationary points

By considering independent variations of each of the variables x_i in turn, with all the others fixed, it is easy to see that if $f(\mathbf{x})$ has a relative minimum or maximum, then it has a corresponding minimum or maximum in each of the variables individually; this in turn requires that $\partial f/\partial x_i = 0$ for all i. In other words, a necessary (but not a sufficient) condition for $f(\mathbf{x})$ to have a relative minimum or maximum at $\mathbf{x} = \mathbf{a}$ is that $\nabla f = \mathbf{0}$ there. If $\nabla f = \mathbf{0}$ at a given point, we say that this point is a stationary point of the function.

To determine the nature of a particular stationary point, we examine the second-order term in the expansion for δf, which can be expressed in matrix notation as

$$\tfrac{1}{2} \sum_{i=1}^{n} \sum_{j=1}^{n} \delta x_i \, H_{ij} \, \delta x_j = \tfrac{1}{2} (\delta \mathbf{x})^{\mathrm{T}} H (\delta \mathbf{x}) \equiv Q (\delta \mathbf{x}), \tag{1}$$

where $\delta \mathbf{x}$ is now regarded as a column vector, $(\delta \mathbf{x})^{\mathrm{T}}$ is its transpose, and H (known as the *Hessian*) is the $n \times n$ matrix of second derivatives at the point $\mathbf{x} = \mathbf{a}$:

$$H_{ij} = \left[\frac{\partial^2 f}{\partial x_i \, \partial x_j} \right]_{\mathbf{x} = \mathbf{a}}$$

We recognize that the expression $Q(\delta \mathbf{x})$ defined by (1) is a quadratic form in the displacements δx_i.

The nature of a stationary point obviously depends on the possible signs of its associated quadratic form (1). A quadratic form $Q(\delta \mathbf{x})$ is said to be *positive definite* if $Q(\delta \mathbf{x}) > 0$ for all $\delta \mathbf{x} \neq \mathbf{0}$. This is clearly a sufficient condition for the stationary point to be a relative minimum. Similarly, if the quadratic form is *negative definite*, i.e. if $Q(\delta \mathbf{x}) < 0$ for all $\delta \mathbf{x} \neq \mathbf{0}$, then the stationary point is a relative maximum. If $Q(\delta \mathbf{x})$ takes both signs, then the variation in the function, δf, can take either sign for small variations away from the stationary point, and we say that we have a saddle point.

If a quadratic form constructed from a given matrix is positive (negative) definite, we also say that the matrix is positive (negative) definite.

There is an intermediate case in which $Q(\delta \mathbf{x})$ vanishes for certain $\delta \mathbf{x} \neq \mathbf{0}$ but is of definite sign for all other values. Such a quadratic form (as well as its associated matrix) is said to be (positive or negative) *semi-definite*. In this case, the behaviour of δf for variations $\delta \mathbf{x}$ in certain directions is determined only by the higher-order terms of the Taylor expansion, so that the nature of the stationary point cannot be resolved by considering only the term involving the Hessian. We shall not consider this case here. An extreme situation of this type is the case in which all the second-order partial derivatives of the function $f(x_1, \ldots, x_n)$ are equal to zero, so that the Hessian is the zero matrix; in this case, the Hessian gives no information at all about the variation of the function $f(x_1, \ldots, x_n)$ for small displacements away from the stationary point.

We turn now to the important problem of determining when the quadratic form (1) is positive definite or negative definite. As a first step, we observe that the Hessian H is symmetric, since it is known from real analysis that the mixed partial derivatives $\partial^2 f / \partial x_i \, \partial x_j$ and $\partial^2 f / \partial x_j \, \partial x_i$ are equal if these derivatives are continuous. Therefore the quadratic form (1) can be brought to diagonal form by a suitable choice of basis. If we remember that the coefficients of the various terms in this diagonal form are the eigenvalues of the matrix H, it is clear that the diagonal form (1) is positive definite (negative definite) if and only if all the eigenvalues of H are positive (negative).

Now it is not actually necessary to determine all the eigenvalues individually to test for either of these conditions. Suppose that we have found the characteristic equation for the matrix H. It is known from elementary algebra (or easily verified) that the condition for all the roots of a polynomial equation to be positive is that the successive coefficients of the polynomial are strictly alternating in sign. Thus it is immediately clear by inspection of the characteristic equation for the Hessian H whether the quadratic form (1) is positive definite. Similarly, the roots of a polynomial equation are all negative when the coefficients of the polynomial all have the same sign, and this provides an equally simple test for a negative definite Hessian.

The case when the quadratic form (1) is semi-definite obviously corresponds to the situation in which one or more of the eigenvalues of H are equal to zero. This situation is again easy to recognize from the characteristic equation for this matrix (by the absence of the constant term in this equation).

If the characteristic equation does not satisfy any of these criteria, there necessarily exist eigenvalues of both signs, and accordingly the quadratic form takes both positive and negative values.

To summarize the discussion so far, we can say that a stationary point is a relative minimum if the quadratic form (1) is positive definite, a relative maximum if this quadratic form is negative definite, and a saddle point if this quadratic form takes both positive and negative values. However, exactly as in the case when the second derivative $f''(a)$ vanishes at a stationary point $x = a$ for a function of a single variable x, the second-order term in the Taylor-series expansion of a function of several variables may also fail to resolve the nature of a stationary point. This happens whenever the Hessian has one or more zero eigenvalues in addition to a set of eigenvalues of identical sign, so that the associated quadratic form is semi-definite. In such cases, it would be necessary to examine the terms of higher order in the Taylor expansion in order to determine the nature of the stationary point.

Let us now consider in detail the important special case of a stationary point for a function $f(x, y)$ of two variables. Here the Hessian has the form

$$H = \begin{pmatrix} f_{xx} & f_{xy} \\ f_{xy} & f_{yy} \end{pmatrix},$$

where $f_{xx} = \partial^2 f/\partial x^2$, etc. The characteristic equation for the matrix H is

$$\lambda^2 - (f_{xx} + f_{yy})\lambda + (f_{xx}f_{yy} - f_{xy}^2) = 0. \tag{2}$$

The stationary point is a relative minimum when both eigenvalues of H are positive, i.e. when the coefficients in (2) alternate in sign. Now f_{xx} and f_{yy} cannot have opposite signs, since $f_{xx}f_{yy} - f_{xy}^2$ must be positive. Therefore a sufficient condition for a relative minimum is given by the pair of inequalities

$$f_{xx} > 0, \quad f_{xx}f_{yy} - f_{xy}^2 > 0. \tag{3}$$

By a similar argument, a sufficient condition for a relative maximum is that

$$f_{xx} < 0, \quad f_{xx}f_{yy} - f_{xy}^2 > 0. \tag{4}$$

The stationary point is a saddle point when the two eigenvalues of H have opposite sign. Since the product of the eigenvalues of H is equal to det H, a sufficient condition for the stationary point to be a saddle point is that

$$f_{xx}f_{yy} - f_{xy}^2 < 0. \tag{5}$$

If none of the conditions (3), (4) or (5) is satisfied, the matrix H necessarily has a zero eigenvalue, so that a knowledge of only the second derivatives of the function $f(x, y)$ is not sufficient to determine the nature of the stationary point.

The connection between the nature of a stationary point and the signs of the eigenvalues of the Hessian at that point can also be understood from a more geometrical standpoint by examining the surfaces on which the quadratic form (1) is constant. As we saw in Sec. 1.6, the nature of the surfaces $Q(\delta x) = $ const depends on the relative signs of these eigenvalues. If all the eigenvalues have the same sign, these surfaces are ellipsoids; but if the eigenvalues are both positive and negative, these surfaces are hyperboloids. In the first case, the surfaces $f(x) = $ const in the immediate vicinity of the stationary point are ellipsoids, and it is clear that the stationary point must be either a minimum or a maximum. In the second case, these surfaces are hyperboloids, and we have a saddle point.

We illustrate these ideas by means of the following example.

Example Find the maximum value of the function

$$f(x, y, z) = (x + y + z)e^{-(x^2 + y^2 + z^2)}.$$

First, we can argue that a maximum certainly exists. Since there is a region in which the function $f(x, y, z)$ is positive, $f(x, y, z) \to 0$ as $x^2 + y^2 + z^2 \to \infty$, and $f(x, y, z)$ is continuous and hence bounded in any finite region, we can deduce that the function takes a maximum value at some point (x, y, z). This point, which is a local maximum of the function, must be a stationary point.

The necessary conditions for a stationary point are

$$f_x(x, y, z) = f_y(x, y, z) = f_z(x, y, z) = 0.$$

Writing $r^2 \equiv x^2 + y^2 + z^2$, we have

$$f_x(x, y, z) = [1 - 2x(x + y + z)]e^{-r^2} = 0 \qquad (6)$$

and hence $x + y + z = 1/2x$. Similarly, the relation $f_y(x, y, z) = 0$ implies that $x + y + z = 1/2y$, and $f_z(x, y, z) = 0$ implies that $x + y + z = 1/2z$. Hence $x = y = z$, so that $3x = 1/2x$ and $x = \pm 1/\sqrt{6}$. Consequently, there are two stationary points

$$(x, y, z) = \pm \left(\frac{1}{\sqrt{6}}, \frac{1}{\sqrt{6}}, \frac{1}{\sqrt{6}} \right) \equiv \pm(x_0, y_0, z_0). \qquad (7)$$

Evaluating the function at these stationary points, we find

$$f\left(\frac{1}{\sqrt{6}}, \frac{1}{\sqrt{6}}, \frac{1}{\sqrt{6}} \right) = \frac{3}{\sqrt{6}} e^{-3/6} = \frac{\sqrt{6}}{2} e^{-1/2},$$

$$f\left(-\frac{1}{\sqrt{6}}, -\frac{1}{\sqrt{6}}, -\frac{1}{\sqrt{6}} \right) = -\frac{\sqrt{6}}{2} e^{-1/2}.$$

The first of these values is clearly the maximum value of the function. Since the function is antisymmetric with respect to reflection about the origin, the second value is its minimum value.

Although we have solved the problem completely, it is instructive to see how the Hessian can be used to check the nature of the stationary points. By differentiating (6), we obtain

$$f_{xx}(x, y, z) = \{-2x[1 - 2x(x + y + z)] - 4x - 2y - 2z\}\, e^{-r^2},$$

$$f_{xy}(x, y, z) = \{-2y[1 - 2x(x + y + z)] - 2x\}\, e^{-r^2}.$$

Similar expressions can be written for the other partial derivatives by permuting the variables x, y, z. At the stationary points $\pm(x_0, y_0, z_0)$ defined in (7), we find

$$f_{xx}[\pm(x_0, y_0, z_0)] = 4f_{xy}[\pm(x_0, y_0, z_0)] = \mp \frac{8}{\sqrt{6}}\, e^{-1/2},$$

so that the Hessian at these points has the values

$$H_\pm = \mp \frac{2}{\sqrt{6}}\, e^{-1/2} \begin{pmatrix} 4 & 1 & 1 \\ 1 & 4 & 1 \\ 1 & 1 & 4 \end{pmatrix} \equiv \mp \frac{2}{\sqrt{6}}\, e^{-1/2}\, N. \tag{8}$$

The characteristic equation of the matrix N is

$$-\lambda^3 + 12\lambda^2 - 45\lambda + 54 = 0.$$

By solving this equation for the eigenvalues of N ($\lambda = 3, 3, 6$), or by simply observing that the coefficients in the characteristic equation alternate in sign, we deduce that N is positive definite. This in turn implies that H_+ is negative definite (corresponding to a maximum of $f(x, y, z)$ at $(x, y, z) = (x_0, y_0, z_0)$), while H_- is positive definite (corresponding to a minimum of $f(x, y, z)$ at $(x, y, z) = -(x_0, y_0, z_0)$).

Still another method of analyzing the Hessian H_+ in this example is based on the fact that N has the special structure

$$N_{ij} = \begin{cases} a & \text{if } i = j, \\ b & \text{if } i \neq j, \end{cases}$$

where a and b are certain constants. Matrices of this type arise in a number of applications, and it is easy to find their eigenvalues and eigenvectors in the general case of n dimensions. Symmetry considerations suggest that $\mathbf{u} \equiv (1 \;\; 1 \dots 1)^T$ is an eigenvector. This is indeed the case, since

$$(N\mathbf{u})_i = \sum_{j=1}^{n} N_{ij} u_j = \sum_{j=1}^{n} N_{ij} = \lambda,$$

where λ, the sum of the elements of row i of the matrix, is independent of i; in other words, $N\mathbf{u} = \lambda\mathbf{u}$, so that λ is the eigenvalue corresponding to the eigenvector $\mathbf{u}$. (The preceding argument actually applies to any matrix in which the sum of the elements of each row has a common value λ.) Next we can show that any vector $\mathbf{v}$ which is orthogonal to the special vector $\mathbf{u}$

is also an eigenvector. Suppose that $\mathbf{v} \equiv (v_1 \ldots v_n)^T$ is orthogonal to $\mathbf{u}$, so that

$$\sum_{i=1}^{n} v_i = 0.$$

Then

$$(N\mathbf{v})_i = \sum_{j=1}^{n} N_{ij} v_j = \sum_{j \neq i} b v_j + a v_i = b \sum_{j=1}^{n} v_j + (a-b) v_i = (a-b) v_i.$$

Thus $\mathbf{v}$ is an eigenvector with eigenvalue $(a - b)$. Applying these results to the specific matrix N defined in (8), we find the eigenvalues $3, 3, 6$, as before.

2.3 Constraints and Lagrange multipliers

We now turn to the problem of finding the points at which a function $f(x_1, \ldots, x_n)$ is stationary when the values of the variables $x_1, \ldots, x_n$ are constrained to satisfy a set of m conditions $g^{(k)}(x_1, \ldots, x_n) = 0$ ($k = 1, \ldots, m$), where $m < n$.

The basic result, which we shall establish below, can be expressed as the following rule. Define the new function

$$\phi(\mathbf{x}) \equiv f(\mathbf{x}) + \sum_{k=1}^{m} \lambda_k g^{(k)}(\mathbf{x}), \tag{1}$$

where the quantities λ_k are undetermined parameters, known as *Lagrange multipliers*. Determine the stationary points of $\phi(\mathbf{x})$ *without* constraints, as a function of the parameters λ_k. Suppose that these parameters λ_k are fixed in such a way that the stationary points of $\phi(\mathbf{x})$ satisfy the m constraints which are imposed. Then the resulting stationary points are precisely the stationary points of the original problem.

As a practical rule of procedure, the solution is determined by solving simultaneously the $(n + m)$ equations

$$\begin{cases} \dfrac{\partial \phi}{\partial x_i} = 0 & (i = 1, \ldots, n), \\[2mm] g^{(k)} = 0 & (k = 1, \ldots, m) \end{cases} \tag{2}$$

for the $(n + m)$ unknowns $x_1, \ldots, x_n ; \lambda_1, \ldots, \lambda_m$.

We give three alternative derivations of this result, each of which has some particular advantage, and which together afford greater insight into the problem. The first derivation shows that all solutions of the system of equations (2) are indeed stationary points of the original problem. The other derivations show that, conversely, all such stationary points satisfy the equations (2).

'Elementary' derivation

Suppose that $x \equiv (x_1 \ldots x_n)^T$ and $\lambda_1, \ldots, \lambda_m$ satisfy the equations (2). Then x, while satisfying all the constraints, is also a stationary point of the function (1) without constraints. Obviously, $\phi(x)$ is also stationary at this point if we restrict ourselves to those variations of x which preserve all the constraint conditions $g^{(k)}(x) = 0$; but this is equivalent to the statement that the function $f(x)$ itself is stationary for variations of x which preserve the constraint conditions.

'Algebraic' derivation

Consider those variations of x which preserve all the constraint conditions. If $f(x)$ is stationary for such variations, we have

$$df = \sum_{i=1}^{n} f_i \, dx_i = 0 \tag{3}$$

$(f_i \equiv \partial f / \partial x_i)$ for all allowed sets of dx_i, while the constraint conditions give the relations

$$dg^{(k)} = \sum_{i=1}^{n} g_i^{(k)} \, dx_i = 0 \quad (k = 1, \ldots, m) \tag{4}$$

among the dx_i. Since the relations (4) are linear, we could use them in principle to eliminate m of the differentials dx_i, say $dx_1, \ldots, dx_m$, from the condition (3) and to rewrite (3) in a form containing only the remaining differentials. This could be done by adding suitable multiples of the equations (4) to (3). In other words, the condition

$$df + \sum_{k=1}^{m} \lambda_k \, dg^{(k)} = \sum_{i=1}^{n} \left[f_i + \sum_{k=1}^{m} \lambda_k \, g_i^{(k)} \right] dx_i = 0$$

can be satisfied with values of the multipliers λ_k such that the coefficients of $dx_1, \ldots, dx_m$ vanish. Since the remaining differentials $dx_{m+1}, \ldots, dx_n$ then represent *independent* variations, their coefficients must also vanish. The vanishing of all n coefficients is equivalent to the condition

$$\nabla \left[f + \sum_{k=1}^{m} \lambda_k g^{(k)} \right] = 0,$$

i.e. to the statement that the function $\phi(\mathbf{x})$ defined by (1) has an unconstrained stationary point.

'Geometric' derivation

We use again the differential conditions (3) and (4) formulated above. The equations (4) can be regarded as vector equations $\nabla g^{(k)} \cdot d\mathbf{x} = 0$, which state that the variations $d\mathbf{x}$ allowed by the constraints are precisely those which are orthogonal to each of the gradient vectors $\nabla g^{(k)}$ ($k = 1, \ldots, m$). The equation $\nabla f \cdot d\mathbf{x} = 0$ obtained from (3) shows that ∇f is orthogonal to all the allowed variations $d\mathbf{x}$; i.e., ∇f lies in the subspace spanned by the vectors $\nabla g^{(k)}$. Thus there exist coefficients λ_k such that

$$\nabla f = - \sum_{k=1}^{m} \lambda_k \, \nabla g^{(k)} . \tag{5}$$

We now establish a general procedure for resolving the nature of stationary points for constrained variations. We recall that

$$\delta f = \delta \mathbf{x} \cdot [\nabla f]_{\mathbf{x}=\mathbf{a}} + \tfrac{1}{2} (\delta \mathbf{x})^{\mathrm{T}} H (\delta \mathbf{x}) + \mathrm{o}(|\delta \mathbf{x}|^2). \tag{6}$$

If the variations $\delta \mathbf{x}$ are restricted to those which satisfy all the constraints $g^{(k)}(\mathbf{x}) = 0$, then in exact analogy with (6) we can write

$$\delta g^{(k)} = 0 = \delta \mathbf{x} \cdot [\nabla g^{(k)}]_{\mathbf{x}=\mathbf{a}} + \tfrac{1}{2} (\delta \mathbf{x})^{\mathrm{T}} G^{(k)} (\delta \mathbf{x}) + \mathrm{o}(|\delta \mathbf{x}|^2), \tag{7}$$

where $G^{(k)}$ is the Hessian for the function $g^{(k)}(\mathbf{x})$. Substituting (5) into (6) and making use of the constraint conditions (7) to eliminate the quantities $\nabla g^{(k)}$, we obtain

$$\delta f = \tfrac{1}{2} (\delta \mathbf{x})^{\mathrm{T}} \left[H + \sum_{k=1}^{m} \lambda_k G^{(k)} \right] (\delta \mathbf{x}) + \mathrm{o}(|\delta \mathbf{x}|^2). \tag{8}$$

Note that the matrix in the square brackets in (8) is simply the Hessian for the function $\phi(\mathbf{x})$ defined in (1).

Suppose now that we have already determined a stationary point and an associated set of Lagrange multipliers λ_k. We can then test for a relative minimum or maximum by determining whether the quadratic form on the right-hand side of (8) is strictly positive or strictly negative for all small displacements that are compatible with the constraints or, equivalently, for all vectors $\delta \mathbf{x}$ in the $(n - m)$-dimensional subspace defined by the set of equations $\delta \mathbf{x} \cdot \nabla g^{(k)} = 0$ ($k = 1, \ldots, m$). Of course, if the quadratic form in (8) is positive or negative definite, it is obviously unnecessary to add the restriction to resolve the nature of the stationary point. If it is not definite, we can rewrite it with respect to a new basis that includes a set of basis vectors for the above-mentioned subspace and then determine whether the quadratic form (in a smaller number of variables) corresponding to variations in this subspace is positive or negative definite. The procedure is illustrated by the following example.

Example   Find the stationary points of the function $f(x, y, z) = x^2 y^3 z^4$ subject to the condition $2x + 3y + 4z = a$ (where a is a positive constant) and determine their nature.

Let

$$\phi(x, y, z) = x^2 y^3 z^4 + \lambda(2x + 3y + 4z - a).$$

We must find all solutions of the simultaneous equations

$$\begin{cases} \phi_x = 2xy^3 z^4 + 2\lambda = 0, \\ \phi_y = 3x^2 y^2 z^4 + 3\lambda = 0, \\ \phi_z = 4x^2 y^3 z^3 + 4\lambda = 0, \\ 2x + 3y + 4z = a. \end{cases}$$

Now since

$$x\phi_x + y\phi_y + z\phi_z = 0 = 9x^2 y^3 z^4 + \lambda (2x + 3y + 4z),$$

we have $\lambda a = -9x^2 y^3 z^4$ and the equations $\phi_x = \phi_y = \phi_z = 0$ give $x = y = z = a/9$. This is the only stationary point, at which

$$f\left(\frac{a}{9}, \frac{a}{9}, \frac{a}{9}\right) = \left(\frac{a}{9}\right)^9.$$

To determine the nature of this stationary point, let us evaluate the Hessian H of the function $\phi(x, y, z)$. We find

$$\phi_{xx} = 2y^3 z^4, \quad \phi_{yy} = 6x^2 yz^4, \quad \phi_{zz} = 12x^2 y^3 z^2,$$

$$\phi_{xy} = 6xy^2 z^4, \quad \phi_{xz} = 8xy^3 z^3, \quad \phi_{yz} = 12x^2 y^2 z^3.$$

At $x = y = z = a/9$, the Hessian is

$$H = 2\left(\frac{a}{9}\right)^7 \begin{pmatrix} 1 & 3 & 4 \\ 3 & 3 & 6 \\ 4 & 6 & 6 \end{pmatrix} \equiv 2\left(\frac{a}{9}\right)^7 M.$$

The characteristic equation of the matrix M is $-\lambda^3 + 10\lambda^2 + 34\lambda + 24 = 0$, so that the quadratic form $(\delta \mathbf{x})^T H(\delta \mathbf{x})$ is neither positive nor negative definite. We therefore investigate whether $(\delta \mathbf{x})^T H(\delta \mathbf{x})$ is of definite sign when restricted to variations $\delta \mathbf{x}$ that satisfy the constraint. Two independent vectors parallel to the plane $2x + 3y + 4z = a$ are given by $(3 \ -2 \ 0)^T$ and $(2 \ 0 \ -1)^T$. (Note that these need not be mutually orthogonal.) Suppose that $(b \ c \ d)^T$ is any third linearly independent vector (for example, a vector perpendicular to the plane). With respect to the basis formed by these three vectors, the Hessian H becomes a matrix of the form

$$H = 2\left(\frac{a}{9}\right)^7 \begin{pmatrix} 3 & -2 & 0 \\ 2 & 0 & -1 \\ b & c & d \end{pmatrix} \begin{pmatrix} 1 & 3 & 4 \\ 3 & 3 & 6 \\ 4 & 6 & 6 \end{pmatrix} \begin{pmatrix} 3 & 2 & b \\ -2 & 0 & c \\ 0 & -1 & d \end{pmatrix} = 2\left(\frac{a}{9}\right)^7 \begin{pmatrix} -15 & -6 & \cdot \\ -6 & -6 & \cdot \\ \cdot & \cdot & \cdot \end{pmatrix},$$

where the dots denote elements that need not be calculated if we are interested in only displacements of the form $\delta\bar{x} = (\delta\bar{x}_1 \ \delta\bar{x}_2 \ 0)^T$ with respect to the new basis. The calculation of the required 2 x 2 submatrix of $\bar{H}$ can be performed by the following simpler procedure:

$$2\left(\frac{a}{9}\right)^7 \begin{pmatrix} 3 & -2 & 0 \\ 2 & 0 & -1 \end{pmatrix} \begin{pmatrix} 1 & 3 & 4 \\ 3 & 3 & 6 \\ 4 & 6 & 6 \end{pmatrix} \begin{pmatrix} 3 & 2 \\ -2 & 0 \\ 0 & -1 \end{pmatrix} = 2\left(\frac{a}{9}\right)^7 \begin{pmatrix} -15 & -6 \\ -6 & -6 \end{pmatrix}.$$

It is easy to verify that this 2 x 2 matrix is negative definite. Consequently, the constrained stationary point is a relative maximum.

Problems

1 Expand by Taylor's theorem $(1 - x^2 - y^2)^{1/2}$ about the point $(x, y) = (0, 0)$ up to fourth-degree terms, and verify that your result agrees with the binomial expansion of $(1 - u)^{1/2}$ with $u = x^2 + y^2$.

2 Show that the function

$$f(x, y) = \exp(y + x \sin y)$$

has neither minima nor maxima.

3 Find all the stationary points of the function

$$f(x, y) = (2x^2 - y^2)e^{x+y}$$

and determine their nature.

4 Find the minimum and maximum values of the function

$$f(x, y) = 3x^2 + 2\sqrt{2}xy + 4y^2$$

on the circle $x^2 + y^2 = 9$.

5 Show that the function

$$F(x, y, z) = x^2 + y^2 + z^2$$

subject to the constraint $x^3 + y^3 + z^3 = 1$ has a total of seven stationary points. Show that one stationary point is a relative maximum and three are relative minima, while the remaining three are neither minima nor maxima.

6 Find the stationary points of the function

$$F(x, y, z) = x^2 - 4xy + y^2 + 2z^2$$

subject to the constraint $x^2 + y^2 + z^2 = 1$ and determine whether each stationary point is a minimum, maximum, or neither.

7 Find the extreme values of the function

$$F(x, y, z) = x^2 + 2y^2 + 3z^2$$

subject to the conditions $x^2 + y^2 + z^2 = 1$ and $x + y + z = 0$.

8 A curve in space is defined by the intersection of the plane $x - y + z = c$ and the hyperboloid $x^2 + y^2 - \frac{1}{2}z^2 = c^2$, where c is a constant. Show that the points on this curve which are nearest to the origin are $(0, -c, 0)$ and $(c, 0, 0)$.

9 Find the points on the curve defined by the intersection of the surfaces $x + y = 1$ and $x^2 + 2y^2 + z^2 = 1$ which are nearest to and furthest from the origin.

10 (i) Show that the function $F(x, y, z) = x^m y^n z^p$ subject to the constraint $x + y + z = 1$, where m, n, p are constants, has a single stationary point at $(x, y, z) = (m/Q, n/Q, p/Q)$, where $Q = m + n + p$.

(ii) In the case $m = n = p > 0$, show by examining the Hessian that the stationary point is a relative minimum.

11 Find the maximum value of the function

$$f(x, y) = \frac{x + 3y}{x^2 + y^2 + xy + 1} \, .$$

12 Find the point on the plane $x + 2y + 3z = 2$ which is nearest the origin.

13 Find the minimum and maximum distances from the point $(1, 1)$ to the curve $5x^2 + 6xy + 5y^2 = 8$ in the xy-plane.

14 Show that there is one stationary point of the function

$$F(x, y, z) = x^2 y^2 z^4$$

subject to the constraint $x + y + 2z = 1$ in the first octant ($x > 0$, $y > 0$, $z > 0$). By examining the appropriate Hessian, show that this stationary point is a relative maximum.

3 The calculus of variations

3.1 Euler's equation

In the previous chapter, we considered the problem of finding extrema of functions of several variables. The calculus of variations is concerned with the determination of extrema of definite integrals which depend on one or more arbitrary *functions*, for variations of these functions within some specified class. A quantity which depends on one or more arbitrary functions is called a *functional*.

The simplest problem of the calculus of variations is as follows. We are given a functional

$$I = \int_a^b F(x, y(x), y'(x)) \, dx, \tag{1}$$

where $F(x, u, v)$ is some specified function of three real variables, while the function $y(x)$ and its derivative $y'(x)$ are undetermined. We wish to find, in some particular class of functions $y(x)$ with prescribed boundary conditions $y(a) = A$ and $y(b) = B$, that function $y = \phi(x)$ which gives to I its minimum value, assuming that such a function exists. Note that there is no loss of generality in seeking a minimum instead of a maximum, since $-I$ is maximized when I is minimized.

This problem can also be formulated in geometrical terms. Each function $y(x)$ in the admissible class corresponds to some curve Γ in the xy-plane joining the points (a, A) and (b, B). We shall sometimes specify such a curve by means of the notation $\Gamma : y = y(x)$. The functional (1) can be regarded as a line integral along such a curve. Although the end-points and the form of the function F in the integrand are fixed, the curve Γ is arbitrary, and the problem is to find that curve $\Gamma_0 : y = \phi(x)$ which minimizes the value of I.

As a simple example, consider the functional

$$I = \int_a^b \sqrt{\left(\frac{dy}{dx}\right)^2 + 1} \, dx \tag{2}$$

for functions $y(x)$ satisfying the boundary conditions $y(a) = A$ and $y(b) = B$. Here I represents the length of the curve joining the points (a, A) and (b, B) in the xy-plane, and it is obvious from elementary considerations that I is minimized when this curve is the straight-line segment Γ_0 given by the equation

$$y = A + \frac{(B - A)(x - a)}{b - a}.$$

Just as we seek *relative* minima (or maxima) in the differential calculus, in the calculus of variations we shall seek *relative* minima of a given functional, for small variations of the unknown function. To define precisely what we mean by 'small' variations, we shall introduce the concept of the 'distance' between two curves Γ_1 and Γ_2, which we shall denote by $\|\Gamma_1 - \Gamma_2\|$. The problem of minimizing a functional such as (2) is then reduced to the problem of finding a curve Γ_0 for which the integral I is smaller than for any neighbouring curve Γ' with the same end-points (see Fig. 3.1).

We have spoken of an 'admissible' class of functions. The importance of imposing definite restrictions on the functions $y(x)$ can be understood qualitatively from the example considered above. Suppose that Γ_0 is the minimizing curve (in this case, the straight-line segment). If we consider only sufficiently 'smooth' curves (in a sense to be defined more precisely below), it is intuitively obvious that any neighbouring curve Γ' (see Fig. 3.1) is only slightly longer than Γ_0, so that in a certain sense the arc length varies continuously as the curve is deformed. However, if we assume only that the functions $y(x)$ are continuous, then there will exist curves such as Γ'' in Fig. 3.1 which are arbitrarily close to the minimizing curve Γ_0 but which nevertheless differ in length from Γ_0 by any pre-assigned amount, so that the nature of the problem is completely changed.

We now make these intuitive ideas more precise mathematically. Consider again the general problem of minimizing a functional of the form (1). Let $I(\Gamma)$ denote the value of the integral I for any curve Γ. Then we

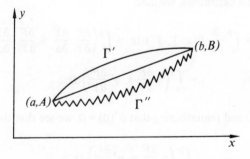

Fig. 3.1

say that a curve Γ_0 provides a *relative minimum* for I if there exists some $\epsilon > 0$ such that $I(\Gamma) \geqslant I(\Gamma_0)$ for all curves Γ in the admissible class for which $\|\Gamma - \Gamma_0\| < \epsilon$. The 'distance' between two curves $\Gamma_1 : y = \phi_1(x)$ and $\Gamma_2 : y = \phi_2(x)$ on the interval $a \leqslant x \leqslant b$ is defined as

$$\|\Gamma_1 - \Gamma_2\| = \max_{x \in [a,b]} |\phi_1(x) - \phi_2(x)|,$$

i.e. the maximum amount by which the functions $\phi_1(x)$ and $\phi_2(x)$ differ from one another within this interval. If $I(\Gamma) \geqslant I(\Gamma_0)$ for *all* Γ in the allowed class, then we have an *absolute minimum*.

Our first task will be to find a necessary condition for a curve $\Gamma_0 : y = \phi(x)$ to provide a relative minimum when the admissible functions $y(x)$ are those that belong to the class $C_2[a, b]$. We shall also assume that the function F is differentiable with respect to its arguments as many times as may be required by the considerations which follow.

Let us consider small variations of the minimizing curve Γ_0. In particular, consider the one-parameter family of varied curves with fixed end-points given by $\Gamma_\alpha : y = \phi(x) + \alpha \eta(x)$, where α is a real parameter and $\eta(x) \in C_2[a, b]$ is some fixed function satisfying the conditions $\eta(a) = \eta(b) = 0$, and let $\psi(\alpha) \equiv I(\Gamma_\alpha)$ be the values of the functional for these curves. In particular, $\psi(0) = I(\Gamma_0)$ is the minimum value of the functional.

Note that for any $\epsilon > 0$, we have $\|\Gamma_\alpha - \Gamma_0\| < \epsilon$ for sufficiently small $|\alpha|$; in other words, the curve Γ_α is 'close' to Γ_0 when $\alpha \approx 0$. This follows from the fact that $\eta(x)$ is continuous and hence bounded on the interval $a \leqslant x \leqslant b$.

If Γ_0 provides a relative minimum, then the function $\psi(\alpha)$ must have a relative minimum at $\alpha = 0$, so that $d\psi/d\alpha = 0$ at $\alpha = 0$. Now

$$\psi(\alpha) = \int_a^b F(x, Y, Y') \, dx,$$

where $Y(x) \equiv \phi(x) + \alpha \eta(x)$ and $Y'(x) \equiv \phi'(x) + \alpha \eta'(x)$. Applying the chain rule for partial derivatives, we have

$$\psi'(\alpha) = \int_a^b \frac{\partial}{\partial \alpha} F(x, Y, Y') dx = \int_a^b \left(\frac{\partial F}{\partial Y} \frac{\partial Y}{\partial \alpha} + \frac{\partial F}{\partial Y'} \frac{\partial Y'}{\partial \alpha} \right) dx$$

$$= \int_a^b \left(\eta \frac{\partial F}{\partial Y} + \eta' \frac{\partial F}{\partial Y'} \right) dx .$$

Setting $\alpha = 0$ and remembering that $\psi'(0) = 0$, we see that the equation

$$\int_a^b \left(\eta \frac{\partial F}{\partial y} + \eta' \frac{\partial F}{\partial y'} \right) dx = 0$$

must hold when $y(x)$ is chosen to be the minimizing function $y = \phi(x)$.
Integrating the second term in the integral by parts, we obtain

$$\int_a^b \left[\eta \frac{\partial F}{\partial y} - \eta \frac{d}{dx}\left(\frac{\partial F}{\partial y'}\right)\right] dx + \left[\eta \frac{\partial F}{\partial y'}\right]_{x=a}^b = 0. \tag{3}$$

The last term on the left-hand side of (3) vanishes because $\eta(a) = \eta(b) = 0$.
Hence

$$\int_a^b \eta \left[\frac{\partial F}{\partial y} - \frac{d}{dx}\left(\frac{\partial F}{\partial y'}\right)\right] dx = 0 \tag{4}$$

must hold when $y = \phi(x)$, for all functions $\eta(x) \in C_2 [a, b]$ such that $\eta(a) = \eta(b) = 0$.

Now the function

$$\frac{d}{dx}\left(\frac{\partial F}{\partial y'}\right) = F_{y'x} + F_{y'y}\, y' + F_{y'y'}\, y'' \tag{5}$$

(where the subscripts denote partial differentiation with respect to the indicated arguments) is continuous, since $y(x) \in C_2 [a, b]$ by hypothesis and all the partial derivatives of F which occur are assumed to be continuous. This implies that the function in the square brackets in the integrand of (4) is a continuous function of x on the interval $a \leqslant x \leqslant b$. From these facts, it can be deduced (see Lemma 1 in Sec. A.3) that the function in the square brackets actually vanishes identically on this interval.

The condition

$$\frac{\partial F}{\partial y} = \frac{d}{dx}\left(\frac{\partial F}{\partial y'}\right) \tag{6}$$

is known as *Euler's equation* and is a necessary condition for a curve $\Gamma : y = \phi(x)$ to be a minimizing curve for the integral I. Euler's equation is the analogue of the condition $\nabla f = 0$ for a stationary point of a function several variables.

Solutions of Euler's equation are called *extremals*. An extremal may or may not correspond to a minimizing or maximizing curve; in general, it represents a curve Γ for which $I(\Gamma)$ is stationary with respect to small variations. It is important to note that Euler's equation (6) is a *second-order* ordinary differential equation for the function $y = y(x)$, since according to (5) its right-hand side contains terms involving both y' and y''. We therefore expect to find, in general, a two-parameter family of extremals and to be able to use the two end-point conditions to select a solution from among them.

We shall not consider here the more difficult problem of establishing sufficient conditions for a relative minimum. In many examples, it is clear from simple geometrical or physical considerations that a minimum or maximum must exist. In these cases, the absolute minimum or maximum of the functional can be determined in principle by finding all the extremals and evaluating the functional for each of them in turn.

We next consider several important special cases of Euler's equation.

(i) If the function F takes the special form $F = F(x, y')$, we have $\partial F/\partial y = 0$ and Euler's equation reduces to $dF_{y'}/dx = 0$. Hence

$$F_{y'} = \text{const.} \tag{7}$$

This is a *first integral* of Euler's equation, i.e. a first-order differential equation which the extremals must satisfy.

(ii) If $F = F(y, y')$, then $F_x = 0$. In this case, applying the chain rule and Euler's equation (6), we have

$$\frac{dF}{dx} = F_y y' + F_{y'} y'' = \frac{dF_{y'}}{dx} y' + F_{y'} y'' = \frac{d(y' F_{y'})}{dx}.$$

Thus we obtain the first integral

$$F - y' F_{y'} = \text{const.} \tag{8}$$

(iii) If $F = F(y')$, then we have the first integral (7) from case (i). Then the fact that $F_{y'}$ is a function of y' alone requires that $y' = \text{const}$, i.e., the extremals are straight lines. This is the case which we considered above in connection with the functional (2).

Example – The brachistochrone problem   A small bead of mass m slides without friction down a curved wire in a vertical plane joining two fixed points A and B under the action of a uniform gravitational field. Find the curve which minimizes the time of descent from A to B. (This is the problem which historically motivated the development of the calculus of variations; the term 'brachistochrone' given to the required curve is from the Greek and means 'shortest time'.)

Suppose that the bead starts from rest at the origin $(0, 0)$ in the xy-plane, where the positive y-axis is taken vertically downward. The kinetic and potential energies of the bead at any instant of time, T and V, are given by $T = \frac{1}{2}m(ds/dt)^2$, where s measures the distance along the unknown curve, and $V = -mgy$, where g is the acceleration due to gravity. Conservation of energy requires that $\frac{1}{2}(ds/dt)^2 - gy = 0$, so that $dt = ds/\sqrt{2gy}$, where $ds = [1 + (dy/dx)^2]^{1/2}dx$. The total time of descent to a given point (a, b) is therefore

$$\Delta t = \frac{1}{\sqrt{2g}} \int_0^a \sqrt{\frac{1+y'^2}{y}} \; dx.$$

We must find the function $y(x)$ which minimizes this integral. According to the special case (ii) considered above, it follows from the absence of an explicit t-dependence of the integrand $F(y, y')$ that there is a first integral of Euler's equation of the form (8), which in this case becomes

$$\frac{1}{\sqrt{y(1+y'^2)}} = c,$$

where c is an arbitrary constant. Differential equations of this type can often be solved by means of the substitution $y' = \tan \psi$. This gives here $\cos \psi/\sqrt{y} = c$, so that

$$y = \frac{1}{c^2} \cos^2 \psi \equiv 2k \cos^2 \psi = k(1 + \cos 2\psi), \tag{9}$$

where k $(k > 0)$ is another constant. Now since $dx = dy/\tan\psi$ and $dy = -4k \sin\psi \cos\psi \, d\psi$ from (9), we have

$$dx = -4k \cos^2 \psi \, d\psi = -2k(1 + \cos 2\psi) \, d\psi.$$

Hence

$$x = k' - k(2\psi + \sin 2\psi), \tag{10}$$

where k' is another arbitrary constant. Equations (9) and (10) can be regarded as the parametric equations of the minimizing curve (which turns out to be a cycloid). The two constants k and k' can obviously be chosen in such a way that the curve passes through the specified point (a, b) in the xy-plane.

3.2 Extremals with corners

Consider the problem of finding extremals for the functional

$$I = \int_a^b y^2 (1 - y')^2 \, dx. \tag{1}$$

The first integral $F - y'F_{y'} = \text{const}$ gives in this case $y^2 - y^2 y'^2 = C$, where C is some constant. For $C = 0$, we have the straight-line solutions $y = 0$ or $y' = \pm 1$. Otherwise, we can separate the variables, giving $y \, dy/\sqrt{y^2 - C} = dx$, which yields on integration the family of hyperbolas $y^2 - (x + k)^2 = C$, where k is a second arbitrary constant.

If we now attempt to find an extremal joining the end-points $(0, 0)$ and $(8, 4)$ in the xy-plane by fixing the constants k and C, we find the unique

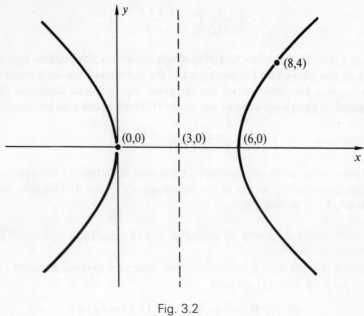

Fig. 3.2

hyperbola $(x - 3)^2 - y^2 = 9$. The symmetry axes of this hyperbola are $x = 3$ and $y = 0$, and there is a gap in the interval $0 < x < 6$ (see Fig. 3.2). Therefore the points $(0, 0)$ and $(8, 4)$ lie on different branches of the hyperbola, so that, contrary to what might be expected at first sight, there is actually no extremal in the class $C_2 [0, 8]$ which joins these two points.

However, we notice that the integrand of (1) vanishes when either $y = 0$ or $y' = 1$ but is positive otherwise. This means that the functional I will certainly have an absolute minimum ($I = 0$) if we allow the end-points to be joined by a curve consisting entirely of line segments on which $y = 0$ or $y' = 1$. Such a curve joining the end-points $(0, 0)$ and $(8, 4)$ certainly exists: it consists of the straight-line segments from $(0, 0)$ to $(4, 0)$ and from $(4, 0)$ to $(8, 4)$. This curve is not in the class $C_2 [0, 8]$, since it has a 'corner' (discontinuous slope) at $x = 4$. Nevertheless, it is clear that the value of the integral I with the given end-points can be made arbitrarily close to zero for curves in the class $C_2 [0, 8]$ by simply 'rounding' the corner.

These considerations suggest that we enlarge the class of admissible curves to include curves with corners. In fact, it turns out to be possible to drop the requirement that the allowed functions $y(x)$ are twice differentiable. For this purpose, we introduce the somewhat more general class of *piecewise smooth* functions as follows. If $y(x)$ is a function defined on the interval $a \leqslant x \leqslant b$, we shall write $y(x) \in \mathrm{PS}[a, b]$ if (i) $y(x) \in$ $C[a, b]$ and (ii) $y'(x) \in \mathrm{PC}[a, b]$, where $\mathrm{PC}[a, b]$ denotes the class of functions which are piecewise continuous on the interval $a \leqslant x \leqslant b$ (i.e., those functions which are continuous at all but a finite number of points of the interval and which have left- and right-hand limits as x approaches each such point). The curves corresponding to such functions $y(x)$, which consist of finitely many smooth arcs, are also said to be piecewise smooth.

We shall now derive a necessary condition for a curve $\Gamma_0 : y = \phi(x)$ to provide a relative minimum for a functional

$$I = \int_a^b F(x, y, y') \, dx, \tag{2}$$

for curves in the class $\mathrm{PS}[a, b]$. In analogy with the derivation of Euler's equation, let us consider a one-parameter family of varied curves $\Gamma_\alpha : y(x) = \phi(x) + \alpha \eta(x)$, for some function $\eta(x) \in \mathrm{PS}[a, b]$ such that $\eta(a) = \eta(b) = 0$. Exactly as in the derivation of Euler's equation, we can show that

$$\int_a^b (\eta F_y + \eta' F_{y'}) \, dx = 0.$$

However, we cannot integrate the second term by parts as before, since we would have

$$\frac{dF_{y'}}{dx} = F_{y'x} + F_{y'y} y' + F_{y'y'} y''$$

and we are no longer assuming the existence of the second derivative $y''(x)$. Instead, we proceed as follows. Defining the quantities

$$A = \int_a^x F_y \, dx, \quad A' = F_y, \quad B = F_{y'},$$

we can write

$$\int_a^b (\eta A' + \eta' B) \, dx = 0.$$

Integrating the first term by parts, we find that

$$0 = \int_a^b (-\eta' A + \eta' B) \, dx + [\eta A]_{x=a}^b = \int_a^b \eta' (B - A) \, dx \tag{3}$$

for all functions $\eta(x)$ satisfying the prescribed conditions $\eta(x) \in \mathrm{PS}[a, b]$ and $\eta(a) = \eta(b) = 0$. Now the function B, and hence also the factor $(B - A)$ in (3), is a continuous function of x except at the corners of $\phi(x)$ (where one of the arguments of F, namely $y'(x)$, is discontinuous along the extremal), so that $(B - A) \in \mathrm{PC}[a, b]$. Under these conditions, we can conclude that $B - A = $ const in the range $a \leqslant x \leqslant b$ (see Lemma 2 in Sec. A.3). Hence $B' = A'$, except at the corners of $\phi(x)$ (where A' and B' may not exist). Reverting to the definitions of A and B, this gives $d(F_{y'})/dx = F_y$, except at the corners.

Thus we have shown that Euler's equation is satisfied *between* the corners of a minimizing curve in the class of piecewise smooth curves. The functions which represent such curves have continuous derivatives between any two corners. This means that we have in fact proved that Euler's equation is satisfied more generally by the minimizing curves of the functional (2), for curves in the class $C_1[a, b]$. Conditions which must be satisfied *at* the corners will be derived later.

As a corollary, we can show that if $\Gamma_0 : y = \phi(x)$ is a minimizing curve in the class PS$[a, b]$, then in fact $\phi(x) \in C_2$ on any interval which excludes both corners and points at which $\partial^2 F/\partial y'^2 = 0$. To prove this, we note that Euler's equation implies that

$$F_{y'x} + F_{y'y} y' + F_{y'y'} y'' = F_y ,$$

except at corners. This means that

$$y'' = \frac{F_y - F_{y'x} - F_{y'y} y'}{F_{y'y'}}$$

is continuous if $F_{y'y'} \neq 0$.

3.3 Variable end-points

Let $\Gamma_0 : y = \phi(x)$ be an extremal joining two specified end-points (x_1, y_1) and (x_2, y_2) and let

$$I = \int_{x_1}^{x_2} F(x, y, y') \, dx \tag{1}$$

be evaluated for this extremal. We shall find an expression for the variation dI in the value of the integral (1) when the end-points are displaced to $(x_1 + dx_1, y_1 + dy_1)$ and $(x_2 + dx_2, y_2 + dy_2)$ and the original extremal Γ_0 is replaced by any neighbouring curve (not necessarily an extremal) joining the new end-points.

As before, we consider a one-parameter family of varied curves $\Gamma_\alpha : y = \phi(x) + \alpha \eta(x)$, where $\eta(x) \in C_2[a, b]$, with $a < x_1 < x_2 < b$; but we shall no longer assume that $\eta(x_1) = \eta(x_2) = 0$. If the end-points as well as the curve which joins them are allowed to vary with α, the value of the functional can be described by

$$I(\alpha) = \int_{x_1(\alpha)}^{x_2(\alpha)} F(x, \phi + \alpha\eta, \phi' + \alpha\eta')\,dx .$$

Differentiating with respect to α, we obtain

$$\frac{dI}{d\alpha} = \int_{x_1}^{x_2} \frac{\partial F}{\partial \alpha}\, dx + \frac{dx_2}{d\alpha}\Big[F\Big]_{x=x_2} - \frac{dx_1}{d\alpha}\Big[F\Big]_{x=x_1} .$$

In exact analogy with the derivation of Euler's equation (cf. equation (3) of Sec. 3.1), we have

$$\int_{x_1}^{x_2} \Big[\frac{\partial F}{\partial \alpha}\Big]_{\alpha=0}\, dx = \int_{x_1}^{x_2} \eta\Big[\frac{\partial F}{\partial y} - \frac{d}{dx}\Big(\frac{\partial F}{\partial y'}\Big)\Big]\, dx + \Big[\eta\,\frac{\partial F}{\partial y'}\Big]_{x=x_1}^{x_2} \quad (2)$$

when $y = \phi(x)$. The integral term on the right-hand side of (2) vanishes because $y = \phi(x)$ is an extremal (i.e., a solution of Euler's equation). However, the last term in (2) no longer vanishes, since $\eta(x)$ is not necessarily equal to zero at the end-points. Thus we can write

$$\Big[\frac{dI}{d\alpha}\Big]_{\alpha=0} = \Big[\eta\,\frac{\partial F}{\partial y'}\Big]_{x=x_1}^{x_2} + \Big[F\frac{dx}{d\alpha}\Big]_{x=x_1}^{x_2} ,$$

so that the variation in I is given by

$$dI = \Big[\eta\,\frac{\partial F}{\partial y'}\Big]_{x=x_1}^{x_2}\, d\alpha + \Big[F\,dx\Big]_{x=x_1}^{x_2} \quad (3)$$

Now the varied curves are described by $y(x, \alpha) = \phi(x) + \alpha\eta(x)$, and we recall that the end-points x_1 and x_2 also depend on the parameter α. Therefore at each end-point $(i = 1, 2)$ we have

$$\frac{dy_i}{d\alpha} = \frac{d\phi}{dx}\frac{dx_i}{d\alpha} + \eta + \alpha\,\frac{d\eta}{dx}\frac{dx_i}{d\alpha} , \quad (4)$$

where all the quantities are evaluated at $x = x_i$. When $\alpha = 0$, (4) becomes $\eta\,d\alpha = dy_i - y_i'dx_i$, where $y_i' \equiv (d\phi/dx)_i$ is the slope function of the extremal at the end-point (x_i, y_i). Hence the expression (3) for dI can be rewritten in the form

$$dI = \Big[(F - y' F_{y'})\,dx + (F_{y'})\,dy\Big]_1^2 , \quad (5)$$

where the indices 1 and 2 refer to the two end-points. This is the *variable end-point theorem*. Note that the form of the variation dI away from an extremal depends only on the displacements of the end-points, and not on the detailed form of the varied curve.

The coefficients of dx and dy in (5) are precisely the quantities which appear in the first integrals of Euler's equation when either of the variables x or y is absent in the integrand $F(x, y, y')$. This is no accident. Consider, for example, the case in which y is absent in F. In this case, Euler's equation is invariant under the transformation $y \to y$ + const, so that the shape of the extremal connecting two end-points (x_1, y_1) and (x_2, y_2) (and hence the corresponding value of I) can depend only on the difference $(y_2 - y_1)$ and not on y_1 and y_2 individually. Thus, for variations of the type $(dx_1, dy_1) = (dx_2, dy_2) = (0, dy)$ (a displacement of both end-points by the same amount in the y-direction), the variable end-point theorem tells us that $[F_{y'}]_1^2 \equiv (F_{y'})_2 - (F_{y'})_1$ must vanish. But this is true for *any* pair of end-points 1 and 2 on a given extremal. Hence $F_{y'}$ = const, in agreement with the first integral of Euler's equation. A similar argument holds in the case when the variable x is absent in F.

The variable end-point theorem can be applied to the problem of finding the curves for which the functional (1) is stationary when one or both of the end-points (x_1, y_1) and (x_2, y_2) are constrained to lie on prescribed curves in the xy-plane specified by equations of the form $\Phi_1(x_1, y_1) = 0$ and $\Phi_2(x_2, y_2) = 0$.

This problem can be solved as follows. First, we note that the required curves must be solutions of Euler's equation, since the functional I is stationary in particular for variations which keep the end-points fixed. In other words, the required curves are among the extremals for the ordinary problem with fixed end-points. This family of extremals is in general described by two parameters, say α and β.

Secondly, we require that

$$dI = \left[(F - y'F_{y'})dx + F_{y'} dy\right]_1^2 \equiv \left[U dx + V dy\right]_1^2 = 0$$

for general variations of the end-points consistent with the constraining curves $\Phi_1(x, y) = 0$ and $\Phi_2(x, y) = 0$. Since $dI = 0$ in particular when either end-point is fixed (for example, $dx_1 = dy_1 = 0$), we have $[U dx + V dy]_i = 0$ at *each* end-point ($i = 1, 2$) separately, provided that the ratio dy_i/dx_i is consistent with the derivative dy/dx calculated from the appropriate condition $\Phi_i(x, y) = 0$.

Thus, we can determine the two parameters α and β characterizing the required extremal and the coordinates (x_1, y_1) and (x_2, y_2) of the unknown end-points by imposing simultaneously the following six conditions: the two end-point conditions $[U dx + V dy]_i = 0$, the two conditions that the end-points satisfy the extremal equation, and the two conditions $\Phi_i(x_i, y_i) = 0$ that these end-points lie on the prescribed curves.

Similarly, in the case when one end-point is fixed and the other is required to lie on some prescribed curve, we have four conditions for the four unknowns.

Example Minimize the functional

$$I = \int_0^X y^2 \, y'^2 \, dx$$

for the end-points $(0, 0)$ and (X, Y), where (X, Y) is constrained to lie on the section of the hyperbola $y^2 - x^2 = 4$ in the first quadrant.

As a first step, we find the extremals. Since x is absent in the integrand, we have the first integral of Euler's equation, $F - y'F_{y'} = $ const, which gives $-y^2 y'^2 = -K^2$, where K is some positive constant. Then $ydy = Kdx$ and the extremals have the form $y^2 = Ax + B$, where A and B are constants. If we restrict ourselves to extremals passing through the origin, we can take $B = 0$.

Next, we apply the end-point condition at $(x, y) = (X, Y)$. This gives

$$(F - y' F_{y'})dx + F_{y'} \, dy = -Y^2 y'^2 \, dx + 2Y^2 y'dy = 0. \qquad (6)$$

(Care must be taken in the interpretation of this condition: here y' is the slope function of the extremal and not of the constraining curve, whereas dy/dx is the slope of the constraining curve, since (dx, dy) represents the allowed end-point variations.)

Since the extremals are $y^2 = Ax$, we have $2yy' = A$ on an extremal. Using this relation to eliminate y' from the end-point condition (6), we have

$$-\tfrac{1}{4}A^2 \, dx + AY \, dy = 0. \qquad (7)$$

But for the displacement (dx, dy) to be consistent with the constraining curve $y^2 - x^2 = 4$, we require that $2Ydy = 2Xdx$, so that (7) reads $(-\tfrac{1}{4}A^2 + AX)dx = 0$. Hence either $A = 0$ or $X = \tfrac{1}{4}A$. If $A = 0$, then $Y = 0$, since $Y^2 = AX$ for any point on the extremal; however, the value $Y = 0$ is inconsistent with the constraining curve $y^2 - x^2 = 4$. We therefore reject the case $A = 0$ and suppose instead that $X = \tfrac{1}{4}A$. Combining this with the equations $Y^2 = AX$ and $Y^2 - X^2 = 4$, we find the solution $X = 2/\sqrt{3}$, $Y = 4/\sqrt{3}, A = 8/\sqrt{3}$, and the required extremal is $y^2 = (8/\sqrt{3})x$.

3.4 Corner conditions

Suppose that we seek a minimizing curve in the class $PS[a, b]$ for a functional

$$I = \int_a^b F(x, y, y') dx$$

with fixed end-points $P \equiv (a, A)$ and $Q \equiv (b, B)$. Under what conditions can such a curve have corners? Let PQ denote some curve (an extremal)

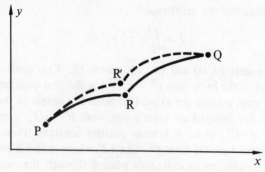

Fig. 3.3

for which I is stationary and which has a single corner at R, so that PR and RQ are extremal arcs without corners (see Fig. 3.3). Suppose that we vary the path PRQ so as to displace the corner by an amount (dx, dy) to a new position R', keeping the end-points P and Q fixed at their original positions. Then the variable end-point theorem (which we have proved for extremals without corners) can be applied to each of the arcs PR and RQ individually. This tells us that the total variation in the functional is given by $dI = dI_1 + dI_2$, where

$$dI_1 = [F - y' F_{y'}]_1 \, dx + [F_{y'}]_1 \, dy,$$

$$dI_2 = -[F - y' F_{y'}]_2 \, dx - [F_{y'}]_2 \, dy.$$

The subscripts 1 and 2 indicate that the quantities are to be evaluated at the corner R on the arcs PR and RQ, respectively, i.e. just to the left and just to the right of the corner. The total variation in the functional can therefore be expressed in the form

$$dI = \left[F - y' F_{y'} \right]_2^1 dx + \left[F_{y'} \right]_2^1 dy.$$

This result shows that the variable end-point theorem actually remains valid for extremals with corners.

Since we are assuming that $dI = 0$ for arbitrary displacements (dx, dy) of the corner, we conclude that

$$[F - y' F_{y'}]_1 = [F - y' F_{y'}]_2 ,$$
$$[F_{y'}]_1 = [F_{y'}]_2 . \tag{1}$$

These relations, known as the *Weierstrass-Erdmann corner conditions*, are necessary conditions which must be satisfied at each corner of an extremal.

Example   Examine the possibility of corners in the extremals in the class

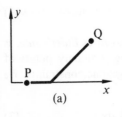 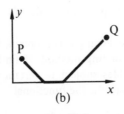 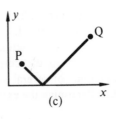

Fig. 3.4

of piecewise smooth curves joining the points $P \equiv (a, A)$ and $Q \equiv (b, B)$ for the functional

$$I = \int_a^b y^2 (1 - y')^2 \, dx \,.$$

We found at the beginning of Sec. 3.2 that the first integral of Euler's equation for this problem gives $y^2 - y^2 y'^2 = C$. When $C = 0$, this leads to the straight-line extremals $y = 0$ or $y' = \pm 1$; a family of hyperbolas is obtained for $C \neq 0$. The corner conditions (1) for this case require that the functions $F_{y'} = -2y^2 (1 - y')$ and $F - y' F_{y'} = y^2 (1 - y'^2)$ are both continuous at any corner. But a corner is characterized by a discontinuity in y'. Therefore corners can occur only at $y = 0$, i.e. only on the x-axis. Since $y^2 - y^2 y'^2 = C$, extremals containing a point at which $y = 0$ correspond to the case $C = 0$. This means that extremals containing corners in this case consist entirely of line segments with $y = 0$ or $y' = \pm 1$. Solutions of this type are possible only for certain configurations of the end-points. Three possibilities are illustrated in Fig. 3.4. An example of a situation in which corners cannot occur is the case in which the end-points are $(1, 1)$ and $(2, 3)$.

3.5 Isoperimetric problems

One of the classical problems of mathematics, which can be solved in many different ways, is to show that, of all curves in the plane which have some specified length, a circle encloses the largest area. More generally, problems in the calculus of variations in which one or more integral constraints are imposed are known as *isoperimetric problems*.

The simplest problem of this type is to find the curves for which a functional

$$I = \int_a^b F(x, y, y') \, dx \tag{1}$$

is stationary when a second functional

$$J = \int_a^b G(x, y, y') \, dx \tag{2}$$

is constrained to have some prescribed value J_0 and the end-points (a, A) and (b, B) are fixed.

The general method of solving this problem, known as *Euler's rule*, is analogous to the corresponding method of finding stationary points of functions of several variables subject to certain algebraic constraints. We first determine the extremals for the functional

$$K = \int_a^b [F(x, y, y') + \lambda G(x, y, y')] \, dx \qquad (3)$$

without constraints, where λ is an undetermined parameter (Lagrange multiplier). These extremals form a three-parameter family of curves $y = y(x; \lambda, \alpha, \beta)$, where α and β are the constants of integration in solving Euler's equation. The required extremals for the problem can be determined by solving simultaneously the three conditions $y(a) = A$, $y(b) = B$ and $J = J_0$ for the three unknown constants λ, α and β.

It is easy to see why the method works. Suppose that Γ is an extremal for the functional (3) without the constraint $J = J_0$ and that Γ satisfies the three conditions stated above. Then Γ is obviously also an extremal for the functional (3) *with* the constraint $J = J_0$. This in turn means that Γ is also an extremal for the original functional (1) with the constraint $J = J_0$.

The method can be generalized in an obvious way to problems involving more than one integral constraint.

Example   Maximize the functional

$$A = \int_0^a y(x) \, dx$$

subject to the constraint

$$\int_0^a \sqrt{1 + y'^2} \, dx = L$$

and the end-point conditions $y(0) = y(a) = 0$. (This is the problem of maximizing the area A under an arc of a curve $y = y(x)$ of length L in the upper half of the xy-plane which joins two given points on the x-axis.)

We first find the extremals for the functional

$$K = \int_0^a [y + \lambda \sqrt{1 + y'^2}] \, dx \equiv \int_0^a H(y, y'; \lambda) \, dx$$

without constraints. Since the variable x is absent in the integrand H, a first integral is $H - y'H_{y'} = \text{const}$, which gives

$$y + \frac{\lambda}{\sqrt{1 + y'^2}} = c,$$

where c is an arbitrary constant, i.e.,

$$y'^2 = \frac{\lambda^2 - (y - c)^2}{(y - c)^2} \; .$$

Separating the variables and integrating, it is readily found that

$$(x - b)^2 + (y - c)^2 = \lambda^2 \; ,$$

where b is another arbitrary constant. Thus the extremals are arcs of circles with centres at $(x, y) = (b, c)$ and with radii λ. The condition $y(0) = y(a)$ requires that $b = \frac{1}{2}a$, as expected from elementary considerations. The remaining two parameters c and λ (i.e., the centre and radius of the circle) can of course be determined by making use of the condition $y(0) = 0$ and the value of L which is specified.

Appendix: Two lemmas

Lemma 1 If $G(x) \in C[a, b]$ and if

$$\int_a^b \eta(x) G(x) \, dx = 0$$

for all functions $\eta(x) \in C_2 [a, b]$ such that $\eta(a) = \eta(b) = 0$, then $G(x) = 0$ for all x in the interval $a \leqslant x \leqslant b$.

PROOF Assume that the hypothesis is true, but that $G(\xi) \neq 0$ for some $\xi \in [a, b]$, say $G(\xi) > 0$. (If this value were negative, we could replace the function G by $-G$ in what follows.) Then $G(x) > 0$ for all x in some subinterval $[\alpha, \beta] \subset [a, b]$. Define the function $\eta(x)$ which is equal to $(x - \alpha)^3 (\beta - x)^3$ for $\alpha \leqslant x \leqslant \beta$ and equal to zero otherwise. Then $\eta(x)$ has the properties $\eta(x) \in C_2 [a, b]$, $\eta(a) = \eta(b) = 0$ and $\eta(x) > 0$ for $x \in (\alpha, \beta)$. Thus

$$\int_a^b \eta(x) G(x) \, dx = \int_\alpha^\beta \eta(x) G(x) \, dx > 0 \; ,$$

which contradicts the hypothesis. Hence we conclude that $G(x) = 0$ for all x in the interval $a \leqslant x \leqslant b$.

Lemma 2 If $E(x) \in PC[a, b]$ and if

$$\int_a^b \eta'(x) E(x) \, dx = 0 \tag{1}$$

for all functions $\eta(x)$ such that $\eta(x) \in PS[a, b]$ and $\eta(a) = \eta(b) = 0$, then $E(x) = \text{const}$ in the interval $a \leqslant x \leqslant b$.

PROOF   Let C be the constant such that

$$\int_a^b [E(x) - C] \, dx = 0$$

and construct the function

$$\eta(x) = \int_a^x [E(x') - C] \, dx' \, .$$

Then $\eta(x)$ belongs to the class of functions defined in the hypothesis of the lemma, which requires that the condition (1) holds. In addition, we have

$$\int_a^b C \eta'(x) \, dx = C \Big[\eta(x)\Big]_{x=a}^b = 0. \tag{2}$$

Subtracting (2) from (1), we obtain

$$\int_a^b \eta'(x) \, [E(x) - C] \, dx = 0.$$

But $\eta'(x) = E(x) - C$, by the definition of $\eta(x)$. Hence

$$\int_a^b [E(x) - C]^2 \, dx = 0,$$

so that $E(x) = C$ for all x in the interval $a \leqslant x \leqslant b$.

Problems

Unless specified otherwise, assume in the following problems that the required extremals have no corners.

1 Find the extremals for the functional

$$I = \int_a^b F(x, y, y') \, dx$$

when the integrand is of the form $F = x^n y'^2$, where n is a constant. Under what conditions can points lying on opposite sides of the y-axis be joined by an extremal?

2 Find the extremals for the integrand $F = (a^2 + y'^2)^{1/2}/y$, where a is a constant.

3 Find the extremals for the integrand $F = y'^2 - k^2 y^2$ with $y(0) = 0$ and $y(1) = a$, where k and a are constants.

4 Find the extremals joining the end-points $(0, 0)$ and $(a, 0)$, where a is a positive constant, when the integrand is $F = y(1 - y'^2)^{1/2}$. Evaluate the integral along each extremal. What are the absolute minimum and maximum values of the functional for functions $y(x)$ in the class $C_2[0, a]$ for the given end-points?

5 Find the curve joining the origin $(0, 0)$ to a variable point (X, Y) on the curve $y^3 = 2 - x$ which minimizes the integral

$$I = \int_0^X (y'^2 - y^2)\,dx.$$

Show that the value of X is approximately 1.83.

6 (i) Find the extremals for the integrand $F = (1 + y'^2)^{1/2}/y$.

(ii) Show in particular that the extremal which joins the origin to a variable point on the line $x + y = 4$ is an arc of the circle $(x - 4)^2 + y^2 = 16$.

7 Find the extremals for the integrand $F = y^2(1 + y'^2)$, with particular reference to the possibility of corners.

8 Find the extremals for the functional

$$I = \int_0^1 (y'^2 + x^2)\,dx$$

subject to the conditions $y(0) = y(1) = 0$ and

$$\int_0^1 y^2\,dx = \tfrac{1}{2}.$$

9 Write down an integral expression for the length of a curve specified in plane polar coordinates in the form $r = r(\theta)$. Hence show that the curve of minimum length between two given points has an equation in polar coordinates of the form $r \cos(\theta + a) = c$, where a and c are constants.

10 The classical isoperimetric problem is to find the closed plane curve of given length L which encloses the largest area. Solve this problem in the class of curves described in polar coordinates by an equation of the form $r = r(\theta)$, $0 \leqslant \theta \leqslant \pi$, with $r(0) = r(\pi) = 0$. Discuss the possibility of corners.

11 Find the extremal which joins a variable point on the y-axis to the fixed point $(1, 1)$ and which minimizes the integral

$$I = \int_0^1 [y(1 + y'^2)]^{1/2}\,dx,$$

and determine the corresponding value of I.

12 Find the extremals for the functional

$$I = \int_0^1 \left(\tfrac{1}{2}y'^2 + yy' + y' + y\right) dx$$

when the values of the function $y(x)$ at the end-points are not specified. Solve the problem first by applying the variable end-point theorem, and secondly by assigning fixed values $y(0) = \alpha$, $y(1) = \beta$, finding the extremals, evaluating the functional for these extremals, and finally determining the values of α and β which give the extreme values of the functional. Verify that the two methods give the same final answer.

4 Fourier series

4.1 Trigonometric approximation

Many physical phenomena are periodic in character. A real function $f(x)$ is said to be periodic with period L $(L > 0)$ if $f(x + L) = f(x)$ for all x. Among the most familiar examples of such functions are $\sin x$ and $\cos x$, which are periodic with period 2π. We shall confine ourselves initially to functions having a period 2π. This involves no loss of generality, since if $f(x)$ has a period 2π, then $f(2\pi x/L)$ has a period L. Of course, if a function $f(x)$ has a period L, then it also has a period nL, where n is any positive integer, but the term 'period' will usually be reserved for the smallest period of the function in question.

Under certain conditions, one can approximate a function $f(x)$ with period 2π by a sum of the form

$$f_N(x) \equiv \tfrac{1}{2}a_0 + \sum_{n=1}^{N} (a_n \cos nx + b_n \sin nx). \tag{1}$$

(The reason for our convention of writing the constant term as $\tfrac{1}{2}a_0$ instead of simply a_0 will become apparent later.) A sum of this form is known as a *trigonometric polynomial* of degree N.

Let us examine certain important properties of the trigonometric functions. If m and n are distinct positive integers $(m \neq n)$, then

$$\int_0^{2\pi} \sin mx \sin nx \, dx = \int_0^{2\pi} \tfrac{1}{2}\{\cos[(m-n)x] - \cos[(m+n)x]\} \, dx$$

$$= \tfrac{1}{2}\left[\frac{\sin[(m-n)x]}{m-n} - \frac{\sin[(m+n)x]}{m+n}\right]_0^{2\pi} = 0.$$

If, however, $m = n$, we find instead

$$\int_0^{2\pi} \sin^2 mx \, dx = \int_0^{2\pi} \tfrac{1}{2}(1 - \cos 2mx) \, dx = \pi.$$

Thus, for any positive integers m and n, we can write

$$\int_0^{2\pi} \sin mx \sin nx \, dx = \pi \delta_{mn}, \tag{2}$$

where δ_{mn} is the Kronecker delta symbol. In a similar way, it can readily be shown that

$$\int_0^{2\pi} \cos mx \cos nx \, dx = \pi \delta_{mn}, \tag{3}$$

$$\int_0^{2\pi} \sin mx \cos nx \, dx = 0 \tag{4}$$

for any positive integers m and n. The integral formulae (2)–(4) will be called the *orthogonality relations* for the trigonometric functions.

We now pose the problem of finding the set of coefficients a_n and b_n in the trigonometric polynomial (1) which provides the best approximation to a particular function $f(x)$ with period 2π. Before tackling this problem, we must obviously specify precisely what constitutes the 'best' approximation. There is no unique answer to this question. For example, we might require that $|f(x) - f_N(x)| < \epsilon$ for all x, where the 'discrepancy' ϵ is to be made as small as possible. In this case, $f_N(x)$ is called the best *uniform approximation* to $f(x)$ in the class of trigonometric polynomials of degree N. An alternative procedure, which turns out to be more convenient for many purposes, is to choose the coefficients so as to minimize the integral

$$J_N \equiv \int_0^{2\pi} [f(x) - f_N(x)]^2 \, dx$$

(assuming, for example, that $f(x) \in PC[0, 2\pi]$, so that this integral necessarily exists). In this case, $f_N(x)$ is said to be the best *approximation in the mean*.

Let us now determine the trigonometric polynomial $f_N(x)$ which gives the best approximation in the mean for some specified function $f(x)$.

Introducing the notation

$$A_N \equiv \frac{1}{\pi} \int_0^{2\pi} f(x) \cos nx \, dx, \quad B_N \equiv \frac{1}{\pi} \int_0^{2\pi} f(x) \sin nx \, dx \tag{5}$$

for $n = 0, 1, \ldots, N$ and using the orthogonality relations (2)–(4), we find

$$\frac{1}{\pi} J_N = \frac{1}{\pi} \int_0^{2\pi} \left[f(x) - \tfrac{1}{2} a_0 - \sum_{n=1}^{N} (a_n \cos nx + b_n \sin nx) \right]^2 dx$$

$$= \frac{1}{\pi} \int_0^{2\pi} [f(x)]^2 \, dx - a_0 A_0 - 2 \sum_{n=1}^{N} (a_n A_n + b_n B_n) +$$

$$+ \tfrac{1}{2} a_0^2 + \sum_{n=1}^{N} (a_n^2 + b_n^2)$$

$$= \frac{1}{\pi} \int_0^{2\pi} [f(x)]^2 \, dx + \frac{1}{2} (a_0 - A_0)^2 + \sum_{n=1}^N (a_n - A_n)^2$$

$$+ \sum_{n=1}^N (b_n - B_n)^2 - \frac{1}{2} A_0^2 - \sum_{n=1}^N (A_n^2 + B_n^2). \tag{6}$$

Clearly, J_N takes its minimum value when $a_n = A_n$ and $b_n = B_n$ ($n = 0$, $1, \ldots$), where the quantities A_n and B_n are given by (5). These quantities are known as the *Fourier coefficients* of the function $f(x)$. (Incidentally, we see here the reason for writing the constant term in the general trigonometric polynomial (1) in the form $\frac{1}{2} a_0$ instead of a_0; if we wrote this term as a_0 (as is done in some books), we would find instead that $a_0 = \frac{1}{2} A_0$, so that the formula for evaluating the Fourier coefficients a_n according to (5) would require modification in the special case $n = 0$.)

Putting now $a_n = A_n$ and $b_n = B_n$ in (6) and using the fact that $J_N \geqslant 0$ by definition, we obtain the following inequality for the Fourier coefficients:

$$\frac{1}{2} A_0^2 + \sum_{n=1}^N (A_n^2 + B_n^2) \leqslant \frac{1}{\pi} \int_0^{2\pi} [f(x)]^2 \, dx. \tag{7}$$

This is *Bessel's inequality*. It becomes an equality if $J_N = 0$, i.e. if $f_N(x)$ provides a perfect representation of the function $f(x)$ *in the mean*. Under what conditions is this possible? It can be shown that, for reasonably well-behaved functions $f(x)$, we have $J_N \to 0$ as $N \to \infty$. In this limit, we are considering the *Fourier series*

$$\frac{1}{2} A_0 + \sum_{n=1}^\infty (A_n \cos nx + B_n \sin nx)$$

and we say that the series *converges in the mean* to $f(x)$.

Of course, even if we know that a Fourier series does converge in the mean to a function $f(x)$, it does not necessarily follow that it converges *pointwise*, i.e. that $f_N(x) \to f(x)$ for all x as $N \to \infty$. However, in the next section we shall prove a fundamental theorem on the pointwise convergence of Fourier series under certain general conditions.

4.2 Pointwise convergence

It is convenient to introduce the following notation for one-sided limits: $f(x^\pm) \equiv \lim f(x \pm \epsilon)$ as ϵ approaches zero through positive values. Then the fundamental theorem on pointwise convergence is as follows:

THEOREM   If $f(x) \in PC[0, 2\pi]$, then the Fourier series

$$\tfrac{1}{2} a_0 + \sum_{n=1}^{\infty} (a_n \cos nx + b_n \sin nx), \tag{1}$$

where

$$a_n = \frac{1}{\pi} \int_0^{2\pi} f(x) \cos nx \, dx, \quad b_n = \frac{1}{\pi} \int_0^{2\pi} f(x) \sin nx \, dx \quad (n = 0, 1, \ldots) \tag{2}$$

converges to $\tfrac{1}{2} [f(x^-) + f(x^+)]$ for each value of x in the range $0 < x < 2\pi$ at which $f(x)$ has both left- and right-hand derivatives. In other words, the series converges to the arithmetic mean of the left- and right-hand limits of the function at each such point.

Note, in particular, that if $f(x)$ is continuous at such a point $x = x_0$, then the Fourier series converges to $f(x_0)$ at that point. If $f(x)$ is piecewise smooth in the range $0 < x < 2\pi$, then the convergence stated in the theorem holds throughout that range. We now turn to the proof of the theorem.

PROOF   For brevity, we have relegated several preliminary lemmas to Sec. A.4, and only the main part of the proof is given here. Let

$$S_N(x) \equiv \tfrac{1}{2} a_0 + \sum_{n=1}^{N} (a_n \cos nx + b_n \sin nx)$$

be the partial sums of the Fourier series (1), where the coefficients a_n and b_n are defined in (2). Then

$$S_N(x) = \frac{1}{\pi} \int_0^{2\pi} f(u) \left[\tfrac{1}{2} + \sum_{n=1}^{N} (\cos nx \cos nu + \sin nx \sin nu) \right] du$$

$$= \frac{1}{\pi} \int_0^{2\pi} f(u) \left\{ \tfrac{1}{2} + \sum_{n=1}^{N} \cos [n(u - x)] \right\} du.$$

But since

$$2 \sin [\tfrac{1}{2}(u - x)] \sum_{n=1}^{N} \cos [n(u - x)] =$$

$$= \sum_{n=1}^{N} \left\{ \sin\left[(n+\tfrac{1}{2})(u-x)\right] - \sin\left[(n-\tfrac{1}{2})(u-x)\right] \right\}$$

$$= \sin\left[(N+\tfrac{1}{2})(u-x)\right] - \sin\left[\tfrac{1}{2}(u-x)\right],$$

we can write

$$S_N(x) = \frac{1}{\pi} \int_0^{2\pi} f(u) \, \frac{\sin\left[(N+\tfrac{1}{2})(u-x)\right]}{2\sin\left[\tfrac{1}{2}(u-x)\right]} \, du$$

$$= \frac{1}{\pi} \int_0^{2\pi} \psi(u) \, \frac{\sin\left[(N+\tfrac{1}{2})(u-x)\right]}{u-x} \, du, \tag{3}$$

where

$$\psi(u) \equiv \frac{f(u)(u-x)}{2\sin\left[\tfrac{1}{2}(u-x)\right]}.$$

Let $x \in (0, 2\pi)$ be a given point at which the function $f(u)$, and hence also $\psi(u)$, has both left- and right-hand derivatives. Under these conditions, we can make use of Lemmas 2 and 3 given in Sec. A.4 to evaluate the last integral in (3) as follows. We first note that, since by hypothesis $f(u) \in$ PC$[0, 2\pi]$, we have also $\psi(u) \in$ PC$[0, 2\pi]$, as will be required for the application of these lemmas; in particular, $\psi(u)$ has, as required, finite one-sided limits as u approaches x from either direction, namely $\psi(x^{\pm}) = f(x^{\pm})$, and the denominator in the definition of $\psi(u)$ does not vanish elsewhere in the range $0 \leqslant u \leqslant 2\pi$. Writing

$$S_N(x) = \frac{1}{\pi} \left[\int_0^x + \int_x^{2\pi} \right] \psi(u) \, \frac{\sin\left[(N+\tfrac{1}{2})(u-x)\right]}{u-x} \, du$$

and putting $v = u - x$, we have

$$S_N(x) = \frac{1}{\pi} \left[\int_{-x}^0 + \int_0^{2\pi-x} \right] \psi(v+x) \, \frac{\sin\left[(N+\tfrac{1}{2})v\right]}{v} \, dv,$$

so that, by Lemmas 2 and 3,

$$\lim_{N \to \infty} S_N(x) = \frac{C}{\pi} \left[\psi(x^-) + \psi(x^+) \right] = \frac{C}{\pi} \left[f(x^-) + f(x^+) \right], \tag{4}$$

where C is a certain constant, whose value does not depend on the particular function $f(x)$ under consideration. It remains only to determine the value of C. This can easily be done by comparing the left- and right-hand sides of (4) for a sufficiently simple function, such as $f(x) = $ const, whose Fourier series contains only a single non-vanishing term. This gives $C = \frac{1}{2}\pi$, which completes the proof of the theorem.

This basic theorem on pointwise convergence can easily be generalized to intervals other than $[0, 2\pi]$. First, it is simple to check that, with only trivial modifications in the limits of integration, our proof of the theorem remains valid if we replace the original integrals over the range $0 \leqslant x \leqslant 2\pi$ by corresponding integrals over the range $A \leqslant x \leqslant A + 2\pi$ for arbitrary A and choose $x \in (A, A + 2\pi)$. Secondly, by making the change of scale $x = 2\pi x'/L$, so that the interval $A \leqslant x \leqslant A + 2\pi$ corresponds to the new interval $B \leqslant x' \leqslant B + L$ with $B = AL/2\pi$, the theorem can be rewritten in terms of the variable x' for an arbitrary interval $B \leqslant x' \leqslant B + L$. The result is that the series

$$\frac{1}{2}a_0 + \sum_{n=1}^{\infty} \left(a_n \cos \frac{2\pi n x'}{L} + b_n \sin \frac{2\pi n x'}{L} \right),$$

where

$$a_n = \frac{2}{L} \int_B^{B+L} f(x') \cos \frac{2\pi n x'}{L} \, dx', \quad b_n = \frac{2}{L} \int_B^{B+L} f(x') \sin \frac{2\pi n x'}{L} \, dx',$$

converges to $\frac{1}{2}[f(x'^-) + f(x'^+)]$ for all $x' \in (B, B + L)$.

It is easy to remember these formulae for the Fourier coefficients by noting that a_n and b_n can be interpreted as twice the average values of $f(x')\cos(2\pi n x'/L)$ and $f(x')\sin(2\pi n x'/L)$, respectively, over the interval $B \leqslant x' \leqslant B + L$. In particular, the constant term $\frac{1}{2}a_0$ in the Fourier series is equal to the average value of the function $f(x')$ itself. Note also that, for a given interval of length L, the Fourier expansion is made in terms of the complete set of sine and cosine functions which have a period L.

Any Fourier series obviously defines a function with some particular period L, and it is of course immaterial how the original function $f(x')$ which it represents is defined outside the interval in question, say $B \leqslant x' \leqslant B + L$. If $f(x')$ is piecewise smooth and periodic with period L, then the Fourier series will converge to $\frac{1}{2}[f(x'^-) + f(x'^+)]$ for *all* x'. This fact can be used to show how the Fourier series for a given function $f(x')$ over an interval $B \leqslant x' \leqslant B + L$ converges at the end-points. For example, at $x' = B$ the series converges to $\frac{1}{2}[f(B + L^-) + f(B^+)]$. A given function $f(x')$ can of course be represented in an interval $B \leqslant x' \leqslant B + L$ by a Fourier series with some specified period *greater* than L; such a representation is not unique, however, because the original function can be extended outside this interval in an arbitrary way.

If we know that a Fourier series for a given function $f(x)$ converges to

$f(x)$ within a certain interval, with the possible exception of a finite set of points, the expressions for the Fourier coefficients of this series follow as a direct consequence of the orthogonality relations for the trigonometric functions. Suppose, for example, that

$$f(x) = \tfrac{1}{2}a_0 + \sum_{n=1}^{\infty} (a_n \cos nx + b_n \sin nx) \tag{5}$$

in the interval $0 \leqslant x \leqslant 2\pi$, except at a finite number of points. For the purposes of evaluating integrals, we can ignore the discrete violations of this equality. Now if we multiply both sides of (5) by one of the functions occurring in the expansion, say $\cos mx$, and then integrate over the range $0 \leqslant x \leqslant 2\pi$, we obtain

$$\int_0^{2\pi} f(x) \cos mx \, dx = \int_0^{2\pi} \cos mx \, [\tfrac{1}{2}a_0 + \sum_{n=1}^{\infty} (a_n \cos nx + b_n \sin nx)] \, dx.$$

If the series in the integrand can be integrated term by term, then only the term with $n = m$ contributes and the result reduces to

$$\int_0^{2\pi} f(x) \cos mx \, dx = \pi a_m,$$

in agreement with the standard formula for the Fourier coefficients a_n. The coefficients b_n can be determined in a similar way.

This is the derivation which is usually given in more elementary treatments of Fourier series. It is purely formal, since it tells us nothing about the existence of a valid Fourier series or the way in which it converges, and it provides no justification for the term-by-term integration which is required.

We conclude this section with an example of the determination of a Fourier series for a specific function.

Example Find the Fourier series of period 2π which represents the function

$$f(x) = \begin{cases} x^2, & 0 < x < \pi, \\ \pi^2, & \pi < x < 2\pi. \end{cases} \tag{6}$$

Following our previous notation, the Fourier coefficient a_0 is given by

$$a_0 = \frac{1}{\pi} \int_0^{\pi} x^2 \, dx + \frac{1}{\pi} \int_{\pi}^{2\pi} \pi^2 \, dx = \frac{4}{3}\pi^2.$$

For $n \neq 0$, we can calculate a_n by integrating twice by parts:

$$a_n = \frac{1}{\pi} \int_0^\pi x^2 \cos nx \, dx + \frac{1}{\pi} \int_\pi^{2\pi} \pi^2 \cos nx \, dx$$

$$= \frac{1}{\pi} \left[\frac{x^2 \sin nx}{n} \right]_0^\pi - \frac{1}{\pi} \int_0^\pi \frac{2x \sin nx}{n} \, dx + 0$$

$$= 0 - \frac{2}{\pi n} \left\{ \left[\frac{-x \cos nx}{n} \right]_0^\pi - \int_0^\pi \frac{(-\cos nx)}{n} \, dx \right\}$$

$$= \frac{2 (-1)^n}{n^2} .$$

Similarly,

$$b_n = \frac{1}{\pi} \int_0^\pi x^2 \sin nx \, dx + \frac{1}{\pi} \int_\pi^{2\pi} \pi^2 \sin nx \, dx,$$

which gives, after some straightforward calculation,

$$b_n = \frac{2}{\pi n^3} \left[(-1)^n - 1 \right] - \frac{\pi}{n} .$$

Hence the Fourier series is

$$\frac{2}{3}\pi^2 + 2 \sum_{n=1}^\infty \frac{(-1)^n \cos nx}{n^2} + \sum_{n=1}^\infty \left\{ \frac{2}{\pi n^3} \left[(-1)^n - 1 \right] - \frac{\pi}{n} \right\} \sin nx. \quad (7)$$

By examining a known Fourier series at specific points, it is often possible to find expressions in closed form for the sums of various simple numerical series. For example, we know that at $x = 0$ the Fourier series (7) for the function (6) must converge to the value $\frac{1}{2}[f(2\pi^-) + f(0^+)] = \frac{1}{2}\pi^2$. Putting $x = 0$ in the series and equating its sum to $\frac{1}{2}\pi^2$, we find

$$\sum_{n=1}^\infty \frac{(-1)^n}{n^2} = -\frac{\pi^2}{12} .$$

Similarly, at $x = \pi$ the series must converge to the value π^2. This yields

$$\sum_{n=1}^\infty \frac{1}{n^2} = \frac{\pi^2}{6} .$$

It is interesting to see how accurately the first few terms of a Fourier series can represent the complete function. A typical situation is illustrated

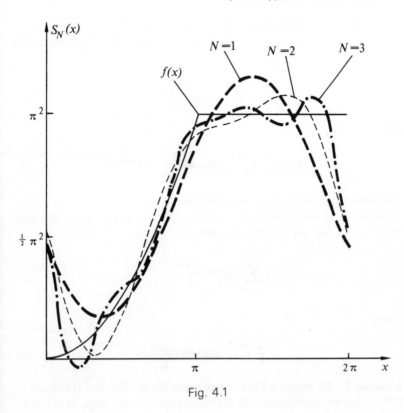

Fig. 4.1

in Fig. 4.1, which shows graphs of the function (6) and of the first three partial sums $S_1(x)$, $S_2(x)$ and $S_3(x)$ of its Fourier series (7).

4.3 Special types of Fourier series

Consider the Fourier series for a function $f(x)$ in a symmetric range about the origin, say $-\frac{1}{2}L \leqslant x \leqslant \frac{1}{2}L$:

$$\frac{1}{2}a_0 + \sum_{n=1}^{\infty} \left(a_n \cos \frac{2\pi n x}{L} + b_n \sin \frac{2\pi n x}{L} \right), \qquad (1)$$

where

$$a_n = \frac{2}{L} \int_{-L/2}^{L/2} f(x) \cos \frac{2\pi n x}{L} \, dx, \quad b_n = \frac{2}{L} \int_{-L/2}^{L/2} f(x) \sin \frac{2\pi n x}{L} \, dx. \qquad (2)$$

If $f(x)$ is an *even* function, i.e. $f(-x) = f(x)$, then $b_n = 0$ for all n (since the integrand in the expression for b_n is odd) and the Fourier series (1) reduces to

$$\tfrac{1}{2} a_0 + \sum_{n=1}^{\infty} a_n \cos \frac{2\pi n x}{L} , \tag{3}$$

where

$$a_n = \frac{4}{L} \int_0^{L/2} f(x) \cos \frac{2\pi n x}{L} \, dx. \tag{4}$$

The series (3) is called a *Fourier cosine series.*

If $f(x)$ is an *odd* function, i.e. $f(-x) = -f(x)$, then $a_n = 0$ for all n and we obtain instead the *Fourier sine series*

$$\sum_{n=1}^{\infty} b_n \sin \frac{2\pi n x}{L} , \tag{5}$$

where

$$b_n = \frac{4}{L} \int_0^{L/2} f(x) \sin \frac{2\pi n x}{L} \, dx. \tag{6}$$

Example 1   To obtain a Fourier sine series for the function $f(x) = \cos x$, $0 < x < \pi$, we consider the odd extension of $f(x)$ to the range $-\pi < x < \pi$:

$$F(x) = \begin{cases} \cos x, & 0 < x < \pi, \\ -\cos x, & -\pi < x < 0. \end{cases}$$

This function $F(x)$, and hence also the original function $f(x)$, is represented by the Fourier sine series

$$\sum_{n=1}^{\infty} b_n \sin nx,$$

where

$$b_n = \frac{2}{\pi} \int_0^{\pi} \cos x \sin nx \, dx$$

$$= \begin{cases} \dfrac{1}{\pi} \left[\dfrac{1 - \cos [(n+1)\pi]}{n+1} + \dfrac{1 - \cos [(n-1)\pi]}{n-1} \right], & n \neq 1, \\ 0, \; n = 1 \end{cases}$$

$$= \begin{cases} 0, n \text{ odd}, \\ \dfrac{1}{\pi}\left[\dfrac{2}{n+1}+\dfrac{2}{n-1}\right] = \dfrac{4n}{\pi(n^2-1)}, & n \text{ even}. \end{cases}$$

Thus, writing $n \equiv 2m$ for even n, the series is

$$\frac{8}{\pi}\sum_{m=1}^{\infty}\frac{m\sin 2mx}{4m^2-1}.$$

In general, any function $f(x)$ defined over a symmetric range $-\frac{1}{2}L \leqslant x \leqslant \frac{1}{2}L$ can be represented as a sum of an even function and an odd function, $f(x) = f_e(x) + f_o(x)$, where

$$f_e(x) = \tfrac{1}{2}[f(x)+f(-x)], \quad f_o(x) = \tfrac{1}{2}[f(x)-f(-x)].$$

It is easy to prove that this decomposition of a function into a sum of even and odd parts is unique. This means that the even and odd components $f_e(x)$ and $f_o(x)$ are represented by the Fourier cosine and sine series which are formed from the even and odd terms, respectively, of the full Fourier series for $f(x)$.

Example 2   Consider the series

$$\frac{2}{3}\pi^2 + 2\sum_{n=1}^{\infty}\frac{(-1)^n\cos nx}{n^2}.$$

What function does this series represent?

This series consists of all the even terms of the Fourier series (7) of Sec. 4.2, which was constructed as the Fourier series representing the function

$$f(x) = \begin{cases} x^2, & 0 < x < \pi, \\ \pi^2, & \pi < x < 2\pi. \end{cases}$$

In the symmetric interval $-\pi < x < \pi$, the original Fourier series represents the periodic extension of $f(x)$, namely

$$F(x) = \begin{cases} \pi^2, & -\pi < x < 0, \\ x^2, & 0 < x < \pi. \end{cases}$$

The given series of even terms must therefore represent the even part of $F(x)$, which is

$$F_e(x) = \tfrac{1}{2}[F(x)+F(-x)] = \tfrac{1}{2}(x^2+\pi^2), \quad -\pi < x < \pi.$$

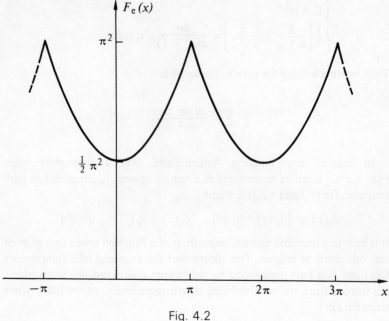

Fig. 4.2

For values of x outside the range $-\pi < x < \pi$, the given series represents the periodic extension of $F_e(x)$. For example, in the range $\pi < x < 3\pi$, the periodic extension is given by $\frac{1}{2}[(x - 2\pi)^2 + \pi^2]$. A graph of the resulting function is shown in Fig. 4.2.

Finally, we shall consider the so-called *complex Fourier series*. Let us take for simplicity a function $f(x)$ defined over the range $0 \leqslant x \leqslant 2\pi$. Its standard Fourier series (1) can be rewritten in the form

$$\frac{1}{2}a_0 + \sum_{n=1}^{\infty} \left[a_n \frac{e^{inx} + e^{-inx}}{2} + b_n \frac{e^{inx} - e^{-inx}}{2i} \right]$$

$$= \frac{1}{2}a_0 + \sum_{n=1}^{\infty} (c_n e^{inx} + d_n e^{-inx}), \tag{7}$$

where

$$c_n \equiv \frac{1}{2}(a_n - ib_n), \quad d_n \equiv \frac{1}{2}(a_n + ib_n).$$

Using the formulae (2) for the original coefficients a_n and b_n, we find

$$c_n = \frac{1}{2\pi} \int_0^{2\pi} f(x)\, e^{-inx}\, dx, \quad d_n = \frac{1}{2\pi} \int_0^{2\pi} f(x)\, e^{inx}\, dx.$$

Defining also $c_0 \equiv \frac{1}{2}a_0$ and $c_{-n} = d_n$ for all $n > 0$, the Fourier series (7) can be written in the compact form

$$\sum_{n=-\infty}^{\infty} c_n\, e^{inx},$$

where

$$c_n = \frac{1}{2\pi} \int_0^{2\pi} f(x)\, e^{-inx}\, dx$$

for *all* integers $n = 0, \pm 1, \pm 2, \ldots$.

4.4 Parseval's theorem

Consider the special case of a Fourier series of period 2π for a piecewise smooth function $f(x)$ defined on the interval $0 \leqslant x \leqslant 2\pi$. We showed in Sec. 4.1 that the Fourier coefficients satisy the relation

$$\frac{1}{\pi} \int_0^{2\pi} [f(x)]^2\, dx - \frac{1}{2}a_0^2 - \sum_{n=1}^{N} (a_n^2 + b_n^2) = \frac{1}{\pi} J_N,$$

where

$$J_N = \int_0^{2\pi} [f(x) - f_N(x)]^2\, dx \tag{1}$$

and $f_N(x)$ is the N-th partial sum of the Fourier series. Now the theorem on pointwise convergence which we proved in Sec. 4.2 tells us that $J_N \to 0$ as $N \to \infty$. This leads to the equality

$$\frac{1}{2}a_0^2 + \sum_{n=1}^{\infty} (a_n^2 + b_n^2) = \frac{1}{\pi} \int_0^{2\pi} [f(x)]^2\, dx,$$

which is known as *Parseval's theorem*.

To derive Parseval's theorem for more general intervals, consider, for example, the change of variable $x = 2\pi x'/L$, so that the original interval $0 \leqslant x \leqslant 2\pi$ corresponds to the new interval $0 \leqslant x' \leqslant L$. In the new variable x', the Fourier series becomes

$$\tfrac{1}{2}a_0^2 + \sum_{n=1}^{\infty} \left(a_n \cos \frac{2\pi n x'}{L} + b_n \sin \frac{2\pi n x'}{L} \right)$$

and Parseval's theorem, when expressed in terms of x', reads

$$\tfrac{1}{2}a_0^2 + \sum_{n=1}^{\infty} (a_n^2 + b_n^2) = \frac{2}{L} \int_0^L [f(x')]^2 \, dx'.$$

A similar result holds, of course, for the more general range $B \leqslant x' \leqslant B + L$.

Parseval's theorem is an expression of the fact that any function in the admissible class can be represented *in the mean* as a Fourier expansion in terms of an appropriate set of trigonometric functions. A set of functions having this property is said to be *complete* with respect to the interval and the class of functions under consideration. If we replace the complete set of functions in Parseval's theorem by a set which is not complete, then the quantity (1) is in general positive instead of zero, so that the equality in Parseval's theorem becomes an inequality (Bessel's inequality).

Parseval's theorem can sometimes be applied to obtain the sums of certain simple infinite series. As an illustration of the method, we write out the specific form of Parseval's theorem for the example given in Sec. 4.3:

$$(\tfrac{8}{\pi})^2 \sum_{m=1}^{\infty} \left(\frac{m}{4m^2 - 1} \right)^2 = \frac{1}{\pi} \int_{-\pi}^{\pi} \cos^2 x \, dx = 1.$$

4.5 Application to partial differential equations

Here we give examples to illustrate the application of Fourier series in obtaining solutions of boundary-value problems for partial differential equations.

Example 1   The temperature $U(x, t)$ along a uniform bar of length L satisfies the one-dimensional heat equation

$$\frac{\partial^2 U}{\partial x^2} = \frac{1}{a^2} \frac{\partial U}{\partial t}, \tag{1}$$

where x is the position coordinate along the bar, measured from one end, t is the time, and a is a constant characterizing the thermal properties of the material. Both ends of the bar are maintained at temperature $U = 0$.

We require a solution in the region $0 \leqslant x \leqslant L$, $t \geqslant 0$ which satisfies the boundary conditions $U(0, t) = U(L, t) = 0$ for all $t \geqslant 0$ and the initial condition $U(x, 0) = f(x)$ for $0 < x < L$, where $f(x)$ is a prescribed function giving the initial temperature distribution along the bar.

To solve this problem, we first apply the method of separation of variables to find acceptable product solutions of the type $U(x, t) = X(x)T(t)$. Substituting this expression into the partial differential equation (1) and dividing by $U(x, t)$, we find

$$\frac{X''(x)}{X(x)} = \frac{1}{a^2} \frac{T'(t)}{T(t)}. \tag{2}$$

Since the left-hand side of (2) is independent of t, while the right-hand side is independent of x, both sides must be equal to a common constant (the so-called separation constant), say k. This condition yields two ordinary differential equations for the functions $X(x)$ and $T(t)$ individually:

$$X''(x) = k\,X(x), \tag{3}$$

$$T'(t) = a^2 k\,T(t). \tag{4}$$

Equation (4) has the general solution $T(t) = C \exp(a^2 kt)$, where C is an arbitrary constant. Now the obvious physical requirement that $T(t)$ remains bounded as $t \to \infty$ can be satisfied only if we have $k < 0$. Thus we can put $k = -\lambda^2$, where λ is another constant, which can be assumed to be positive without loss of generality. Then $T(t) = C \exp(-a^2 \lambda^2 t)$, while the equation (3) for $X(x)$ gives $X(x) = A \cos \lambda x + B \sin \lambda x$, where A and B are arbitrary constants. The boundary conditions which are imposed at $x = 0$ and $x = L$ imply that $X(0) = 0$ and $X(L) = 0$, respectively, which in turn require that $A = 0$ and $\sin \lambda L = 0$ (since the alternative possibility $B = 0$ would give only the trivial solution $U(x, t) = 0$); to satisfy the last condition, we must take $\lambda = n\pi/L$, where n is a (positive) integer. Note that it would not be possible to find a non-trivial solution of (3) satisfying the boundary conditions at $x = 0, L$ if we had $k \geqslant 0$.

Thus we have constructed the infinite family of product solutions

$$U(x, t) = b \sin \frac{n\pi x}{L} \, e^{-(n\pi a/L)^2 t}, \tag{5}$$

where b is an arbitrary constant and n is some positive integer. Each such solution satisfies the original partial differential equation (1) and the boundary conditions at $x = 0, L$. All these conditions are also satisfied by an arbitrary linear superposition of product solutions of the type (5):

$$U(x, t) = \sum_{n=1}^{\infty} b_n \sin \frac{n\pi x}{L} \, e^{-(n\pi a/L)^2 t}. \tag{6}$$

This conclusion depends only on the *linearity* of the partial differential equation (1) and on the fact that the boundary conditions imposed at $x = 0, L$ are *homogeneous* (i.e. they equate the function at certain points to zero).

We can now choose the coefficients b_n in (6) so as to satisfy the given initial condition at $t = 0$. This condition requires that

$$f(x) = \sum_{n=1}^{\infty} b_n \sin \frac{n\pi x}{L}, \quad 0 < x < L. \tag{7}$$

We recognize (7) as a Fourier sine series whose coefficients are given by

$$b_n = \frac{2}{L} \int_0^L f(x) \sin \frac{n\pi x}{L} \, dx. \tag{8}$$

Thus the solution to the problem is given by the series (6) with the coefficients (8).

Example 2   The steady-state temperature distribution within a circular disc covering the region $x^2 + y^2 \leqslant C^2$ of the xy-plane satisfies Laplace's equation in two dimensions:

$$\frac{\partial^2 U}{\partial x^2} + \frac{\partial^2 U}{\partial y^2} = 0.$$

Find a solution of this equation satisfying prescribed boundary conditions on the circumference of the disc.

To solve this problem, we first transform Laplace's equation to polar coordinates (r, θ), given by the relations $x = r \cos \theta, y = r \sin \theta$. After straightforward calculations, this gives

$$\frac{\partial^2 U}{\partial r^2} + \frac{1}{r} \frac{\partial U}{\partial r} + \frac{1}{r^2} \frac{\partial^2 U}{\partial \theta^2} = 0.$$

We next construct suitable product solutions of this equation by the method of separation of variables. Substituting $U(r, \theta) = R(r)H(\theta)$ into the partial differential equation and multiplying by r^2/U, we find

$$\frac{r^2 R'' + rR'}{R} = -\frac{H''}{H} = k,$$

where k is the separation constant. The function $H(\theta)$ must satisfy the periodicity condition $H(\theta + 2\pi) = H(\theta)$ in order to give a single-valued solution $U(r, \theta)$. This can be achieved only by choosing the separation constant k to be positive. Putting $k = n^2$, we find that $H(\theta)$ must satisfy the differential equation $H''(\theta) = -n^2 H(\theta)$, whose general solution is

$$H(\theta) = A \cos n\theta + B \sin n\theta.$$

Moreover, the periodicity condition requires that n is an integer, and there is no loss of generality in restricting ourselves to the values $n = 0, 1, 2 \ldots$.
Consider next the differential equation for $R(r)$:

$$r^2 R''(r) + rR'(r) - n^2 R(r) = 0.$$

This is Euler's differential equation, which, as is easily verified, has the general solution

$$R(r) = \begin{cases} \alpha r^n + \beta r^{-n}, & n \neq 0, \\ \alpha + \beta \log r, & n = 0, \end{cases}$$

where α and β are arbitrary constants. In order to construct a physically acceptable solution $U(r, \theta)$, we must ensure that $R(0)$ is finite. We must therefore take $\beta = 0$ for arbitrary n.

Putting all the results together and taking the most general superposition of product solutions, we obtain the more general solution

$$U(r, \theta) = \sum_{n=0}^{\infty} r^n (a_n \cos n\theta + b_n \sin n\theta).$$

It remains only to fix the constants a_n and b_n. We do this by imposing the prescribed boundary condition on the circle $x^2 + y^2 = C^2$. Suppose that $U(C, \theta) = F(\theta)$, where $F(\theta)$ is given for $0 \leqslant \theta \leqslant 2\pi$. Then we require that

$$F(\theta) = a_0 + \sum_{n=1}^{\infty} C^n (a_n \cos n\theta + b_n \sin n\theta)$$

for $0 \leqslant \theta \leqslant 2\pi$. We recognize this series as a Fourier series of period 2π for the function $F(\theta)$ in this range. The Fourier coefficients are given by

$$2a_0 = \frac{1}{\pi} \int_0^{2\pi} F(\theta) \, d\theta,$$

$$C^n a_n = \frac{1}{\pi} \int_0^{2\pi} F(\theta) \cos n\theta \, d\theta,$$

$$C^n b_n = \frac{1}{\pi} \int_0^{2\pi} F(\theta) \sin n\theta \, d\theta.$$

Example 3 Find a solution of Laplace's equation in three dimensions,

$$\frac{\partial^2 U}{\partial x^2} + \frac{\partial^2 U}{\partial y^2} + \frac{\partial^2 U}{\partial z^2} = 0$$

in the rectangular parallelepiped $0 \leqslant x \leqslant a, 0 \leqslant y \leqslant b, 0 \leqslant z \leqslant c$ satisfying the boundary conditions $U(x, y, c) = F(x, y)$, where $F(x, y)$ is a prescribed function, while $U = 0$ on the remaining five faces of the parallelepiped.

We begin by seeking product solutions of the form $U(x, y, z) = X(x)Y(y)Z(z)$. Substituting this form into Laplace's equation and dividing by U, we have

$$\frac{X''}{X} + \frac{Y''}{Y} + \frac{Z''}{Z} = 0.$$

Now since each term of this equation is a function of a different variable, the three terms must actually be equal to constants, say k_1, k_2 and k_3, respectively, with $k_1 + k_2 + k_3 = 0$. In order to satisfy the boundary conditions at $x = 0$ and $x = a$, we must have $X(0) = X(a) = 0$. Exactly as in Example 1, it is possible to find a non-trivial solution of the equation $X''(x) = k_1 X(x)$ with these boundary conditions only by choosing $k_1 = -(n\pi/a)^2$, where n is an integer, which can be taken to be positive; the acceptable solutions are $X(x) = B \sin(n\pi x/a)$. Similarly, the acceptable solutions of the equation $Y''(y) = k_2 Y(y)$ have the form $Y(y) = C \sin(m\pi y/b)$, where m is a positive integer.

The differential equation for $Z(z)$ takes the form $Z''(z) = -(k_1 + k_2) Z(z)$, where k_1 and k_2 take the values determined above. The solutions of this equation satisfying the boundary condition $Z(0) = 0$ are $Z(z) = E \sinh \xi_{nm} z$, where $\xi_{nm}^2 = (n\pi/a)^2 + (m\pi/b)^2$. Thus the most general superposition of product solutions satisfying all the homogeneous boundary conditions is

$$U(x, y, z) = \sum_{n=1}^{\infty} \sum_{m=1}^{\infty} A_{nm} \sin \frac{n\pi x}{a} \sin \frac{m\pi y}{b} \sinh \xi_{nm} z.$$

Finally, to fix the coefficients A_{nm}, we apply the remaining boundary condition at $z = c$. This gives

$$F(x, y) = \sum_{n=1}^{\infty} \sum_{m=1}^{\infty} (A_{nm} \sinh \xi_{nm} c) \sin \frac{n\pi x}{a} \sin \frac{m\pi y}{b}$$

for $0 \leqslant x \leqslant a, 0 \leqslant y \leqslant b$. This is an example of a *double Fourier series*. Assuming that such a representation of the function $F(x, y)$ is possible, it is easy to determine the coefficients A_{nm}. Multiplying the expansion for $F(x, y)$ by $\sin(k\pi x/a)\sin(p\pi y/b)$, where k and p are arbitrary positive integers, integrating over the rectangular region $0 \leqslant x \leqslant a, 0 \leqslant y \leqslant b$, and then applying the orthogonality relations

$$\int_0^a \sin\frac{n\pi x}{a} \sin\frac{k\pi x}{a} \, dx = \tfrac{1}{2}a\delta_{nk},$$

$$\int_0^b \sin\frac{m\pi y}{b} \sin\frac{p\pi y}{b} \, dy = \tfrac{1}{2}b\delta_{mp},$$

we obtain

$$\int_0^a dx \int_0^b dy \, F(x,y) \sin\frac{k\pi x}{a} \sin\frac{p\pi y}{b} = \tfrac{1}{4}ab A_{kp} \sinh\xi_{kp}c,$$

which determines A_{kp}.

REMARK   Similar solutions satisfying prescribed boundary conditions at $x = a$ or at $y = b$, but with homogeneous boundary conditions on all the other faces, can be written down by simply interchanging the roles of the variables x, y and z. To obtain a solution satisfying non-homogeneous boundary conditions only on the face $z = 0$, for example, it is sufficient to make the substitution $z' = c - z$, so that, in terms of the variables (x, y, z'), the problem is transformed into the one considered above. By taking the sum of six solutions, each of which satisfies prescribed non-homogeneous boundary conditions on only one of the six faces, it is possible to construct a more general solution of Laplace's equation satisfying arbitrary boundary conditions over the entire surface of the parallelepiped.

Appendix: Lemmas for the theorem on pointwise convergence

Lemma 1 (the Riemann-Lebesgue lemma)   If $\psi(x) \in PC[a, b]$, then

$$\lim_{N\to\infty} \int_a^b \psi(x) \sin Nx \, dx = 0.$$

PROOF   Making the change of variable $x = u + \pi/N$, we have

$$\int_a^b \psi(x) \sin Nx \, dx = -\int_{a-\pi/N}^{b-\pi/N} \psi(u + \pi/N) \sin Nu \, du,$$

where we have used the fact that $\sin(Nu + \pi) = -\sin Nu$. Hence

$$2\int_a^b \psi(x) \sin Nx \, dx = \int_a^b \psi(x) \sin Nx \, dx - \int_{a-\pi/N}^{b-\pi/N} \psi(u+\pi/N) \sin Nu \, du$$

$$= I + J - K,$$

where

$$I = \int_{b-\pi/N}^{b} \psi(x) \sin Nx \, dx,$$

$$J = \int_{a}^{b-\pi/N} [\psi(x) - \psi(x + \pi/N)] \sin Nx \, dx,$$

$$K = \int_{a-\pi/N}^{a} \psi(x + \pi/N) \sin Nx \, dx.$$

Now since $\psi(x) \in PC[a, b]$, the function $\psi(x)$ is bounded in this interval. In other words, there is a constant M such that $|\psi(x)| < M$ for all $x \in [a, b]$. Then

$$|I| < \int_{b-\pi/N}^{b} |\psi(x)| \, dx < \frac{M\pi}{N},$$

so that $I \to 0$ as $N \to \infty$. By an analogous argument, we also have $K \to 0$ as $N \to \infty$. A different argument is required to show that the remaining integral J also vanishes as $N \to \infty$. Since $\psi(x)$ is piecewise continuous on the closed interval $[a, b]$, it is uniformly continuous on this interval; i.e., for any $\epsilon > 0$, we can choose a value N_0 such that

$$|\psi(x + \pi/N) - \psi(x)| < \epsilon$$

whenever $N > N_0$. Hence, if $N > N_0$, we have

$$|J| < \epsilon (b - a - \pi/N),$$

so that $J \to 0$ as $N \to \infty$. This completes the proof.

Lemma 2   If $\psi(x) \in PC[0, a]$ for some $a > 0$ and $\psi(x)$ has a right-hand derivative at $x = 0$, then

$$\lim_{N \to \infty} \int_{0}^{a} \psi(x) \frac{\sin Nx}{x} \, dx = C \psi(0^+),$$

where the constant C is defined by

$$C = \int_{0}^{\infty} \frac{\sin x}{x} \, dx. \tag{1}$$

(We remark that C actually has the value $\frac{1}{2}\pi$, as is shown in Sec. 4.2 by comparing the sum of the Fourier series for a simple function with the function itself. The fact that $C = \frac{1}{2}\pi$ is a standard result, which can be established directly in various ways. For example, given a knowledge of complex variable theory, it is easy to evaluate the integral (1) by appropriately closing the contour of integration in the complex plane and applying the calculus of residues. However, we shall not present a direct proof that $C = \frac{1}{2}\pi$ here, since the numerical value of C is not actually required in advance for our derivation of the theorem in Sec. 4.2.)

PROOF   Writing

$$\psi(x) = \psi(0^+) + [\psi(x) - \psi(0^+)],$$

we have

$$\int_0^a \psi(x)\, \frac{\sin Nx}{x}\, dx = \psi(0^+)\int_0^a \frac{\sin Nx}{x}\, dx + \int_0^a \phi(x)\sin Nx\, dx, \quad (2)$$

where $\phi(x) \equiv [\psi(x) - \psi(0^+)]/x$. Now $\phi(x) \in PC[0, a]$; in particular, the limit $\phi(0^+)$ exists because $\psi(x)$ has a right-hand derivative at $x = 0$. Hence, by Lemma 1, the last integral in (2) vanishes as $N \to \infty$. Using this fact and putting $Nx = u$ in the remaining integral, we have

$$\lim_{N \to \infty} \int_0^a \psi(x)\, \frac{\sin Nx}{x}\, dx = \psi(0^+)\lim_{N \to \infty} \int_0^a \frac{\sin Nx}{x}\, dx$$

$$= \psi(0^+)\lim_{N \to \infty} \int_0^{Na} \frac{\sin u}{u}\, du = C\psi(0^+).$$

Lemma 3   If $\psi(x) \in PC[b, 0]$ for some $b < 0$ and $\psi(x)$ has a left-hand derivative at $x = 0$, then

$$\lim_{N \to \infty} \int_b^0 \psi(x)\, \frac{\sin Nx}{x}\, dx = C\psi(0^-),$$

where C is the same constant as in Lemma 2.

PROOF   The result follows at once by making the change of variable $x' = -x$ in the result of Lemma 2.

Problems

1 Find the Fourier series of period 2π for the functions

(i) $f(x) = \begin{cases} -1, & -\pi < x < 0, \\ 1, & 0 < x < \pi; \end{cases}$

(ii) $f(x) = |x|, \quad -\pi < x < \pi;$

(iii) $f(x) = \begin{cases} \sin x, & 0 < x < \pi, \\ 0, & \pi < x < 2\pi. \end{cases}$

Use the results of parts (i) and (ii) to show that

(a) $\displaystyle\sum_{k=0}^{\infty} \frac{(-1)^k}{2k+1} = \frac{\pi}{4}$; (b) $\displaystyle\sum_{k=0}^{\infty} \frac{1}{(2k+1)^2} = \frac{\pi^2}{8}$; (c) $\displaystyle\sum_{k=0}^{\infty} \frac{1}{(2k+1)^4} = \frac{\pi^4}{96}$.

2 Find the Fourier sine series of period 2π for the function $f(x) = e^x$ in the range $0 < x < \pi$. What function does the series represent for $-\pi < x < 0$ and $\pi < x < 2\pi$?

3 Find the Fourier series of period 2π for the function $f(x) = e^x$ in the range $-\pi < x < \pi$. Deduce that

$$\sum_{n=1}^{\infty} \frac{1}{n^2+1} = \tfrac{1}{2}(\pi \coth \pi - 1).$$

4 Find the Fourier series of period 3 which represents the function

$$f(x) = \begin{cases} 2, & 0 < x < 1, \\ 1, & 1 < x < 2, \\ 0, & 2 < x < 3. \end{cases}$$

5 Find the Fourier cosine series of period 2π which represents the function $f(x) = \cos \lambda x$ in the range $0 < x < \pi$, where the constant λ is not an integer. Hence evaluate the following series when λ is not an integer:

(a) $\displaystyle\sum_{n=1}^{\infty} \frac{1}{n^2 - \lambda^2}$; (b) $\displaystyle\sum_{n=1}^{\infty} \frac{(-1)^n}{n^2 - \lambda^2}$.

Study the behaviour of the Fourier series when $\lambda \to N$, where N is an integer.

6 A function $f(x)$ has the property $f(x + \pi) = -f(x)$ for all x.

(i) Prove that $f(x)$ is periodic with period 2π.

(ii) Show that the Fourier series of period 2π for $f(x)$ contains only terms of the type $\cos mx$ and $\sin mx$ for odd m.

7 Determine what special properties a Fourier series of period L has when the function $f(x)$ which it represents is (i) symmetric about both $x = 0$ and $x = \frac{1}{4}L$; or (ii) symmetric about $x = 0$ and antisymmetric about $x = \frac{1}{4}L$.

8 Find a solution $U = U(x, y)$ of Laplace's equation inside the square $0 \leqslant x \leqslant a$, $0 \leqslant y \leqslant a$, given that U vanishes everywhere on the boundary except on the segment $\frac{1}{3}a < x < \frac{2}{3}a$, $y = a$, where it has the constant value U_0.

9 Find a solution of the heat equation

$$a^2 \frac{\partial^2 U}{\partial x^2} = \frac{\partial U}{\partial t}$$

which satisfies the boundary conditions $\partial U/\partial x = 0$ when $x = 0$ or $x = L$ and the initial condition $U(x, 0) = H(x)$, where $H(x)$ is a given function.

10 Solve the partial differential equation

$$\frac{\partial^2 U}{\partial x^2} - \frac{\partial^2 U}{\partial t^2} + U = 0$$

subject to the conditions $U(0, t) = U(1, t) = 0$, $\partial U/\partial t = 0$ when $t = 0$, and $U(x, 0) = \sin^3 \pi x$.

11 Find solutions $U = U(r, \theta)$ of Laplace's equation in plane polar co-ordinates satisfying the boundary condition

$$U(1, \theta) = \begin{cases} C, & 0 < \theta < \frac{1}{2}\pi, \\ 0, & \frac{1}{2}\pi < \theta < 2\pi, \end{cases}$$

where C is a constant (i) in the region $r < 1$, with $U(r, \theta)$ remaining finite as $r \to 0$; (ii) in the region $r > 1$, with $U(r, \theta) \to 0$ as $r \to \infty$.

12 Find a solution $U = U(r, \theta)$ of Laplace's equation in plane polar co-ordinates in the circular sector $0 \leqslant r \leqslant R$, $0 \leqslant \theta \leqslant \alpha$ satisfying the boundary conditions $U(r, 0) = U(r, \alpha) = 0$ and $U(R, \theta) = C\theta$, where C is a constant.

13 Find a solution of the one-dimensional wave equation

$$\frac{\partial^2 U}{\partial x^2} = \frac{1}{a^2} \frac{\partial^2 U}{\partial t^2}$$

in the region $0 \leqslant x \leqslant L$, $t > 0$ satisfying the boundary conditions

$$\frac{\partial U}{\partial x}(0, t) = \frac{\partial U}{\partial x}(L, t) = 0$$

for all $t > 0$ and the initial conditions

$$U(x, 0) = \sin \frac{\pi x}{L}, \qquad \frac{\partial U}{\partial t}(x, 0) = 0$$

for $0 \leqslant x \leqslant L$.

14 Find the Fourier series of period 2π which represents the function $f(x) = |\sin x|$ for $-\pi < x < \pi$. Hence sum the series

$$S = \sum_{n=0}^{\infty} \frac{1}{4(2n+1)^2 - 1}.$$

15 The temperature $U(x, t)$ along a bar of length L, with radiation heat loss, obeys the partial differential equation

$$\frac{\partial U}{\partial t} = k \frac{\partial^2 U}{\partial x^2} - cU,$$

where k and c are positive constants. Find a solution for times $t > 0$, given the boundary conditions $U(0, t) = U(L, t) = 0$ $(t > 0)$ and the initial condition $U(x, 0) = U_0$ $(0 < x < L)$, where U_0 is a constant.

16 The steady-state temperature distribution U in a flat plate satisfies Laplace's equation in two dimensions. If the temperature at the circumference of a circular plate of radius R is maintained at $U(R, \theta) = U_0 |\sin \theta|$ in plane polar coordinates (r, θ), where U_0 is a constant, find the temperature $U(r, \theta)$ at an arbitrary point of the plate.

17 Show that Laplace's equation in cylindrical polar coordinates (r, θ, z) has solutions of the form

$$U(r, \theta, z) = R(r)(A \cos n\theta + B \sin n\theta)e^{\pm mz},$$

where m and n are constants and $R(r)$ is a solution of the differential equation

$$r^2 R''(r) + rR'(r) + (m^2 r^2 - n^2)R(r) = 0.$$

5 Fourier and Laplace transforms

5.1 Fourier transforms

We begin by recalling the form of the complex Fourier series representation for a given function $f(x)$, which is assumed to be piecewise smooth on the interval $-\pi \leqslant x \leqslant \pi$ and periodic with period 2π:

$$\tfrac{1}{2}[f(x^-) + f(x^+)] = \sum_{n=-\infty}^{\infty} c_n e^{inx}, \tag{1}$$

where

$$c_n = \frac{1}{2\pi} \int_{-\pi}^{\pi} f(x) e^{-inx} dx. \tag{2}$$

For simplicity, we shall generally assume in what follows that $f(x) = \tfrac{1}{2}[f(x^-) + f(x^+)]$ at each value of x. This condition holds, of course, if the function $f(x)$ is actually continuous for all x. In the more general case of a function with a discrete set of discontinuities, we can simply redefine the function $f(x)$ at each discontinuity so that it has the value $\tfrac{1}{2}[f(x^-) + f(x^+)]$, without altering the values of any integrals. If we work with this modified function, we can then write simply $f(x)$ instead of $\tfrac{1}{2}[f(x^-) + f(x^+)]$ in equations such as (1).

Equations (1) and (2) can easily be generalized to the case of functions defined on an arbitrary symmetric interval $[-\tfrac{1}{2}L, \tfrac{1}{2}L]$ by making the change of variable $x = 2\pi x'/L$. Doing this, and then writing x instead of x', we obtain

$$f(x) = \sum_{n=-\infty}^{\infty} c_n e^{2\pi inx/L}, \tag{3}$$

where

$$c_n = \frac{1}{L} \int_{-L/2}^{L/2} f(x) e^{-2\pi inx/L} dx. \tag{4}$$

Let us consider the limiting form of (3) and (4) for the case of an infinite interval by taking the limit $L \to \infty$ (without paying undue attention to mathematical rigour at this stage). Observing that the integrand in (4) depends on n only through the ratio n/L, we define the quantities $y_n \equiv 2\pi n/L$ and

$$g(y_n) \equiv Lc_n = \int_{-L/2}^{L/2} f(x)\, e^{-ixy_n}\, dx. \tag{5}$$

The Fourier series (3) can then be written in the form

$$f(x) = \sum_{n=-\infty}^{\infty} \frac{g(y_n)}{L}\, e^{ixy_n}\, \frac{L}{2\pi}\, \Delta y, \tag{6}$$

where $\Delta y \equiv 2\pi/L$ is the spacing between successive values of y_n. Since $\Delta y \to 0$ as $L \to \infty$, the sum (6) becomes a corresponding integral in this limit,

$$f(x) = \frac{1}{2\pi} \int_{-\infty}^{\infty} g(y)\, e^{ixy}\, dy, \tag{7}$$

while (5) becomes

$$g(y) = \int_{-\infty}^{\infty} f(x)\, e^{-ixy}\, dx. \tag{8}$$

The pair of equations (7) and (8) is sometimes adopted as the definition of the Fourier transform and inverse transform. There is no universally accepted convention as to which of these relations defines the transform and which defines the inverse transform, and different normalization conventions are also in use. In this book, we shall adopt a more symmetric notation by rewriting (7) and (8) in terms of the functions $\widetilde{F}(x) \equiv \sqrt{2\pi}\, f(x)$ and $F(y) \equiv g(y)$:

$$\widetilde{F}(x) = \frac{1}{\sqrt{2\pi}} \int_{-\infty}^{\infty} F(y)\, e^{ixy}\, dy, \tag{9}$$

$$F(y) = \frac{1}{\sqrt{2\pi}} \int_{-\infty}^{\infty} \widetilde{F}(x)\, e^{-ixy}\, dx. \tag{10}$$

The two functions $F(y)$ and $\widetilde{F}(x)$ occur on an equal footing in this pair of equations. For any appropriately well-behaved function $F(y)$, we shall say that $\widetilde{F}(x)$, as defined by (9), is the *Fourier transform* of $F(y)$; accordingly, the relation (10) expresses $F(y)$ as the *inverse Fourier transform* of $\widetilde{F}(x)$. Note that the functions $F(y)$ and $\widetilde{F}(x)$ may both be complex. The fact that the relations (9) and (10) express each of these functions in terms of the other means that the inverse Fourier transform is essentially unique.

The integral representation for a function $F(y)$ obtained by substituting (9) into (10),

$$F(y) = \frac{1}{2\pi} \int_{-\infty}^{\infty} dx \, e^{-ixy} \int_{-\infty}^{\infty} dy' \, F(y') \, e^{ixy'}, \tag{11}$$

is known as *Fourier's integral theorem* and is obviously equivalent to the pair of integral equations (9) and (10).

Although the foregoing arguments are by no means mathematically rigorous, they clearly show that there is an intimate connection between Fourier series and Fourier transforms. Without entering into the full details, we shall outline briefly a method of constructing a more rigorous proof of Fourier's integral theorem.

Suppose that the function $F(y)$ is piecewise smooth on the entire real axis and, in addition, is absolutely integrable:

$$\int_{-\infty}^{\infty} |F(y)| \, dy < \infty.$$

Then the right-hand side of (11) is equal to

$$\frac{1}{2\pi} \lim_{X \to \infty} \int_{-X}^{X} dx \int_{-\infty}^{\infty} dy' \, F(y') \, e^{ix(y'-y)}$$

$$= \frac{1}{2\pi} \lim_{X \to \infty} \int_{-\infty}^{\infty} F(y') \, \frac{2 \sin [X(y'-y)]}{y'-y} \, dy'$$

$$= \frac{1}{\pi} \lim_{X \to \infty} \int_{-\infty}^{\infty} F(u+y) \, \frac{\sin Xu}{u} \, du = \tfrac{1}{2}[F(y^-) + F(y^+)],$$

where in the last two steps we have made the change of variable $u = y' - y$ and then applied a variant of Lemmas 2 and 3 of the appendix to chapter 4 (in which the range of integration extends along the entire real axis). Thus, exactly as in the case of a Fourier series, the Fourier integral representation (11) reproduces the arithmetic mean of the left- and right-hand limits of the function at each value of its argument. As discussed above, we shall replace the quantity $\tfrac{1}{2}[F(y^-) + F(y^+)]$ by $F(y)$ in all subsequent equations.

We now examine some special cases. Suppose first that the function $F(y)$ is *even*, i.e., $F(-y) = F(y)$. Then its Fourier transform can be written

$$\widetilde{F}(x) = \frac{1}{\sqrt{2\pi}} \int_{-\infty}^{0} F(y) \, e^{ixy} \, dy + \frac{1}{\sqrt{2\pi}} \int_{0}^{\infty} F(y) \, e^{ixy} \, dy. \tag{12}$$

Putting $y = -y'$ in the first integral in (12) and using the fact that $F(-y') = F(y')$, we have

$$\widetilde{F}(x) = \frac{1}{\sqrt{2\pi}} \int_0^\infty F(y') \, e^{-ixy'} \, dy' + \frac{1}{\sqrt{2\pi}} \int_0^\infty F(y) \, e^{ixy} \, dy$$

$$= \sqrt{\frac{2}{\pi}} \int_0^\infty F(y) \cos xy \, dy \equiv \widetilde{F}_c(x). \tag{13}$$

Equation (13) is taken as the definition of the *Fourier cosine transform* $\widetilde{F}_c(x)$ of the function $F(y)$. Thus, for an *even* function $F(y)$, we have $\widetilde{F}(x) = \widetilde{F}_c(x)$, i.e., the Fourier cosine transform is the same as the ordinary Fourier transform. The form of the integral in (13) also shows that if $F(y)$ is even, then its ordinary Fourier transform $\widetilde{F}(x)$ is also even. Using this fact, we can write the inverse transform as

$$F(y) = \frac{1}{\sqrt{2\pi}} \int_{-\infty}^0 \widetilde{F}(x) \, e^{-ixy} \, dx + \frac{1}{\sqrt{2\pi}} \int_0^\infty \widetilde{F}(x) \, e^{-ixy} \, dx$$

$$= \frac{1}{\sqrt{2\pi}} \int_0^\infty \widetilde{F}(x') \, e^{ix'y} \, dx' + \frac{1}{\sqrt{2\pi}} \int_0^\infty \widetilde{F}(x) \, e^{-ixy} \, dx$$

$$= \sqrt{\frac{2}{\pi}} \int_0^\infty \widetilde{F}(x) \cos xy \, dx,$$

which we recognize as the Fourier cosine transform of $\widetilde{F}(x)$ and hence also of $\widetilde{F}_c(x)$. In other words, the functions $F(y)$ and $\widetilde{F}_c(x)$ are Fourier cosine transforms of each other. Provided that we restrict ourselves to the range $y > 0$, this property remains true even if the original function $F(y)$ is not assumed to be even. This follows from the observation that the definition of $\widetilde{F}_c(x)$ depends only on the values of $F(y)$ for $y > 0$, so that the preceding argument involving an even function can still be applied in the general case by working with the even function which coincides with $F(y)$ for $y > 0$.

Exactly analogous considerations apply when $F(y)$ is *odd*, i.e., $F(-y) = -F(y)$. In this case, we find instead that

$$\widetilde{F}(x) = i\sqrt{\frac{2}{\pi}} \int_0^\infty F(y) \sin xy \, dy \equiv i\widetilde{F}_s(x), \tag{14}$$

where $\widetilde{F}_s(x)$ is defined as the *Fourier sine transform* of $F(y)$. We see that in this case $\widetilde{F}(x)$ is also an odd function, and use of this fact in the inverse transform leads to the result

$$F(y) = \sqrt{\frac{2}{\pi}} \int_0^\infty \widetilde{F}_s(x) \sin xy \, dx,$$

which we recognize as the Fourier sine transform of $\widetilde{F}_s(x)$. In other words,

$F(y)$ and $\widetilde{F}_s(x)$ are Fourier sine transforms of each other. This remains true even if $F(y)$ is not assumed to be an odd function, provided that the restriction is made to the range $y > 0$.

5.2 The Dirac delta function

We now introduce a notational device which proves to be very convenient when considering Fourier transforms, as well as for many other applications. We first formally interchange the order of integration in Fourier's integral theorem and write

$$F(y) = \frac{1}{2\pi} \int_{-\infty}^{\infty} dy' \, F(y') \int_{-\infty}^{\infty} dx \, e^{ix(y' - y)}. \tag{1}$$

We define the so-called *Dirac δ-function* by the equation

$$\delta(z) \equiv \frac{1}{2\pi} \int_{-\infty}^{\infty} e^{ixz} \, dx, \tag{2}$$

so that (1) reads

$$F(y) = \int_{-\infty}^{\infty} F(y') \, \delta(y' - y) \, dy'. \tag{3}$$

The operation of interchanging the order of integration which leads to these equations cannot actually be mathematically justified (in the ordinary sense of classical analysis), since the improper integral (2) is clearly divergent, so that there is actually no function $\delta(z)$ having the properties (2) and (3). Nevertheless, it is possible to ascribe a definite meaning to equations such as these. The idea is essentially to *define* the entire set of symbols on the right-hand side of (3) to be a representation of the function $F(y)$, so that the formal manipulations leading to equations (1)–(3) automatically reproduce the correct result, $F(y)$, for the original double integral.

Although '$\delta(z)$' in isolation has no more meaning as a numerical quantity than the 'dx' in a definite integral, it is convenient to think of the δ-function as if it were an actual function having certain peculiar properties.

The main formal properties which we shall require are as follows:
(i) the property (3); (ii) $\delta(z) = 0$ for $z \neq 0$; (iii) $\delta(-z) = \delta(z)$. Property (ii) merely reflects the fact that the value of the integral (3) depends only on the value of the function $F(y')$ at the single point $y' = y$. Property (iii) can be derived by making the substitution $x = -x'$ in the original integral (2)

which defines the δ-function:

$$\delta(z) = \frac{1}{2\pi} \int_{-\infty}^{\infty} e^{-ix'z} \, dx' = \delta(-z).$$

It follows from properties (i) and (ii) that the δ-function has the general property

$$\int_{a}^{b} F(y') \, \delta(y' - y) \, dy' = \begin{cases} F(y) \text{ if } a < y < b, \\ 0 \text{ if } y \notin [a, b]. \end{cases}$$

We do not define the value of the integral when $y = a$ or $y = b$.

The Dirac δ-function $\delta(y)$ can also be thought of as the formal limit of certain sequences of ordinary functions $F_n(y)$ $(n = 1, 2, \ldots)$ which have the following properties:

(i) $F_n(y) \to 0$ as $n \to \infty$ for any fixed $y \neq 0$;

(ii) $\int_{-\infty}^{\infty} F_n(y) dy = 1$ for all n.

An example of a sequence of functions having these properties is provided by the set of 'Gaussian' functions

$$F_n(y) = \frac{n}{\sqrt{2\pi}} \exp\left(-\tfrac{1}{2} n^2 \, y^2\right). \tag{4}$$

We first note that the function $F_n(y)$ has a central peak at $y = 0$ of height $F_n(0) = n/\sqrt{2\pi}$ and width proportional to $1/n$ (where the width can be defined as the distance from the peak at which $F_n(y)$ falls off to some standard fraction of its maximum value). This peak becomes progressively higher and narrower with increasing n, as is illustrated in Fig. 5.1, where we compare the graphs of $F_1(y)$ and $F_2(y)$.

Clearly, the functions (4) have the property that $F_n(y) \to 0$ as $n \to \infty$ for any fixed $y \neq 0$. Now consider the integral

$$\int_{-\infty}^{\infty} F_n(y) \, dy = \frac{1}{\sqrt{\pi}} \int_{-\infty}^{\infty} e^{-x^2} \, dx, \tag{5}$$

where we have made the substitution $x = ny/\sqrt{2}$. The integral on the right-hand side of (5) can be readily evaluated by writing its square as a double integral in the plane and transforming the latter to plane polar coordinates:

$$\left[\int_{-\infty}^{\infty} e^{-x^2} \, dx\right]^2 = \int_{-\infty}^{\infty} dx \int_{-\infty}^{\infty} dy \, e^{-(x^2 + y^2)} \tag{6}$$

$$= \int_{0}^{2\pi} d\theta \int_{0}^{\infty} dr \, r e^{-r^2} = (2\pi)(\tfrac{1}{2}) = \pi.$$

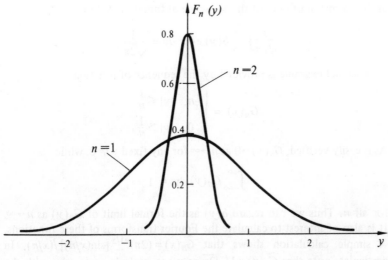

Fig. 5.1

Thus we have

$$\int_{-\infty}^{\infty} F_n(y)\,dy = 1$$

for all n, as required, and the sequence of functions $F_n(y)$ serves as a 'model' for the Dirac δ-function.

It turns out that the Fourier transforms of the functions (4) are also of Gaussian form. To see this, we calculate

$$\widetilde{F}_n(x) = \frac{1}{\sqrt{2\pi}}\int_{-\infty}^{\infty} F_n(y)\,e^{ixy}\,dy = \frac{n}{2\pi}\int_{-\infty}^{\infty} \exp\left(-\tfrac{1}{2}n^2 y^2 + ixy\right)dy$$

$$= \frac{n}{2\pi}\int_{-\infty}^{\infty} \exp\left[-\tfrac{1}{2}\left(ny - \frac{ix}{n}\right)^2 - \tfrac{1}{2}\frac{x^2}{n^2}\right]dy.$$

Having completed the square in the exponent, we can evaluate the integral by making the change of variable $u = (ny - ix/n)/\sqrt{2}$ and using the result (6):

$$\widetilde{F}_n(x) = \frac{1}{\sqrt{2}\,\pi} \exp(-\tfrac{1}{2}\frac{x^2}{n^2})\int_{-\infty}^{\infty} \exp(-u^2)\,du = \frac{1}{\sqrt{2\pi}} \exp(-\tfrac{1}{2}\frac{x^2}{n^2}). \quad (7)$$

The expression (7) is a Gaussian function with a fixed maximum height $1/\sqrt{2\pi}$ and a width proportional to n. Note that $\widetilde{F}_n(x) \to 1/\sqrt{2\pi}$ as $n \to \infty$. This is precisely what would be obtained by taking the Fourier transform of the formal limit $\delta(y)$ of the sequence of functions $F_n(y)$:

$$\frac{1}{\sqrt{2\pi}}\int_{-\infty}^{\infty}\delta(y)\,e^{ixy}\,dy = \frac{1}{\sqrt{2\pi}}\ .$$

A second example is provided by the sequence of functions

$$G_n(y) = \begin{cases} \frac{1}{2}n, & |y| \leqslant \frac{1}{n}, \\[2mm] 0, & |y| > \frac{1}{n}. \end{cases}$$

As is easily verified, $G_n(y) \to 0$ as $n \to \infty$ for any fixed $y \neq 0$, while

$$\int_{-\infty}^{\infty} G_n(y)\,dy = 1$$

for all n. Thus we can regard $\delta(y)$ as the formal limit of $G_n(y)$ as $n \to \infty$. It is also of interest to calculate the Fourier transforms of these functions. A simple calculation shows that $\widetilde{G}_n(x) = (2\pi)^{-1/2}\,[\sin(x/n)]/(x/n)$. In particular, note that $\widetilde{G}_n(x) \to 1/\sqrt{2\pi}$ as $n \to \infty$, again in agreement with the value obtained directly by calculating the Fourier transform of $\delta(y)$.

As an application of the Dirac δ-function, we now derive two important properties of Fourier transforms.

The convolution theorem for Fourier transforms

If
$$F(y) = \int_{-\infty}^{\infty} A(y - y')\,G(y')\,dy', \tag{8}$$

then
$$\widetilde{F}(x) = \sqrt{2\pi}\,\widetilde{A}(x)\,\widetilde{G}(x). \tag{9}$$

This theorem states that if a function $F(y)$ is expressed as a 'convolution integral' (8) in terms of two other functions, then the Fourier transforms of the three functions satisfy the simple multiplicative relation (9).

PROOF   Expressing the factors in the integrand of (8) in terms of their Fourier transforms, we have

$$F(y) = \int_{-\infty}^{\infty} dy'\,\frac{1}{\sqrt{2\pi}}\int_{-\infty}^{\infty} dx\,\widetilde{A}(x)\,e^{-ix(y-y')}\,\frac{1}{\sqrt{2\pi}}\int_{-\infty}^{\infty} dx'\,\widetilde{G}(x')\,e^{-ix'y'}$$

$$= \int_{-\infty}^{\infty} dx\,\widetilde{A}(x)\,e^{-ixy}\int_{-\infty}^{\infty} dx'\,\widetilde{G}(x')\,\frac{1}{2\pi}\int_{-\infty}^{\infty} dy'\,e^{i(x-x')\,y'}$$

$$= \int_{-\infty}^{\infty} dx\,\widetilde{A}(x)\,e^{-ixy}\int_{-\infty}^{\infty} dx'\,\widetilde{G}(x')\,\delta(x-x')$$

$$= \int_{-\infty}^{\infty} \widetilde{A}(x)\,e^{-ixy}\,\widetilde{G}(x)\,dx, \tag{10}$$

which we recognize as the inverse Fourier transform of the function $\sqrt{2\pi}\,\widetilde{A}(x)\widetilde{G}(x)$. Taking the Fourier transforms of both sides of (10), we have $\widetilde{F}(x) = \sqrt{2\pi}\,\widetilde{A}(x)\widetilde{G}(x)$, as required.

THEOREM *(Parseval's identity)*   A function $F(y)$ and its Fourier transform $\widetilde{F}(x)$ satisfy the relation

$$\int_{-\infty}^{\infty} |F(y)|^2\, dy = \int_{-\infty}^{\infty} |\widetilde{F}(x)|^2\, dx. \tag{11}$$

PROOF   The left-hand side of (11) is

$$\int_{-\infty}^{\infty} F(y)F^*(y)\,dy = \int_{-\infty}^{\infty} dy \frac{1}{\sqrt{2\pi}} \int_{-\infty}^{\infty} dx\, \widetilde{F}(x) e^{-ixy} \frac{1}{\sqrt{2\pi}} \int_{-\infty}^{\infty} dx'\, \widetilde{F}^*(x') e^{ix'y}$$

$$= \int_{-\infty}^{\infty} dx\, \widetilde{F}(x) \int_{-\infty}^{\infty} dx'\, \widetilde{F}^*(x') \frac{1}{2\pi} \int_{-\infty}^{\infty} dy\, e^{i(x'-x)y}$$

$$= \int_{-\infty}^{\infty} dx\, \widetilde{F}(x) \int_{-\infty}^{\infty} dx'\, \widetilde{F}^*(x')\, \delta(x'-x) =$$

$$= \int_{-\infty}^{\infty} \widetilde{F}(x)\, \widetilde{F}^*(x)\, dx,$$

which is equal to the right-hand side of (11).

Some simple consequences of Parseval's identity are of special interest. If $F(y)$ (and hence also $\widetilde{F}(x)$) is an *even* function, then $\widetilde{F}(x) = \widetilde{F}_c(x)$ and we find

$$\int_0^{\infty} |F(y)|^2\, dy = \int_0^{\infty} |\widetilde{F}_c(x)|^2\, dx. \tag{12}$$

If $F(y)$ (and hence also $\widetilde{F}(x)$) is *odd*, then $\widetilde{F}(x) = i\widetilde{F}_s(x)$ and we find

$$\int_0^{\infty} |F(y)|^2\, dy = \int_0^{\infty} |\widetilde{F}_s(x)|^2\, dx. \tag{13}$$

Since the Fourier cosine and sine transforms are defined by integrals over only the positive range of arguments, the relations (12) and (13) remain valid for arbitrary functions which are neither even nor odd.

The various forms of Parseval's identity are sometimes useful for the evaluation of definite integrals. As an example, consider the integral

$$I \equiv \int_0^{\infty} \left(\frac{\sin y}{y}\right)^2 dy.$$

We notice that

$$\frac{\sin y}{y} = \int_0^1 \cos yx \, dx = \sqrt{\frac{2}{\pi}} \int_0^\infty H(x) \cos yx \, dx,$$

where

$$H(x) = \begin{cases} \sqrt{\frac{\pi}{2}}, & 0 \leqslant x \leqslant 1, \\ 0, & x > 1, \end{cases}$$

so that the functions $(\sin y)/y$ and $H(x)$ are Fourier cosine transforms of each other. Hence

$$I = \int_0^\infty |H(x)|^2 \, dx = \tfrac{1}{2}\pi.$$

The convolution theorem and Parseval's identity acquire a simple interpretation in situations when the function $F(y)$ represents the time dependence of some physical quantity. It is more appropriate in such cases to adopt a different notation for the independent variables which we have so far been calling x and y and to write the Fourier transform and inverse transform as

$$\widetilde{F}(\omega) = \frac{1}{\sqrt{2\pi}} \int_{-\infty}^\infty F(t) \, e^{i\omega t} \, dt, \quad F(t) = \frac{1}{\sqrt{2\pi}} \int_{-\infty}^\infty \widetilde{F}(\omega) \, e^{-i\omega t} \, d\omega.$$

A time-dependent quantity $F(t)$ is then expressed as a superposition of pure (sinusoidal) frequency components $e^{-i\omega t}$, and its Fourier transform $\widetilde{F}(\omega)$ specifies the frequency spectrum, i.e. the amplitude associated with each frequency component in the superposition.

Consider a physical system ('black box') in which some time-dependent 'response' or 'output' $F(t)$ is linearly related to an 'input' $G(t)$ by the law

$$F(t) = \int_{-\infty}^\infty A(t - t') \, G(t') \, dt' \tag{14}$$

(see Fig. 5.2). Equation (14) allows the relation between the input and the output to depend only on the interval of time between them, and not on

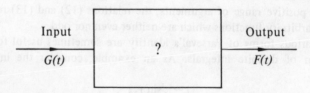

Fig. 5.2

the absolute time; in other words, it is assumed that the properties of the system are time-independent. The principle of causality, according to which the input at a given time cannot influence the output at any earlier time, requires that $A(\tau) = 0$ for $\tau < 0$. Apart from this restriction, the function $A(\tau)$ can be arbitrary, depending on the nature of the physical system. Applying the convolution theorem to (14), we have $\tilde{F}(\omega) = \sqrt{2\pi}\tilde{A}(\omega)\tilde{G}(\omega)$. This shows that each individual frequency component of the output is simply proportional to the corresponding frequency component of the input. For this reason, it is often more convenient to discuss the frequency spectra of physical quantities than their time dependence when analyzing linear systems.

In many physical situations, the quantity $|F(t)|^2$ represents an energy transmitted per unit time. By virtue of Parseval's identity, $|\tilde{F}(\omega)|^2$ can then be interpreted as an energy per unit of frequency in the frequency spectrum, so that the two sides of Parseval's identity represent the total energy.

5.3 Application to partial differential equations

When the method of separation of variables is used to obtain product solutions of partial differential equations, it sometimes happens that the separation constant can take arbitrary values within some continuous range, even after all the homogeneous boundary conditions have been imposed. This situation can occur when the region in the space of the independent variables in which the equation is to be solved is of infinite extent. The non-homogeneous boundary conditions then lead to expressions for prescribed functions as continuous superpositions (integrals) of certain product solutions, instead of discrete superpositions (summations) as in Sec. 4.5. When the basic product solutions involve trigonometric functions, Fourier transforms play the role analogous to that of the Fourier series in the problems considered in Sec. 4.5.

Example 1   Consider the heat equation for the temperature distribution $U(x, t)$ along a uniform semi-infinite bar ($0 \leqslant x < \infty$),

$$\frac{\partial^2 U}{\partial x^2} = \frac{1}{a^2}\frac{\partial U}{\partial t}, \tag{1}$$

where a solution is to be found in the region $0 \leqslant x < \infty$, $t \geqslant 0$, satisfying the boundary condition $U(0, t) = 0$ for all $t \geqslant 0$ and the initial condition $U(x, 0) = f(x)$ for all $x \geqslant 0$, where $f(x)$ is a prescribed function which gives the initial temperature distribution. This problem is completely analogous to the boundary-value problem for a bar of finite length L considered in Example 1 of Sec. 4.5 and corresponds to the limiting case $L \to \infty$.

As before, separation of variables leads to the product solutions

$$U(x, t) = (A \cos \lambda x + B \sin \lambda x)\, e^{-a^2 \lambda^2 t}, \tag{2}$$

and the boundary condition at $x = 0$ requires that $A = 0$. However, since there is no longer any second boundary condition at another value of x, there is now no restriction on λ, although it is obviously sufficient to consider only values $\lambda \geqslant 0$. The most general superposition of such product solutions satisfying the partial differential equation (1) and the homogeneous boundary condition at $x = 0$ is therefore of the form

$$U(x, t) = \int_0^\infty B(\lambda) \sin \lambda x\, e^{-a^2 \lambda^2 t}\, d\lambda.$$

The prescribed initial condition at $t = 0$ requires that

$$f(x) = \int_0^\infty B(\lambda) \sin \lambda x\, d\lambda.$$

This condition states that $f(x)$ is the Fourier sine transform of the function $\sqrt{\pi/2}\, B(\lambda)$. Hence

$$B(\lambda) = \frac{2}{\pi} \int_0^\infty f(x) \sin \lambda x\, dx$$

and the required solution is given by the double integral

$$U(x, t) = \frac{2}{\pi} \int_0^\infty d\lambda \sin \lambda x\, e^{-a^2 \lambda^2 t} \int_0^\infty dx'\, f(x') \sin \lambda x'.$$

Example 2   Consider the heat equation (1) for a uniform bar of infinite extent in both directions $(-\infty < x < \infty)$, subject to the initial condition $U(x, 0) = f(x)$, where the function $f(x)$ is now specified for all x.

In the absence of any boundary condition at a specific value of x, it is convenient to rewrite the product solution (2) in the form

$$U(x, t) = C e^{i\lambda x}\, e^{-a^2 \lambda^2 t}$$

(with no restriction on λ), so that the general superposition

$$U(x, t) = \int_{-\infty}^\infty C(\lambda)\, e^{i\lambda x}\, e^{-a^2 \lambda^2 t}\, d\lambda$$

is also a solution. The prescribed initial condition then requires that

$$f(x) = \int_{-\infty}^{\infty} C(\lambda)\, e^{i\lambda x}\, d\lambda.$$

Hence

$$C(\lambda) = \frac{1}{2\pi} \int_{-\infty}^{\infty} f(x)\, e^{-i\lambda x}\, dx$$

and the required solution is given by

$$U(x, t) = \frac{1}{2\pi} \int_{-\infty}^{\infty} d\lambda\, e^{i\lambda x}\, e^{-a^2 \lambda^2 t} \int_{-\infty}^{\infty} dx'\, f(x')\, e^{-i\lambda x'}.$$

5.4 Laplace transforms

The conditions under which the Fourier transform

$$\widetilde{F}(\omega) = \frac{1}{\sqrt{2\pi}} \int_{-\infty}^{\infty} F(t)\, e^{i\omega t}\, dt$$

of a function $F(t)$ can be defined are quite restrictive, and the integral defining $\widetilde{F}(\omega)$ does not converge even for such simple functions as $F(t) = t$, $F(t) = \sin at$, etc.

For many purposes, it is sufficient to restrict the discussion to functions $F(t)$ which vanish (or which can be defined to be zero) for $t < 0$, as in the case of physical processes which begin at some particular time and in whose behaviour we are interested for subsequent times. In this case, although the integral defining $\widetilde{F}(\omega)$ may not converge for real values of ω, it often does converge for a range of values of ω on the positive imaginary axis of the ω-plane. This is true for a wide class of functions $F(t)$, including functions which increase polynomially or even exponentially as $t \to \infty$. Assuming that $F(t) = 0$ for all $t < 0$ and putting $\omega = is$ ($s > 0$), we have

$$\widetilde{F}(is) = \frac{1}{\sqrt{2\pi}} \int_{0}^{\infty} F(t)\, e^{-st}\, dt.$$

We define the *Laplace transform* of $F(t)$ to be the function $\overline{F}(s) \equiv \sqrt{2\pi}\, \widetilde{F}(is)$, i.e.

$$\overline{F}(s) = \int_{0}^{\infty} F(t)\, e^{-st}\, dt, \qquad (1)$$

whenever this integral converges.

The following theorem provides sufficient conditions for the convergence of the integral (1).

THEOREM   If $F(t)$ is piecewise continuous on any finite interval of positive t and satisfies the inequality $|F(t)| \leqslant Me^{at}$ for all sufficiently large t, for some constants M and a, then $\overline{F}(s)$ is defined for all $s > a$.

PROOF   We first note that $F(t)$ is integrable on any finite interval and satisfies an inequality of the form $|F(t)| \leqslant Ne^{at}$ for all t. Since $|e^{-st}F(t)| \leqslant Ne^{-(s-a)t}$, it follows from the comparison theorem for integrals that the integral (1) is convergent whenever the integral

$$\int_0^\infty Ne^{-(s-a)t}\, dt$$

is convergent, i.e. when $s > a$.

A function $F(t)$ which has an upper bound of the type $|F(t)| \leqslant Me^{at}$ for all sufficiently large t is said to be *of exponential order*. Practically all the familiar functions which arise in applications satisfy this condition. This applies even to certain functions which grow faster than an exponential function. For example, the function $F(t) = t^4 e^{2t}$ is of exponential order, since $F(t)/e^{3t} \to 0$ as $t \to \infty$. An example of a function which is not of exponential order is $G(t) = e^{t^2}$.

Under the hypotheses of the theorem proved above, we have

$$|\overline{F}(s)| \leqslant \int_0^\infty |F(t)\, e^{-st}|\, dt \leqslant N \int_0^\infty e^{-(s-a)t}\, dt = \frac{N}{s-a}$$

for all $s > a$, so that $\overline{F}(s) \to 0$ as $s \to \infty$; even more precisely, we can assert that $\overline{F}(s) = O(1/s)$. This shows that functions which do not tend to zero in this way as $s \to \infty$ (such as 1, s or $\sin s$) cannot be Laplace transforms of functions which are piecewise continuous and of exponential order.

We shall sometimes denote the Laplace transform of a function $F(t)$ by the notation $\mathcal{L}[F(t)]$. The symbol s will be reserved for the independent variable of the Laplace transform, and we shall say that a transform exists if the defining integral (1) converges for at least some range of s. Laplace transforms of many simple functions can be evaluated by direct calculation of the defining integral. For example,

$$\mathcal{L}[e^{at}] = \int_0^\infty e^{-(s-a)t}\, dt = \frac{1}{s-a} \quad (s > a) \tag{2}$$

and

$$\mathcal{L}[\sin at] = \int_0^\infty e^{-st} \sin at\, dt = \text{Im} \int_0^\infty e^{-(s-ia)t}\, dt$$

$$= \text{Im}\left[\frac{1}{s-ia}\right] = \frac{a}{s^2+a^2} \quad (s>0), \tag{3}$$

where the range of s in which the result is valid is indicated in parentheses in each case. An important special case of (2) is the relation

$$\mathcal{L}[1] = \frac{1}{s} \quad (s>0). \tag{4}$$

If we allow the Dirac δ-function, we can write

$$\mathcal{L}[\delta(t-a)] = \int_0^\infty e^{-st}\, \delta(t-a)\, dt = e^{-sa} \tag{5}$$

for any $a>0$. The limiting form of (5) when $a \to 0^+$ is often written as

$$\mathcal{L}[\delta(t)] = 1. \tag{6}$$

It is important to remember that (6) must be interpreted in this way, since the integral in (5) has the limit zero as $a \to 0^-$ and is undefined if $a=0$. Note that $\mathcal{L}[\delta(t)]$ according to (6), unlike the Laplace transforms of ordinary piecewise continuous functions of exponential order, does not tend to zero as $s \to \infty$.

Certain fundamental properties of Laplace transforms enable us to build up the transforms of many new functions from the known transforms of simpler functions. We begin by giving four of the properties which are most useful in practice; here a and b are arbitrary constants and $F(t)$ and $G(t)$ are any functions satisfying the sufficient conditions assumed earlier for the existence of the Laplace transform.

(a) **Linearity** $\mathcal{L}[aF(t)+bG(t)] = a\mathcal{L}[F(t)] + b\mathcal{L}[G(t)]$.

(b) **Transforms of derivatives** $\mathcal{L}[F'(t)] = s\mathcal{L}[F(t)] - F(0^+)$.

(c) **First shifting theorem** If $\mathcal{L}[F(t)] = \bar{F}(s)$, then $\mathcal{L}[e^{at}F(t)] = \bar{F}(s-a)$.

(d) **Derivatives of transforms** $\mathcal{L}[tF(t)] = -d\bar{F}(s)/ds$.

Property (a) follows directly from the definition of the Laplace transform. To prove property (b), we first integrate by parts:

$$\mathcal{L}[F'(t)] = \int_0^\infty e^{-st} F'(t)\, dt = [e^{-st} F(t)]_0^\infty + s\int_0^\infty e^{-st} F(t)\, dt$$

$$= [e^{-st} F(t)]_0^\infty + s\mathcal{L}[F(t)].$$

If $F(t)$ is of exponential order, then $e^{-st}F(t) \to 0$ as $t \to \infty$ for sufficiently large s. This gives the result (b). Note that by writing $F(0^+)$ we are allowing for the possibility that the function $F(t)$ may be discontinuous at $t = 0$. By repeated application of the property (b), we can obtain expressions for the transforms of higher derivatives; for example,

$$\mathcal{L}[F''(t)] = s^2 \mathcal{L}[F(t)] - sF(0^+) - F'(0^+).$$

Property (c) follows from the fact that

$$\mathcal{L}[e^{at} F(t)] = \int_0^\infty e^{-(s-a)t} F(t)\, dt.$$

Property (d) can be established by differentiating under the integral sign in the definition of the Laplace transform:

$$\frac{d\overline{F}(s)}{ds} = -\int_0^\infty te^{-st} F(t)\, dt.$$

By repeated application of this property, we can derive the more general relation

$$\mathcal{L}[t^n F(t)] = (-1)^n \frac{d^n \overline{F}(s)}{ds^n}.$$

Before discussing further general properties of Laplace transforms, let us consider some examples of the application of the properties derived so far in evaluating Laplace transforms.

Example 1   Knowing the result $\mathcal{L}[\sin at] = a/(s^2 + a^2)$ $(s > 0)$, it follows from property (b) that $\mathcal{L}[a \cos at] = as/(s^2 + a^2)$ and hence, by the linearity property,

$$\mathcal{L}[\cos at] = \frac{s}{s^2 + a^2} \quad (s > 0). \tag{7}$$

Example 2   Evaluate $\mathcal{L}[t^n]$, where n is any non-negative integer.

We observe that $d(t^n)/dt = nt^{n-1}$. Hence, by property (b), $\mathcal{L}[nt^{n-1}] = s\mathcal{L}[t^n]$, which can be written as a recurrence relation $\mathcal{L}[t^n] = (n/s)\mathcal{L}[t^{n-1}]$ $(n = 1, 2, \ldots)$. We already know the result when $n = 0$: $\mathcal{L}[1] = 1/s$ $(s > 0)$. Repeated application of the recurrence relation then leads to the general formula

$$\mathcal{L}[t^n] = \frac{n!}{s^{n+1}} \quad (s > 0). \tag{8}$$

This in turn enables us to evaluate the Laplace transform of any polynomial in t, by virtue of the linearity property.

Example 3   Evaluate $\mathcal{L}[te^{2t} \sin 3t]$.

Since $\mathcal{L}[\sin 3t] = 3/(s^2 + 9)$, by property (d) we have

$$\mathcal{L}[t \sin 3t] = \frac{6s}{(s^2 + 9)^2} .$$

Finally, by property (c),

$$\mathcal{L}[te^{2t} \sin 3t] = \frac{6(s - 2)}{[(s - 2)^2 + 9]^2} .$$

Example 4   Evaluate the Laplace transform of the Laguerre polynomial of degree n, which can be defined as

$$L_n(t) \equiv \frac{e^t}{n!} \frac{d^n(t^n e^{-t})}{dt^n} \quad (n = 0, 1, \dots).$$

Starting with our previous result (8), by the first shifting theorem we have $\mathcal{L}[e^{-t}t^n] = n!/(s + 1)^{n+1}$. Hence, by property (b),

$$\mathcal{L}\left[\frac{d(e^{-t} t^n)}{dt}\right] = s\, \mathcal{L}[e^{-t} t^n]$$

for $n = 1, 2, \dots$. By repeated application of the same rule,

$$\mathcal{L}\left[\frac{d^n(e^{-t} t^n)}{dt^n}\right] = s^n\, \mathcal{L}[e^{-t} t^n] = \frac{s^n n!}{(s + 1)^{n+1}} .$$

Finally, by property (c),

$$\mathcal{L}\left[e^t\, \frac{d^n (e^{-t} t^n)}{dt^n}\right] = \frac{(s - 1)^n\, n!}{s^{n+1}}$$

and hence

$$\mathcal{L}[L_n(t)] = \frac{(s - 1)^n}{s^{n+1}} .$$

By exploiting our previous results for Fourier transforms and the relation between Fourier and Laplace transforms, it is possible to derive a general inversion formula for the inverse Laplace transform. This shows that the inverse Laplace transform, if it exists for a particular function, is essentially unique. However, it is often simplest in practice to determine inverse Laplace transforms by applying the basic general properties of

Laplace transforms in conjunction with tables of transforms of 'standard' functions. In this connection, it is useful to rewrite the properties (c) and (d) above in a form that refers specifically to inverse transforms. Writing $\overline{F}(s) \equiv G(s)$, i.e., $F(t) \equiv \mathcal{L}^{-1}[G(s)]$, where $\mathcal{L}^{-1}$ denotes the inverse Laplace transform, and taking the inverse transforms of the identities (c) and (d), these properties can be expressed as follows.

(c') $\mathcal{L}^{-1}[G(s-a)] = e^{at}\,\mathcal{L}^{-1}[G(s)]$.

(d') $\mathcal{L}^{-1}[dG(s)/ds] = -t\,\mathcal{L}^{-1}[G(s)]$.

Example 5   The method of partial fractions is often useful in finding the inverse transforms of rational functions. Thus

$$\mathcal{L}^{-1}\left[\frac{1}{s(s^2+1)}\right] = \mathcal{L}^{-1}\left[\frac{1}{s} - \frac{s}{s^2+1}\right] = 1 - \cos t.$$

Example 6   As an application of property (c'), we have

$$\mathcal{L}^{-1}\left[\frac{s}{s^2+4s+5}\right] = \mathcal{L}^{-1}\left[\frac{(s+2)-2}{(s+2)^2+1}\right] = e^{-2t}\,\mathcal{L}^{-1}\left[\frac{s-2}{s^2+1}\right]$$

$$= e^{-2t}\,\mathcal{L}^{-1}\left[\frac{s}{s^2+1} - \frac{2}{s^2+1}\right] = e^{-2t}\,(\cos t - 2\sin t).$$

Example 7   As an application of property (d'), we have

$$\mathcal{L}^{-1}\left[\frac{2as}{(s^2+a^2)^2}\right] = \mathcal{L}^{-1}\left[\frac{d}{ds}\left(-\frac{a}{s^2+a^2}\right)\right] = -t\,\mathcal{L}^{-1}\left[-\frac{a}{s^2+a^2}\right] = t\sin at.$$

(e) The convolution theorem for Laplace transforms

If
$$F(t) = \int_0^t A(t-t')\,G(t')\,dt'$$

for all $t > 0$, then $\overline{F}(s) = \overline{A}(s)\overline{G}(s)$.

PROOF   Without loss of generality, we can assume that $A(\tau) = G(\tau) = 0$ for all $\tau < 0$. In this case we can write

$$F(t) = \int_{-\infty}^{\infty} A(t-t')\,G(t')\,dt',$$

so that $\widetilde{F}(\omega) = \sqrt{2\pi}\,\widetilde{A}(\omega)\widetilde{G}(\omega)$ by the convolution theorem for Fourier transforms. Putting $\overline{F}(s) = \sqrt{2\pi}\,\widetilde{F}(is)$, etc., we obtain the required result.

The convolution theorem is an important tool in the evaluation of inverse Laplace transforms.

Example 8   An alternative solution of the problem of Example 5 is as follows. By identifying the functions $\bar{A}(s) \equiv 1/s$ and $\bar{B}(s) \equiv 1/(s^2 + 1)$ as the inverse transforms of known functions, namely $A(t) = 1$ and $B(t) = \sin t$, the problem reduces to that of calculating $F(t) \equiv \mathcal{L}^{-1}[\bar{A}(s)\bar{B}(s)]$. In view of the convolution theorem and the uniqueness of the inverse transform, $F(t)$ must be given by

$$F(t) = \int_0^t A(t - t') B(t') dt' = \int_0^t \sin t' \, dt' = 1 - \cos t.$$

Example 9   Evaluate the inverse Laplace transform

$$F(t) \equiv \mathcal{L}^{-1}\left[\frac{2a}{(s^2 + a^2)^2}\right].$$

Here it is most convenient to make the identification $\bar{A}(s) \equiv 1/s$ and $\bar{B}(s) \equiv 2as/(s^2 + a^2)^2$, corresponding to $A(t) = 1$ and $B(t) = t \sin at$ (see Example 7). Hence

$$F(t) = \int_0^t A(t - t') B(t') dt' = \int_0^t t' \sin at' \, dt' = \frac{1}{a^2}(\sin at - at \cos at).$$

The results of Examples 7 and 9 and equation (3) can be rearranged into the standard formulae

$$\mathcal{L}[t \sin at] = \frac{2as}{(s^2 + a^2)^2}, \tag{9}$$

$$\mathcal{L}[t \cos at] = \frac{s^2 - a^2}{(s^2 + a^2)^2}. \tag{10}$$

We conclude this section with two further properties of Laplace transforms which are closely related to the properties (b) and (d) derived earlier.

(f) Transforms of integrals $\mathcal{L}[\int_0^t F(t')dt'] = (1/s)\,\mathcal{L}[F(t)]$.

(g) Integrals of transforms $\mathcal{L}[F(t)/t] = \int_s^\infty \bar{F}(s')ds'$.

To establish the property (f), let us define the function

$$G(t) \equiv \int_0^t F(t') \, dt',$$

which has the properties $dG(t)/dt = F(t)$ and $G(0) = 0$. Then, by property (b), we have

$$\mathcal{L}[F(t)] = s\,\mathcal{L}[G(t)] - G(0)$$

and we obtain the required result for $\mathcal{L}[G(t)]$.

To establish the property (g), let

$$\bar{H}(s) \equiv \int_s^\infty \bar{F}(s')\,ds'.$$

Then $d\bar{H}(s)/ds = -\bar{F}(s)$, and $\bar{H}(s)$ has the property $\bar{H}(s) \to 0$ as $s \to \infty$, as is required of a Laplace transform. By the property (d), we have $\bar{F}(s) = \mathcal{L}[tH(t)]$ and hence $F(t) = tH(t)$. Solving for $H(t)$ and taking its Laplace transform, we obtain the required result.

The forms of the properties (f) and (g) which refer specifically to inverse Laplace transforms are as follows.

(f') $\mathcal{L}^{-1}[\bar{F}(s)/s] = \int_0^t F(t')\,dt'.$

(g') $\mathcal{L}^{-1}\left[\int_s^\infty \bar{F}(s')\,ds'\right] = F(t)/t.$

Example 10   Evaluate

$$\mathcal{L}^{-1}\left[\frac{1}{s^2\,(s-2)}\right].$$

We know that $\mathcal{L}^{-1}[1/(s-2)] = e^{2t}$. Applying the property (f'), we have

$$\mathcal{L}^{-1}\left[\frac{1}{s(s-2)}\right] = \int_0^t e^{2t'}\,dt' = \frac{1}{2}\,(e^{2t}-1),$$

$$\mathcal{L}^{-1}\left[\frac{1}{s^2\,(s-2)}\right] = \frac{1}{2}\int_0^t (e^{2t'}-1)\,dt' = \frac{1}{4}\,(e^{2t}-2t-1).$$

Example 11   Evaluate

$$\mathcal{L}^{-1}\left[\log\left(\frac{s+a}{s+b}\right)\right],$$

where a and b are constants.

Let $\bar{G}(s) \equiv \log\,[(s+a)/(s+b)]$. Then

$$\frac{d\bar{G}(s)}{ds} = \frac{1}{s+a} - \frac{1}{s+b}.$$

Since $\bar{G}(s)$ vanishes as $s \to \infty$, as expected for a Laplace transform, we have

$$\bar{G}(s) = \int_s^\infty \left[\frac{1}{s'+b} - \frac{1}{s'+a}\right]\,ds'.$$

Applying the property (g'), we obtain the required inverse transform

$$G(t) = \frac{1}{t}(e^{-bt} - e^{-at}).$$

5.5 Applications to ordinary differential equations

We illustrate the main ideas by means of a number of specific examples.

Example 1   Solve the differential equation

$$\frac{d^2x}{dt^2} - x = t + 1$$

subject to the initial conditions $x(0) = 0$ and $x'(0) = 1$.

The Laplace transform of the differential equation is $\mathcal{L}[x''] - \mathcal{L}[x] = \mathcal{L}[t + 1] = 1/s^2 + 1/s$. We have seen that $\mathcal{L}[x''] = s^2\mathcal{L}[x] - sx(0) - x'(0)$. With the given initial conditions, this gives $\mathcal{L}[x''] = s^2\mathcal{L}[x] - 1$. The transform of the original differential equation therefore becomes an algebraic equation for $\bar{x}(s) \equiv \mathcal{L}[x]$:

$$(s^2 - 1)\,\bar{x}(s) - 1 = \frac{1}{s^2} + \frac{1}{s}\,.$$

Solving for $\bar{x}(s)$ and expressing the result in terms of partial fractions, we find

$$\bar{x}(s) = \frac{s^2 + s + 1}{s^2(s^2 - 1)} = \frac{3}{2}\frac{1}{s - 1} - \frac{1}{2}\frac{1}{s + 1} - \frac{1}{s^2} - \frac{1}{s}\,.$$

Finally, taking the inverse transform, we obtain the required solution:

$$x(t) = \frac{3}{2}e^t - \frac{1}{2}e^{-t} - t - 1.$$

This method can be used more generally to solve linear ordinary differential equations with constant coefficients, subject to prescribed initial conditions at $t = 0$. If the Laplace transform of the non-homogeneous term in the differential equation is known, the problem is reduced to finding the required solution as the inverse transform of a known function. Note that the calculation automatically incorporates the initial conditions. To find the *general* solution of such a differential equation, we can proceed in exactly the same way, carrying out the analysis in terms of *arbitrary* initial conditions at $t = 0$; the parameters specifying these initial conditions will then play the role of the arbitrary constants in the solution.

As the following example demonstrates, similar methods can be used to solve simultaneous differential equations.

Example 2   Find a solution of the simultaneous differential equations

$$\begin{cases} \dfrac{dx}{dt} + y = e^t, \\[2mm] x - \dfrac{dy}{dt} = \sin t \end{cases}$$

subject to the initial conditions $x(0) = 1$ and $y(0) = 0$.

The Laplace transforms of these equations are

$$\mathcal{L}[x'] + \mathcal{L}[y] = \frac{1}{s - 1},$$

$$\mathcal{L}[x] - \mathcal{L}[y'] = \frac{1}{s^2 + 1}.$$

Writing $\mathcal{L}[x'] = s\,\mathcal{L}[x] - x(0) = s\bar{x}(s) - 1$, where $\bar{x}(s) \equiv \mathcal{L}[x]$, and a similar equation for $\mathcal{L}[y']$, we obtain the pair of equations

$$s\bar{x}(s) + \bar{y}(s) = 1 + \frac{1}{s - 1},$$

$$\bar{x}(s) - s\bar{y}(s) = \frac{1}{s^2 + 1}.$$

Solving algebraically for $\bar{x}(s)$ and $\bar{y}(s)$ and expressing the results in terms of partial fractions, we find

$$\bar{x}(s) = \frac{1}{2}\left[\frac{1}{s - 1} + \frac{1}{s^2 + 1} + \frac{s}{s^2 + 1} + \frac{2}{(s^2 + 1)^2}\right],$$

$$\bar{y}(s) = \frac{1}{2}\left[\frac{1}{s - 1} + \frac{1}{s^2 + 1} - \frac{s}{s^2 + 1} - \frac{2s}{(s^2 + 1)^2}\right].$$

The inverse transforms of the various terms in these equations can be obtained from the results of the preceding section. This gives the required solution:

$$x(t) = \frac{1}{2}\left[e^t + \sin t + \cos t + (\sin t - t \cos t)\right],$$

$$y(t) = \frac{1}{2}\left[e^t + \sin t - \cos t - t \sin t\right].$$

Example 3   Laplace transform methods are sometimes also useful in finding solutions of ordinary differential equations with non-constant (particularly polynomial) coefficients. As an illustration, consider Laguerre's differential equation of order n ($n = 0, 1, \ldots$):

$$t\,\frac{d^2 x}{dt^2} + (1 - t)\frac{dx}{dt} + nx = 0.$$

Taking the Laplace transforms of the various terms which occur, we have

$$\mathcal{L}[x'] = s\bar{x} - x(0),$$

$$\mathcal{L}[tx'] = -\frac{d}{ds}[s\bar{x}(s) - x(0)] = -s\frac{d\bar{x}}{ds} - \bar{x},$$

$$\mathcal{L}[x''] = s^2\bar{x} - sx(0) - x'(0),$$

$$\mathcal{L}[tx''] = -\frac{d}{ds}[s^2\bar{x}(s) - sx(0) - x'(0)] = -s^2\frac{d\bar{x}}{ds} - 2s\bar{x} + x(0).$$

Combining these results, we find that the transform of the original differential equation can be written in the form

$$(s^2 - s)\frac{d\bar{x}}{ds} = (n + 1 - s)\bar{x}, \tag{1}$$

where the dependence on $x(0)$ has dropped out. This is a first-order differential equation for $\bar{x}(s)$. It is easy to see that, more generally, if the coefficients in the original differential equation are polynomials in t of maximum degree m, then the Laplace transform of this equation is a new differential equation of order m for the transform $\bar{x}(s)$; this is so because each multiplication by t in the original differential equation corresponds to a differentiation with respect to s in the transformed equation.

Separating the variables in the differential equation (1), we obtain

$$\frac{d\bar{x}}{\bar{x}} = \left(\frac{n}{s-1} - \frac{n+1}{s}\right) ds,$$

whose general solution is easily found to be $\bar{x}(s) = C(s-1)^n/s^{n+1}$, where C is an arbitrary constant. This expression can be identified as $C\mathcal{L}[L_n(t)]$, where $L_n(t)$ is the Laguerre polynomial of degree n (see Example 4 in Sec. 5.4). Hence we obtain the solution $x(t) = CL_n(t)$. Note, however, that this solution contains only a single arbitrary constant and is therefore not the general solution of Laguerre's differential equation. (It turns out that the second independent solution is divergent as $t \to 0$ in such a way that it does not possess a Laplace transform.)

5.6 Green's functions

In this section we shall develop a systematic procedure for solving initial-value problems for linear ordinary differential equations with constant coefficients with the aid of Laplace transforms.

Consider a differential equation of the form

$$P(D)[x(t)] = h(t),$$ (1)

where

$$P(D) = \sum_{k=0}^{n} a_k D^k \quad \left(D \equiv \frac{d}{dt} \right)$$

is a polynomial differential operator of degree n and $h(t)$ is a given function; we seek a solution of (1) subject to the homogeneous initial conditions

$$x(0) = x'(0) = \ldots = x^{(n-1)}(0) = 0.$$

The Laplace transform of the differential equation (1) is $\mathcal{L}[P(D)x] = \bar{h}(s)$. Let us assume that the transform $\bar{h}(s)$ is known. Now $\mathcal{L}[Dx] = s \mathcal{L}[x] - x(0) = s\bar{x}$ and, more generally, we can show by induction that $\mathcal{L}[D^k x] = s^k \bar{x}$ $(k = 0, 1, \ldots, n)$. Linearity then implies that $\mathcal{L}[P(D)x] = P(s)\bar{x}$, so that the Laplace transform of the differential equation becomes $P(s)\bar{x}(s) = \bar{h}(s)$. In other words, the Laplace transform of the required solution is $\bar{x}(s) = \bar{h}(s)\bar{G}(s)$, where $\bar{G}(s) \equiv 1/P(s)$. Let us suppose that $G(t) \equiv \mathcal{L}^{-1}[1/P(s)]$ is known. By the convolution theorem, we can write

$$x(t) = \int_0^t G(t - t') h(t') dt'.$$ (2)

The general formula (2) expresses the solution of the problem directly in terms of the given non-homogeneous term $h(t)$, which can be specified arbitrarily, and the function $G(t)$, which clearly depends on the differential operator $P(D)$ but not on the specific form of the function $h(t)$. The function $G(t)$ in (2) is called the *Green's function* for the initial-value problem.

Example 1   Find the solution of the differential equation

$$\frac{d^2 x}{dt^2} + 2 \frac{dx}{dt} + 5x = h(t),$$

where $h(t)$ is a given function, subject to the initial conditions $x(0) = x'(0) = 0$.

Here the differential operator is $P(D) = D^2 + 2D + 5$, so that the Green's function is

$$G(t) = \mathcal{L}^{-1}\left[\frac{1}{s^2 + 2s + 5} \right] = \frac{1}{2} \mathcal{L}^{-1}\left[\frac{2}{(s+1)^2 + 4} \right] = \frac{1}{2} e^{-t} \sin 2t.$$

Therefore the required solution is given by

$$x(t) = \frac{1}{2} \int_0^t e^{-(t-t')} \sin\left[2(t-t')\right] h(t')\, dt'.$$

Consider next a similar type of initial-value problem, but with homogeneous initial conditions specified at some other point $t = T$:

$$P(D)[x(t)] = h(t), \quad x(T) = \ldots = x^{(n-1)}(T) = 0.$$

We can reduce this problem to one of the previous type by making the change of variable $\tau = t - T$ and defining the function $y(\tau) \equiv x(t)$, so that $dy/d\tau = dx/dt$, etc. In the new variables, the problem therefore becomes

$$P(D)[y(\tau)] = h(\tau + T), \quad y(0) = \ldots = y^{(n-1)}(0) = 0 \qquad (3)$$

(where now $D \equiv d/d\tau$). As we have seen, the solution of this problem is given by

$$y(\tau) = \int_0^\tau G(\tau - \tau')\, h(\tau' + T)\, d\tau',$$

where $G(\tau) \equiv \mathcal{L}^{-1}[1/P(s)]$. Putting now $\tau = t - T$ and $\tau' = t' - T$, we obtain the solution of the original problem in the form

$$x(t) = \int_T^t G(t - t')\, h(t')\, dt'. \qquad (4)$$

Note that the solution (4) has the same structure as our previous result (2), apart from the lower limit of integration. This means that a single Green's function serves to solve all initial-value problems of the type (3) (with a given differential operator) for any choice of the point $t = T$ at which the initial conditions are imposed.

Finally, we consider the problem of solving the differential equation $P(D)[x(t)] = h(t)$ subject to the more general (non-homogeneous) initial conditions $x(T) = C_0, \ldots, x^{(n-1)}(T) = C_{n-1}$, where $C_0, \ldots, C_{n-1}$ are given constants. The method of solving this problem is to express its solution as a superposition of the form $x(t) = u(t) + v(t)$, where $u(t)$ satisfies the original non-homogeneous differential equation with the homogeneous initial conditions $u(T) = \ldots = u^{(n-1)}(T) = 0$, while $v(t)$ satisfies the corresponding homogeneous differential equation $P(D)[x(t)] = 0$ with the original non-homogeneous initial conditions.

Example 2   Find the solution of the initial-value problem

$$\frac{d^2x}{dt^2} + 2\frac{dx}{dt} + 5x = h(t), \quad x(3) = 2, \quad x'(3) = -1.$$

Using the Green's function constructed in Example 1, we know that the function

$$u(t) = \frac{1}{2} \int_3^t e^{-(t-t')} \sin \left[2(t-t') \right] h(t') \, dt'$$

satisfies the given differential equation and the conditions $u(3) = u'(3) = 0$. We must also determine the function $v(t)$ which satisfies the homogeneous differential equation $v'' + 2v' + 5v = 0$ and the conditions $v(3) = 2$, $v'(3) = -1$. Let $v(t) \equiv w(t-3)$, so that $w'' + 2w' + 5w = 0$, with $w(0) = 2$ and $w'(0) = -1$. This initial-value problem can of course be solved by elementary methods. The solution based on Laplace transform methods is as follows. Putting $\bar{w}(s) \equiv \mathcal{L}[w(t)]$, we find $\mathcal{L}[w'] = s\bar{w} - 2$ and $\mathcal{L}[w''] = s^2 \bar{w} - 2s + 1$, so that the Laplace transform of the differential equation reads $(s^2 + 2s + 5)\bar{w} - 2s - 3 = 0$. Therefore

$$\bar{w}(s) = \frac{2s+3}{(s+1)^2 + 4} = \frac{2(s+1)}{(s+1)^2 + 4} + \frac{1}{2} \frac{2}{(s+1)^2 + 4} .$$

This gives

$$w(t) = 2 e^{-t} \cos 2t + \frac{1}{2} e^{-t} \sin 2t$$

and hence

$$v(t) = w(t-3) = e^{-(t-3)} \left\{ 2 \cos \left[2(t-3) \right] + \frac{1}{2} \sin \left[2(t-3) \right] \right\} .$$

Finally, the solution to the original problem is given by the sum $x(t) = u(t) + v(t)$.

5.7 Further applications of Laplace and Fourier transforms

Certain boundary-value problems for partial differential equations can be solved by directly taking an appropriate transform of the differential equation with respect to one of the independent variables. We shall illustrate the basic idea of the method by means of several examples.

Example 1 Find a solution $U = U(x, t)$ of the one-dimensional wave equation

$$\frac{\partial^2 U}{\partial x^2} = \frac{1}{a^2} \frac{\partial^2 U}{\partial t^2} \tag{1}$$

in the region $x \geqslant 0, t \geqslant 0$, satisfying the initial conditions

$$U(x, 0) = 0, \qquad \left[\frac{\partial U(x, t)}{\partial t} \right]_{t=0} = 0$$

for all $x \geq 0$ and the boundary condition

$$U(0, t) = f(t)$$

for all $t \geq 0$, where $f(t)$ is a prescribed function. [This boundary-value problem arises, for example, in studying the transverse oscillations of a semi-infinite elastic string under tension, with zero initial displacement and velocity and with a time-dependent displacement of the end at $x = 0$ governed by the law $U(0, t) = f(t)$.]

This problem can be solved by introducing the Laplace transform with respect to the variable t, regarding the independent variable x as a parameter. Thus the transform of the function $U(x, t)$ is

$$\bar{U}(x, s) = \int_0^\infty e^{-st} U(x, t) \, dt,$$

and the transform of the left-hand side of the wave equation (1) is $\partial^2 \bar{U}/\partial x^2$. Using the general formula for the Laplace transform of a derivative, we have $\mathcal{L}[\partial U/\partial t] = s\mathcal{L}[U(x, t)] - U(x, 0) = s\bar{U}(x, s)$, where we have used the initial condition for the function $U(x, t)$. Applying the same rule once again and making use of the initial condition for $\partial U/\partial t$, we find $\mathcal{L}[\partial^2 U/\partial t^2] = s^2 \bar{U}(x, s)$. Consequently, the transform of the partial differential equation (1) becomes

$$\frac{\partial^2 \bar{U}}{\partial x^2} = \frac{s^2}{a^2} \bar{U}. \tag{2}$$

Since the new differential equation (2) does not contain any derivatives with respect to s, it can be solved as though it were an ordinary differential equation with the independent variable x, in which s merely plays the role of a parameter. The general solution of (2) is therefore

$$\bar{U}(x, s) = A(s) e^{(s/a)x} + B(s) e^{-(s/a)x}, \tag{3}$$

where $A(s)$ and $B(s)$ are arbitrary functions.

Our next step is to determine the functions $A(s)$ and $B(s)$. On the basis of physical considerations, we seek a solution $U(x, t)$ which tends to zero as $x \to \infty$ for any fixed t, and we therefore assume that the transform $\bar{U}(x, s)$ also tends to zero as $x \to \infty$ for fixed s. (The quantities s and a may be assumed to be positive.) This means that the function $A(s)$ must vanish identically. To fix the remaining unknown function $B(s)$, we set $x = 0$ in (3) and apply the boundary condition $U(0, t) = f(t)$. This gives $B(s) = \bar{f}(s)$, where $\bar{f}(s)$ is the Laplace transform of the given function $f(t)$, which we assume is known. Thus the transform of the required solution is given by

$$\bar{U}(x, s) = \bar{f}(s) e^{-(x/a)s}. \tag{4}$$

The function (4) is equal to the product of a known transform and an exponential function. The inverse Laplace transform of such a function can always be determined in the following way. Writing $c \equiv x/a$ for brevity, we have

$$e^{-cs} \, \overline{f}(s) = \int_0^\infty e^{-s(t+c)} f(t) \, dt = \int_c^\infty e^{-st'} f(t'-c) \, dt',$$

where $t' \equiv t + c$. If, as is usually done when considering Laplace transforms, we assume that the function $f(t)$ is equal to zero for all negative values of its argument, we can extend the range of the last integral down to the point $t' = 0$ without altering the value of the integral. This finally gives

$$e^{-cs} \, \overline{f}(s) = \mathcal{L}\left[f(t-c)\right],$$

a general result which is sometimes known as the *second shifting theorem*.

Thus the inverse transform of (4) (i.e., the solution to the original boundary-value problem) is

$$U(x, t) = f\left(t - \frac{x}{a}\right), \qquad (5)$$

with the understanding that the function f is defined to be zero for negative values of its argument. The solution (5) has a simple physical interpretation: it represents a 'wave' propagating in the positive x-direction with velocity a, and the amplitude is identically zero for $x > at$, since any disturbance originating at the point $x = 0$ at positive time t has not yet reached this region.

Example 2   Find a solution of the partial differential equation

$$\frac{\partial U}{\partial x} + x \, \frac{\partial U}{\partial y} = x$$

in the quadrant $x \geqslant 0, y \geqslant 0$, subject to the boundary conditions $U(0,y) = 0$ for all $y \geqslant 0$ and $U(x, 0) = 0$ for all $x \geqslant 0$.

Following the method of the previous example, we take the Laplace transform of the differential equation with respect to the variable y. This gives

$$\frac{\partial \overline{U}}{\partial x} + xs\overline{U} = \frac{x}{s}, \qquad (6)$$

where

$$\overline{U}(x, s) = \int_0^\infty e^{-sy} \, U(x, y) \, dy.$$

Equation (6) can be treated as an ordinary differential equation with the independent variable x. It is a first-order linear differential equation, which can be solved by multiplying it by the integrating factor $\exp(\frac{1}{2}sx^2)$. This leads to the solution

$$\bar{U}(x, s) = \frac{1}{s^2} + \bar{C}(s)\, e^{-sx^2/2},$$

where $\bar{C}(s)$ is an arbitrary function. Applying the second shifting theorem to the last term, we have

$$U(x, y) = y + C(y - \tfrac{1}{2}x^2), \tag{7}$$

where $C(y)$ is the inverse transform of the function $\bar{C}(s)$, and it is understood that $C(y)$ is equal to zero for negative values of its argument. Finally, we fix the function $C(y)$ in (7) by applying the prescribed boundary condition at $x = 0$. This gives $0 = y + C(y)$ for all $y \geqslant 0$. Consequently, the solution (7) becomes

$$U(x, y) = \begin{cases} y, & y - \tfrac{1}{2}x^2 \leqslant 0, \\ \tfrac{1}{2}x^2, & y - \tfrac{1}{2}x^2 \geqslant 0. \end{cases}$$

As the next example demonstrates, certain boundary-value problems can be solved by similar techniques involving the use of the Fourier transform.

Example 3 Find a solution of the one-dimensional heat equation

$$\frac{\partial^2 U}{\partial x^2} = \frac{1}{a^2}\frac{\partial U}{\partial t} \tag{8}$$

satisfying the initial condition $U(x, 0) = f(x)$ for all x, where $f(x)$ is a prescribed function (cf. Example 2 of Sec. 5.3, where this same problem is solved by the method of separation of variables).

We introduce the Fourier transform with respect to the variable x:

$$\widetilde{U}(\omega, t) = \frac{1}{\sqrt{2\pi}} \int_{-\infty}^{\infty} e^{i\omega x}\, U(x, t)\, dx.$$

Then the transform of $\partial U/\partial t$ is $\partial \bar{U}/\partial t$. To determine the transform of the left-hand side of the differential equation (8), we require a formula for the Fourier transform of the derivative of a function. Such a formula can easily be derived in exactly the same way as the corresponding formula for the Laplace transform of a derivative. The result is that if the Fourier transform of a function $F(t)$ is $\widetilde{F}(\omega)$, then the Fourier transform of $dF(t)/dt$ is $-i\omega\widetilde{F}(\omega)$, provided that $F(t) \to 0$ as $t \to \pm\infty$. If we apply this rule twice in succession, adopting the reasonable physical assumption that U and $\partial U/\partial x$ both vanish as $x \to \pm\infty$ for any fixed t, the Fourier transform of the differential equation (8) becomes

$$-\omega^2 \, \tilde{U} = \frac{1}{a^2} \frac{\partial \tilde{U}}{\partial t} \, . \tag{9}$$

The general solution of (9) is

$$\tilde{U}(\omega, t) = \tilde{K}(\omega) \, e^{-a^2 \omega^2 t}, \tag{10}$$

where $\tilde{K}(\omega)$ is an arbitrary function. It follows from the prescribed initial condition that $\tilde{U}(\omega, 0) = \tilde{f}(\omega)$. Consequently, $\tilde{K}(\omega) = \tilde{f}(\omega)$. Taking the inverse Fourier transform of (10) and writing $\tilde{f}(\omega)$ in terms of $f(x)$, we have

$$U(x, t) = \frac{1}{2\pi} \int_{-\infty}^{\infty} d\omega \, e^{-i\omega x} \, e^{-a^2 \omega^2 t} \int_{-\infty}^{\infty} dx' \, f(x') \, e^{i\omega x'},$$

which is identical to the solution of this problem found in Sec. 5.3 by the method of separation of variables.

As the following example illustrates, integral transforms can also be used to solve certain integral equations.

Example 4   Consider the integral equation

$$y(x) = x + \int_0^x (x' - x) \, y(x') \, dx'$$

for the unknown function $y(x)$. Taking the Laplace transform of this equation, noticing that the integral term has the form of a convolution integral, we find

$$\bar{y}(s) = \frac{1}{s^2} - \frac{1}{s^2} \, \bar{y}(s).$$

Thus

$$\bar{y}(s) = \frac{1}{s^2 + 1} \, ,$$

so that the required solution is

$$y(x) = \sin x.$$

5.8 The inversion formula for Laplace transforms

We have seen that many problems require the determination of an inverse Laplace transform. For reasonably simple functions, this can usually be done using tables of 'standard' transforms in conjunction with the various special properties of the Laplace transform. However, it sometimes happens that this approach is intractable. It is then necessary to resort to a method which allows the direct computation of the inverse transform.

The practical implementation of the method which we shall develop here, unlike the remainder of this book, requires a detailed knowledge of the theory of analytic functions of a complex variable, and a brief discussion of this method is included here for the benefit of the reader with this background knowledge. (This section may be omitted without loss of continuity.)

To derive the inversion formula, we begin with Fourier's integral theorem for a function $F(t)$:

$$F(t) = \frac{1}{2\pi} \int_{-\infty}^{\infty} du \; e^{-iut} \int_{-\infty}^{\infty} dt' \; F(t') \, e^{iut'}.$$

Suppose now that we are given a function $f(t)$ which is equal to zero for negative values of t and which satisfies the usual sufficient conditions for the existence of the Laplace transform. Let c be any real constant such that the integral

$$I = \int_{0}^{\infty} e^{-ct} \, |f(t)| \, dt$$

exists. Then it follows from the Fourier integral representation for the function $e^{-ct} f(t)$ that

$$f(t) = \frac{1}{2\pi} \int_{-\infty}^{\infty} du \; e^{(c - iu)t} \int_{0}^{\infty} dt' \; e^{-(c - iu)t'} f(t').$$

This is a representation for the function $f(t)$ which is somewhat more general than the ordinary Fourier integral representation, since we have here an additional parameter c at our disposal.

If we make the substitution $c - iu = s$ and introduce the Laplace transform

$$\bar{f}(s) = \int_{0}^{\infty} e^{-st} f(t) \, dt,$$

we obtain

$$f(t) = \frac{1}{2\pi i} \int_{c - i\infty}^{c + i\infty} e^{ts} \, \bar{f}(s) \, ds, \qquad (1)$$

where the integration is along the infinite vertical line parallel to the imaginary axis of the complex s-plane and c units to the right of it.

Equation (1) provides a general formula for the inverse Laplace transform of the function $\overline{f}(s)$, known as the *Bromwich integral* or the *Fourier-Mellin integral*.

In many practical situations, integrals of the form (1) can be most easily evaluated by the methods of contour integration in the complex plane and the calculus of residues. For simplicity, suppose that the given function $\overline{f}(s)$ is analytic throughout the complex s-plane apart from some finite number of poles, and let us take the real constant c to be sufficiently large that all the poles lie to the left of the vertical line $\mathrm{Re}(s) = c$ in the complex s-plane. We close the path of integration in the integral (1) by means of an infinitely large semicircle to the left of this vertical line, assuming that the function $\overline{f}(s)$ tends to zero sufficiently fast to ensure that the integral over the semicircular contour vanishes as its radius tends to infinity. Then the residue theorem of complex-variable theory asserts that the value of the integral (1) is

$$f(t) = \sum_k \operatorname*{Res}_{s = s_k} \left[e^{ts}\, \overline{f}(s) \right], \qquad (2)$$

where s_k are the positions of the poles of the function $\overline{f}(s)$ and the right-hand side of (2) represents the sum of the residues of the function $e^{ts}\overline{f}(s)$ at these poles.

Example 1   Evaluate

$$f(t) \equiv \mathcal{L}^{-1} \left[\frac{s}{s^2 + 4s + 5} \right]$$

(cf. Example 6 of Sec. 5.4).

A simple calculation shows that the given function $\overline{f}(s)$ has simple poles at $s = -2 + i$ and $s = -2 - i$ with residues $\frac{1}{2} + i$ and $\frac{1}{2} - i$, respectively. Thus equation (2) gives

$$f(t) = (\tfrac{1}{2} + i)\, e^{(-2+i)t} + (\tfrac{1}{2} - i)\, e^{(-2-i)t} = e^{-2t}\,(\cos t - 2\sin t).$$

Example 2   Evaluate

$$f(t) \equiv \mathcal{L}^{-1} \left[\frac{2as}{(s^2 + a^2)^2} \right]$$

(cf. Example 7 of Sec. 5.4).

Here the given function $\overline{f}(s)$ has double poles at $s = ia$ and $s = -ia$, and the residues of the function $e^{ts}\overline{f}(s)$ at these poles are found to be $-\frac{1}{2}ite^{iat}$ and $\frac{1}{2}ite^{-iat}$, respectively. Equation (2) then gives $f(t) = t \sin at$.

Appendix: Summary of the properties of Laplace transforms

The table given below contains a summary of the most important general properties of Laplace transforms and the transforms of some elementary functions. Using this information, it is possible to construct the transforms and inverse transforms of many more complex functions. The references in the third column of the table indicate the point in the text at which the indicated property is derived; the letters refer to the general theorems established in Sec. 5.4, and the numbers refer to the equations of that section.

Function $f(t)$	Transform $\bar{f}(s)$	Reference
$aF(t) + bG(t)$	$a\bar{F}(s) + b\bar{G}(s)$	(a)
$dF(t)/dt$	$s\bar{F}(s) - F(0^+)$	(b)
$e^{at}F(t)$	$\bar{F}(s-a)$	(c)
$tF(t)$	$-d\bar{F}(s)/ds$	(d)
$\int_0^t A(t-t')G(t')dt'$	$\bar{A}(s)\bar{G}(s)$	(e)
$\int_0^t F(t')dt'$	$\bar{F}(s)/s$	(f)
$F(t)/t$	$\int_s^\infty \bar{F}(s')ds'$	(g)
1	$1/s$	(4)
t^n	$n!/s^{n+1}$	(8)
e^{at}	$1/(s-a)$	(2)
$\delta(t)$	1	(6)
$\delta(t-a)$	e^{-as}	(5)
$\sin at$	$a/(s^2 + a^2)$	(3)
$\cos at$	$s/(s^2 + a^2)$	(7)
$t \sin at$	$2as/(s^2 + a^2)^2$	(9)
$t \cos at$	$(s^2 - a^2)/(s^2 + a^2)^2$	(10)

Problems

1 Find the Fourier transform, Fourier cosine transform and Fourier sine transform of the function

$$F(t) = \begin{cases} 1, & 0 < t < a, \\ 0, & \text{otherwise.} \end{cases}$$

Hence evaluate the integral

$$\int_0^\infty \frac{\sin au \cos bu \, du}{u}.$$

2 Find a solution of Laplace's equation

$$\frac{\partial^2 U}{\partial x^2} + \frac{\partial^2 U}{\partial y^2} = 0$$

in the first quadrant $x > 0$, $y > 0$, subject to the boundary conditions $U(0, y) = 0$ for all $y > 0$ and $U(x, 0) = f(x)$ for all $x > 0$, where $f(x)$ is a given function, and the condition that $U(x, y)$ remains bounded as $x^2 + y^2 \to \infty$.

3 Find a solution of Laplace's equation in the half-plane $y > 0$, subject to the boundary condition $U(x, 0) = f(x)$ for all x, where $f(x)$ is a given function, and the condition that $U(x, y)$ remains bounded as $x^2 + y^2 \to \infty$.

4 Find a solution of Laplace's equation in the semi-infinite strip $x > 0$, $0 < y < a$, subject to the boundary conditions $U(0, y) = 0$ for $0 < y < a$, $U(x, 0) = 0$ for $x > 0$, and $U(x, a) = f(x)$ for $x > 0$, where $f(x)$ is a given function, and the condition that $U(x, y)$ remains bounded as $x \to \infty$.

5 Find the inverse Laplace transform of the function $1/(s^3 - 1)$.

6 Use Laplace transform methods to solve the following initial-value problems:

(i) $x'' + 2x' + 2x = 0$, $x(0) = 1$, $x'(0) = -1$;

(ii) $x'' - x' - 2x = e^t$, $x(0) = 1$, $x'(0) = -1$;

(iii) $x'' + x = e^{-t} \sin t$, $x(0) = 0$, $x'(0) = 2$;

(iv) $x'' + x' = te^{-t}$, $x(0) = x'(0) = 0$;

(v) $x'' + 4x' + 4x = 1 - e^{-t}$, $x(0) = 0$, $x'(0) = -\frac{1}{2}$;

(vi) $x''' - 6x'' + 11x' - 6x = e^t + e^{2t}$, $x(0) = x'(0) = x''(0) = 0$.

7 Solve the simultaneous differential equations

$$\begin{cases} \dfrac{dx}{dt} = 2x - 3y, \\[2mm] \dfrac{dy}{dt} = y - 2x \end{cases}$$

subject to the initial conditions $x(0) = 8$ and $y(0) = 3$.

8 Solve the simultaneous differential equations

$$\begin{cases} \dfrac{dx}{dt} - y = e^t, \\[2mm] \dfrac{dy}{dt} + x = \sin t \end{cases}$$

subject to the initial conditions $x(0) = 0$ and $y(0) = 2$.

9 Solve the simultaneous differential equations

$$\begin{cases} 2\dfrac{dx}{dt} + \dfrac{dy}{dt} + 5x = 5, \\[2mm] \dfrac{dx}{dt} + \dfrac{dy}{dt} + 11x + 2y = 0 \end{cases}$$

subject to the initial conditions $x(0) = 1$ and $y(0) = -4$.

10 Bessel's differential equation of order n $(n \geqslant 0)$ is

$$x^2 \frac{d^2y}{dx^2} + x\frac{dy}{dx} + (x^2 - n^2)y = 0$$

and possesses a solution $y = J_n(x)$ which is finite at $x = 0$. Show that the function $F(x) \equiv x^n J_n(x)$ satisfies the differential equation

$$x\frac{d^2F}{dx^2} + (1 - 2n)\frac{dF}{dx} + xF = 0$$

and hence that the Laplace transform of the function $F(x)$ is $\bar{F}(s) = C_n(s^2 + 1)^{-n-\frac{1}{2}}$, where C_n is a constant.

11 Solve the following initial-value problems using the method of Green's functions:

(i) $x'' + x = 1$, $x(0) = 0$, $x'(0) = 1$;

(ii) $x'' - x' - 2x = e^t$, $x(0) = 1$, $x'(0) = -1$.

12 (i) A function $x(t)$ satisfies the differential equation $x'' - x = h(t)$, where $h(t)$ is a given function, and the initial conditions $x(0) = x'(0) = 0$. Determine the Green's function associated with this initial-value problem and use it to construct the function $x(t)$.

(ii) If $h(t) = e^{-t} \sin t$, find the solution of the differential equation which satisfies the initial conditions $x(0) = 1$ and $x'(0) = 2$.

13 Find the Laplace transform of the function

$$F(t) = \begin{cases} \int_0^t x^2 e^{-x} \cos(t - x)\, dx, & t > 0, \\ 0, & t < 0. \end{cases}$$

14 Find the Laplace transforms of the following functions:

(i) $F(t) = (\sin at)/t$;

(ii) $F(t) = \sin at \sinh at$;

(iii) $F(t) = (1 - e^{-t})/t$.

15 Find the inverse Laplace transforms of the following functions:

(i) $\cot^{-1}(s + 1)$;

(ii) $(s^4 - a^4)^{-1}$.

16 Prove the following generalizations of Parseval's identity:

(i) For the ordinary Fourier transform,

$$\int_{-\infty}^{\infty} F(t)G^*(t)dt = \int_{-\infty}^{\infty} \widetilde{F}(\omega)\widetilde{G}^*(\omega)d\omega.$$

(ii) For the Fourier cosine and sine transforms,

$$\int_0^{\infty} F(t)G^*(t)dt = \int_0^{\infty} \widetilde{F}_{c,s}(\omega)\widetilde{G}^*_{c,s}(\omega)d\omega.$$

17 Use a method based on Fourier transforms to solve the one-dimensional wave equation

$$\frac{\partial^2 U}{\partial x^2} = \frac{1}{a^2}\frac{\partial^2 U}{\partial t^2}$$

in the region $-\infty < x < \infty$, $t > 0$, subject to the initial conditions

$$U(x, 0) = F(x), \qquad \left[\frac{\partial U(x, t)}{\partial t}\right]_{t=0} = G(x),$$

where $F(x)$ and $G(x)$ are given functions, and show that the solution can be expressed in the form

$$U(x, t) = \tfrac{1}{2}[F(x - at) + F(x + at)] + \frac{1}{2a}\int_{x-at}^{x+at} G(x')dx'.$$

(This expression is known as 'd'Alembert's solution'.)

18 Show that if the Fourier transform of $F(t)$ is $\widetilde{F}(\omega)$, then the Fourier transform of $dF(t)/dt$ is $-i\omega\widetilde{F}(\omega)$, provided that $F(t)\to 0$ as $t\to\pm\infty$.

19 By taking an appropriate Laplace transform, find a solution of the partial differential equation

$$x\frac{\partial U}{\partial x} + \frac{\partial U}{\partial y} = x$$

in the quadrant $x \geqslant 0$, $y \geqslant 0$, subject to the boundary conditions $U(0, y) = 0$ for all $y \geqslant 0$ and $U(x, 0) = 0$ for all $x \geqslant 0$.

20 Solve the following integral equations:

(i) $y(x) = x - \int_0^x (x' - x)y(x')dx'$;

(ii) $y(x) = 1 + \int_0^x (x' - x)y(x')dx'$.

6 General theory of ordinary differential equations

6.1 Existence and uniqueness theorems

Many of the differential equations which are encountered in practical applications cannot be solved exactly in closed form. In such cases, one may resort to numerical or other approximate methods. It is clearly important to be able to say beforehand that a solution actually exists.

A simple example of an initial-value problem which possesses no solution is the differential equation $t(dx/dt) + x = 0$ subject to the condition $x(0) = 1$.

Even if a solution to a particular problem is known to exist, it is obviously also desirable to be able to show that this solution is unique. The uniqueness of the solution to a physical problem whose mathematical formulation leads to a differential equation is sometimes obvious from simple physical considerations, but it is often by no means immediately obvious that the corresponding mathematical problem also possesses a unique solution, since the mathematical formulation of a physical problem generally involves simplifying assumptions, idealizations and approximations. Small changes in the initial data of a mathematical problem can sometimes produce fundamental changes in the character of the solution.

For example, there are two distinct solutions of the differential equation $dx/dt = x^{1/2}$ subject to the condition $x(0) = 0$, namely $x(t) = 0$ and $x(t) = \frac{1}{4}t^2$. However, it can be shown that the solution becomes unique if the original initial condition is replaced by $x(0) = \epsilon$, where ϵ is any (arbitrarily small) positive constant.

An initial-value problem may even have infinitely many solutions. For example, the function $x(t) = Ct + 1$, where C is an arbitrary constant, is a solution of the differential equation $t(dx/dt) - x + 1 = 0$ subject to the initial condition $x(0) = 1$.

Various sets of sufficient conditions for the existence and uniqueness of initial-value and boundary-value problems are known. We shall discuss here one of the simplest existence and uniqueness theorems, whose statement is as follows.

Picard's theorem   If the function $f(t, x)$ and its partial derivative $\partial f / \partial x$ are defined and continuous in some region S of the tx-plane containing the interior point (t_0, x_0), then in some neighbourhood of the point $t = t_0$ the differential equation $dx/dt = f(t, x)$ possesses a solution $x = \phi(t)$ satisfying the condition $\phi(t_0) = x_0$. Moreover, this solution is unique within the region S.

Instead of presenting the complete proof of this theorem, which is rather involved, we confine ourselves in this section to an outline of the general idea of the method. The minutiae of the proof are relegated to Sec. A.6.

As a first step, it is easy to see that a function $\phi(t)$ is a solution of the initial-value problem

$$\frac{d\phi}{dt} = f(t, \phi(t)), \qquad \phi(t_0) = x_0 \tag{1}$$

if and only if $\phi(t)$ satisfies the integral equation

$$\phi(t) = x_0 + \int_{t_0}^{t} f(t', \phi(t')) \, dt'. \tag{2}$$

The subsequent analysis of the problem is based entirely on the integral equation (2).

Since a function which is differentiable is also continuous, it is obviously sufficient to consider only functions $\phi(t)$ which are continuous in some neighbourhood of the point $t = t_0$, say $|t - t_0| \leqslant r$. If, in this neighbourhood, we have $|\phi(t) - x_0| \leqslant a$, so that the graph of the function $x = \phi(t)$ in the tx-plane does not go above or below the rectangular region R specified by the inequalities $|t - t_0| \leqslant r$ and $|x - x_0| \leqslant a$ (see Fig. 6.1), we shall write $\phi \in \Omega_R$ (where Ω_R is the class of functions satisfying this condition). If $\phi \in \Omega_R$ for such a rectangular region R contained within the original

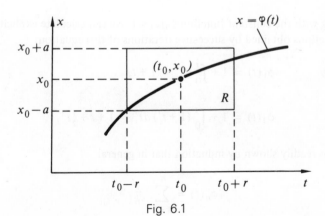

Fig. 6.1

region S specified in the hypothesis of the theorem, it is possible to define another function $\phi^*(t)$ by the equation

$$\phi^*(t) = x_0 + \int_{t_0}^{t} f(t', \phi(t')) \, dt'. \tag{3}$$

For conciseness of notation, we shall introduce an operator A such that (3) can be written $\phi^* = A\phi$.

It is easy to see that the function $\phi^*(t)$ defined by (3) is continuous, although it is not necessarily true that $\phi^* \in \Omega_R$. However, it can be shown that by choosing the region R sufficiently small we can ensure that $\phi^* \in \Omega_R$ whenever $\phi \in \Omega_R$. This means that, if $\phi_0 \in \Omega_R$, it is possible to define the complete sequence of functions $\phi_1 = A\phi_0$, $\phi_2 = A\phi_1$, etc.

The essence of the proof of the existence theorem is to show that, for an appropriate choice of the initial function ϕ_0 of the sequence, namely the constant function $\phi_0(t) = x_0$, the sequence of functions $\{\phi_0, \phi_1, \phi_2, \ldots\}$ converges in some neighbourhood of the point $t = t_0$ to a well-defined limiting function $\phi(t)$ and that this limiting function satisfies the integral equation $\phi = A\phi$; this means that $x = \phi(t)$ is the required solution. Furthermore, it can be shown that this solution is unique. Note that the proof of existence which we have outlined is a constructive proof, i.e., it actually provides an explicit method by which the solution can be determined with any desired degree of accuracy.

As an example of how this constructive procedure can actually be implemented in practice, consider the differential equation $dx/dt = x$ subject to the initial condition $x(0) = 1$. The corresponding integral equation is

$$\phi(t) = 1 + \int_0^t \phi(t') \, dt'.$$

Starting with the constant function $\phi_0(t) = 1$, we can calculate explicitly the functions obtained by successive iterations of this equation:

$$\phi_1(t) = 1 + \int_0^t dt' = 1 + t,$$

$$\phi_2(t) = 1 + \int_0^t (1 + t') \, dt' = 1 + t + \tfrac{1}{2}t^2,$$

etc. It is readily shown by induction that in general

$$\phi_n(t) = \sum_{k=0}^{n} \frac{t^k}{k!}.$$

Hence the (unique) solution is given by

$$\lim_{n\to\infty} \phi_n(t) = e^t,$$

and this solution is valid for all t.

It should be pointed out that Picard's theorem merely asserts the existence of a solution in some neighbourhood of the initial point, and without further analysis we cannot necessarily conclude that this solution is valid throughout the entire region in which the hypothesis of the theorem holds. For example, the differential equation $dx/dt = x^2 + 1$ subject to the condition $x(0) = 0$ possesses the solution $x(t) = \tan t$, which has discontinuities at $t = \pm\frac{1}{2}\pi$.

Picard's theorem can be extended to systems of simultaneous differential equations, and we shall now indicate very briefly how this can be done. Consider, for example, the following initial-value problem for two simultaneous first-order differential equations:

$$\begin{cases} \dfrac{dx}{dt} = f(t, x, y), & x(t_0) = x_0, \\[2mm] \dfrac{dy}{dt} = g(t, x, y), & y(t_0) = y_0, \end{cases}$$

where the functions $f(t, x, y), g(t, x, y)$ and their partial derivatives satisfy appropriate continuity conditions. The given system is clearly equivalent to the pair of integral equations

$$\begin{cases} x(t) = x_0 + \int_{t_0}^{t} f(t', x(t'), y(t'))\, dt', \\[2mm] y(t) = y_0 + \int_{t_0}^{t} g(t', x(t'), y(t'))\, dt', \end{cases}$$

which we can write more concisely in an operator notation in the form $x = A(x, y)$ and $y = B(x, y)$. In analogy with the proof of Picard's theorem, we can then define sequences of functions $\{x_0, x_1, \ldots\}$ and $\{y_0, y_1, \ldots\}$ by the rule $x_{n+1} = A(x_n, y_n)$ and $y_{n+1} = B(x_n, y_n)$, starting with the constant functions $x_0(t) = x_0$ and $y_0(t) = y_0$. As in the case of an initial-value problem for a single differential equation, it can be shown that the functions $x_n(t)$ and $y_n(t)$ tend to definite limiting functions as $n \to \infty$ and that these limiting functions provide the solution to the problem.

Finally, we shall indicate briefly how these results can be used to derive an existence and uniqueness theorem for differential equations of higher order. Consider a differential equation of order n of the form

$$x^{(n)}(t) = f(t, x(t), x'(t), \ldots, x^{(n-1)}(t)),$$

subject to a set of initial conditions

$$x(t_0) = a_0, \quad x'(t_0) = a_1, \ldots, \quad x^{(n-1)}(t_0) = a_{n-1}.$$

Defining the new variables $y_0(t) \equiv x(t), y_1(t) \equiv x'(t), \ldots, y_{n-1}(t) \equiv x^{(n-1)}(t)$, it is easy to see that the original problem is equivalent to the following initial-value problem for n simultaneous first-order differential equations:

$$y_0'(t) \quad = y_1(t),$$
$$y_1'(t) \quad = y_2(t),$$
$$\cdots \cdots \cdots$$
$$y_{n-2}'(t) = y_{n-1}(t),$$
$$y_{n-1}'(t) = f(t, y_0(t), y_1(t), \ldots, y_{n-1}(t)),$$

subject to the initial conditions

$$y_0(t_0) = a_0, \ldots, \quad y_{n-1}(t_0) = a_{n-1}.$$

The existence and uniqueness theorem for this system of simultaneous differential equations can then be translated back into an existence and uniqueness theorem for the original initial-value problem for a differential equation of order n, provided that the function f and its partial derivatives are continuous in some neighbourhood of the point $(t_0, a_0, \ldots, a_{n-1})$.

6.2 Solutions of linear differential equations

The most general form of a linear differential equation of order n is

$$p_n(t) \frac{d^n x}{dt^n} + \ldots + p_1(t) \frac{dx}{dt} + p_0(t) x(t) = h(t). \tag{1}$$

We shall assume throughout this chapter that the functions $p_n(t), \ldots, p_0(t)$ and $h(t)$ are continuous in some interval $a \leqslant t \leqslant b$. We shall sometimes assume in addition that the coefficient $p_n(t)$ of the highest derivative in the differential equation is non-zero throughout the interval $a \leqslant t \leqslant b$, in which case the differential equation is said to be *normal* in that interval. It will often be convenient to write the differential equation (1) in the symbolic form $Lx = h$, where L is the differential operator

$$L \equiv p_n(t) \frac{d^n}{dt^n} + \ldots + p_0(t).$$

We begin by recalling several elementary properties of linear differential equations, all of which are immediate consequences of the fact that the operator L is *linear*.

(i) The superposition principle: If $x = u_1(t)$ and $x = u_2(t)$ are solutions of the homogeneous differential equation $Lx = 0$, then $x = \alpha u_1(t) + \beta u_2(t)$ is also a solution of this equation, for arbitrary values of the constants α and β.

(ii) If $x = u(t)$ is a solution of the homogeneous differential equation $Lx = 0$ and $x = v(t)$ is a solution of the non-homogeneous differential equation $Lx = h$, then $x = u(t) + v(t)$ is a solution of the equation $Lx = h$.

(iii) The general solution of the non-homogeneous differential equation $Lx = h$ is given by the sum of the general solution of the corresponding homogeneous differential equation $Lx = 0$ and a particular solution of the equation $Lx = h$.

The remainder of this section concerns properties of the solutions of homogeneous linear differential equations of the form $Lx = 0$.

DEFINITION 1   A set of functions $u_1(t), \ldots, u_n(t)$ is *linearly dependent* on the interval $a \leqslant t \leqslant b$ if there exist constants α_i, not all zero, such that

$$\sum_{i=1}^{n} \alpha_i u_i(t) = 0 .$$

for all t in the range $a \leqslant t \leqslant b$. If this condition is not satisfied, we say that the functions $u_1(t), \ldots, u_n(t)$ are *linearly independent* on this interval.

THEOREM 1   A linear differential equation $Lx = 0$ of order n has at most n linearly independent solutions on the interval $a \leqslant t \leqslant b$.

PROOF   Suppose that $x = u_i(t)$ $(i = 1, \ldots, m$, where $m > n)$ are solutions, and let us select a point $t_0 \in (a, b)$. Consider the system of equations

$$\sum_{i=1}^{m} c_i u_i^{(k)}(t_0) = 0 \qquad (k = 0, \ldots, n-1), \qquad (2)$$

[where the superscript (k) indicates the k-th derivative, and $u^{(0)}(t) \equiv u(t)$] as a set of n simultaneous algebraic equations in the m unknowns c_i. Since by hypothesis $m > n$, these equations have at least one non-trivial solution $c_1, \ldots, c_m$. Choosing any such solution, let us define the function

$$v(t) \equiv \sum_{i=1}^{m} c_i u_i(t).$$

Then $Lv = 0$ by the superposition principle, and $v^{(k)}(t_0) = 0$ for $k = 0, \ldots,$ $n - 1$ by virtue of the n equations (2). Thus $v(t)$ is a solution of the differential equation satisfying a complete set of homogeneous initial conditions at the point $t = t_0$. Since $x(t) = 0$ is obviously a solution with these properties, it follows from the uniqueness theorem discussed in the preceding section that $v(t) = 0$ for $a \leqslant t \leqslant b$. In other words, the functions $u_i(t)$ are linearly dependent on this interval.

DEFINITION 2   The *Wronskian* of a set of functions $u_1(t), \ldots, u_m(t)$ [assumed to be $(m - 1)$-times differentiable] is the function defined by the determinant

$$W(t) \equiv \begin{vmatrix} u_1(t) & \ldots u_m(t) \\ u_1'(t) & \ldots u_m'(t) \\ \cdot & \cdot \\ \cdot & \cdot \\ \cdot & \cdot \\ u_1{}^{(m-1)}(t) & \ldots u_m{}^{(m-1)}(t) \end{vmatrix}. \tag{3}$$

Note that the value of the Wronskian (in particular, its sign) depends on the order in which the functions are given.

THEOREM 2   If the functions $u_1(t), \ldots, u_m(t)$, all having derivatives of order $m - 1$, are linearly dependent on the interval $a \leqslant t \leqslant b$, then their Wronskian satisfies the condition $W(t) = 0$ for all t in this interval.

PROOF   Suppose that

$$\sum_{i=1}^{m} \alpha_i u_i(t) = 0$$

for all t in the range $a \leqslant t \leqslant b$, where the constants α_i are not all zero. Then

$$\sum_{i=1}^{m} \alpha_i u_i{}^{(k)}(t) = 0 \qquad (k = 0, \ldots, m - 1).$$

For any fixed point $t \in [a, b]$, these m equations are satisfied for non-trivial values of the α_i. Regarding them as a set of simultaneous algebraic equations for the α_i, the condition for the existence of a non-trivial solution is the vanishing of the determinant of their coefficients. This determinant is precisely the Wronskian (3).

Example 1   Consider the familiar differential equation $x'' + x = 0$, two of whose solutions are $x = \sin t$ and $x = \cos t$. A simple calculation shows that their Wronskian is $W(t) = -1$, which is non-zero for all t. Thus Theorem 2 tells us that the functions $\sin t$ and $\cos t$ are linearly independent on any interval. Theorem 1 then implies that the general solution of the differential equation is $x(t) = \alpha_1 \sin t + \alpha_2 \cos t$.

The converse of Theorem 2 is false; i.e., the vanishing of the Wronskian does *not* imply linear dependence of the functions. This can be demonstrated by means of the following counterexample. Let $u_1(t) = t^3$ and $u_2(t) = |t|^3$. The Wronskian of these functions is found to be $W(t) = 0$ for all t. However, the two functions are linearly independent on the interval $-1 \leqslant t \leqslant 1$, for example. For suppose that $\alpha_1 u_1(t) + \alpha_2 u_2(t) = 0$ for all t in this interval. Putting $t = \pm 1$, we find the two equations $\pm \alpha_1 + \alpha_2 = 0$, which together imply that $\alpha_1 = \alpha_2 = 0$.

Although the vanishing of the Wronskian is by itself not a sufficient condition for linear dependence, we have the following theorem.

THEOREM 3   If, on the interval $a \leqslant t \leqslant b$, the functions $x = u_i(t)$ $(i = 1, \ldots, n)$ are solutions of the n-th order linear differential equation $Lx = 0$ for which the Wronskian $W(t)$ vanishes at some point $t_0 \in (a, b)$, then the functions $u_i(t)$ are linearly dependent on the interval $a \leqslant t \leqslant b$.

Note that the hypothesis of the theorem requires the vanishing of the Wronskian at only a single point.

PROOF   Consider the equations

$$\sum_{i=1}^{n} \alpha_i u_i^{(k)}(t_0) = 0 \qquad (k = 0, \ldots, n-1) \qquad (4)$$

as a set of n simultaneous algebraic equations for the α_i. If $W(t_0) = 0$, then the determinant of the coefficients of these equations vanishes, so that the equations have a non-trivial solution $\alpha_1, \ldots, \alpha_n$. Let

$$v(t) \equiv \sum_{i=1}^{n} \alpha_i u_i(t).$$

Then $v^{(k)}(t_0) = 0$ for $k = 0, \ldots, n-1$; i.e., the function $x = v(t)$ satisfies the differential equation with homogeneous initial conditions at $t = t_0$. Hence $v(t) = 0$ for all $t \in [a, b]$ by the uniqueness theorem, and the conclusion of the theorem follows.

Corollary   If, for a set of n solutions of the n-th order differential equation

$Lx = 0$ on the interval $a \leqslant t \leqslant b$, the Wronskian satisfies $W(t_0) = 0$ for some $t_0 \in (a, b)$, then $W(t) = 0$ for *all* $t \in [a, b]$.

PROOF   By Theorem 3, the solutions are linearly dependent on the interval $a \leqslant t \leqslant b$. Theorem 2 then implies that $W(t) = 0$ for all $t \in [a, b]$.

THEOREM 4   A set of solutions $x = u_i(t)$ $(i = 1, \ldots, n)$ of an n-th order linear differential equation $Lx = 0$ is linearly dependent on the interval $a \leqslant t \leqslant b$ if and only if the set of n (n-dimensional) vectors

$$\mathbf{U}_i(t_0) \equiv \begin{pmatrix} u_i(t_0) \\ u_i'(t_0) \\ \vdots \\ u_i^{(n-1)}(t_0) \end{pmatrix} \quad (i = 1, \ldots, n)$$

is linearly dependent, where $t_0 \in (a, b)$ is any fixed point in the interval.

PROOF   By Theorems 2 and 3, the solutions are linearly dependent on the interval if and only if $W(t_0) = 0$. But $W(t_0)$ is the determinant of the coefficients of the equations (4) as a system of simultaneous algebraic equations for the α_i, which in vector notation can be written as the single equation

$$\sum_{i=1}^{n} \alpha_i \mathbf{U}_i(t_0) = \mathbf{0} .$$

This means that $W(t_0) = 0$ if and only if these equations have a non-trivial solution $\alpha_1, \ldots, \alpha_n$, i.e. if and only if the vectors $\mathbf{U}_i(t_0)$ are linearly dependent.

Example 2   Consider again the solutions $x = \sin t \equiv u_1(t)$ and $x = \cos t \equiv u_2(t)$ of the differential equation $x'' + x = 0$ (cf. Example 1). At $t = 0$ the corresponding vectors defined in Theorem 4 are

$$\mathbf{U}_1(0) = \begin{pmatrix} 0 \\ 1 \end{pmatrix}, \qquad \mathbf{U}_2(0) = \begin{pmatrix} 1 \\ 0 \end{pmatrix} .$$

These two vectors are obviously linearly independent. This implies that the two solutions are linearly independent on any interval which includes the point $t = 0$.

THEOREM 5   A linear differential equation $Lx = 0$ of order n has exactly n linearly independent solutions on the interval $a \leqslant t \leqslant b$.

PROOF   Theorem 1 asserts that there are *at most n* linearly independent solutions. Let us choose any point $t_0 \in (a, b)$. For each value of the index $i = 0, \ldots, n - 1$, let $x = u_i(t)$ be the solution of the differential equation satisfying the set of initial conditions $u_i^{(k)}(t_0) = \delta_{ik}$ $(k = 0, \ldots, n - 1)$. The existence of these solutions is guaranteed by the existence theorem discussed in the preceding section, and these n solutions are linearly independent by Theorem 4.

Thus we have shown that the solutions of a linear differential equation of order n form an n-dimensional vector space. This vector space, or function space, is called the *solution space* of the differential equation.

THEOREM 6   Let $W(t)$ be the Wronskian of any set of n solutions $x = u_i(t)$ $(i = 1, \ldots, n)$ of the n-th order linear differential equation

$$p_n(t) x^{(n)}(t) + \ldots + p_1(t) x'(t) + p_0(t) x(t) = 0 \tag{5}$$

on the interval $a \leqslant t \leqslant b$, and suppose that the differential equation is normal on this interval. Then

$$W(t) = W(t_0) \exp \left[-\int_{t_0}^{t} \frac{p_{n-1}(t')}{p_n(t')} \, dt' \right], \tag{6}$$

where $t_0 \in [a, b]$ is any point of the interval.

Equation (6) is known as *Abel's formula* (or *Liouville's formula*). Note that it expresses the t-dependence of the Wronskian purely in terms of the first two coefficients in the differential equation.

PROOF   The derivative of the Wronskian is

$$W'(t) = \frac{d}{dt} \begin{vmatrix} u_1(t) & \ldots & u_n(t) \\ \vdots & & \vdots \\ u_1^{(n-1)}(t) & \ldots & u_n^{(n-1)}(t) \end{vmatrix} = \Delta_1 + \ldots + \Delta_n,$$

where Δ_r denotes the determinant formed from the determinant (3) by differentiating the elements in row r, leaving all the other rows unchanged. Since a determinant vanishes if it has two identical rows, we have $\Delta_r = 0$ for $i = 1, \ldots, n - 1$, so that

$$W'(t) = \begin{vmatrix} u_1(t) & \ldots & u_n(t) \\ \vdots & & \vdots \\ u_1^{(n-2)}(t) & \ldots & u_n^{(n-2)}(t) \\ u_1^{(n)}(t) & \ldots & u_n^{(n)}(t) \end{vmatrix}. \tag{7}$$

From the differential equation (5), we have

$$u_i^{(n)}(t) = -\frac{p_{n-1}(t)}{p_n(t)} u_i^{(n-1)}(t) - \ldots - \frac{p_0(t)}{p_n(t)} u_i(t) \qquad (8)$$

for $i = 1, \ldots, n$. If we substitute the expression (8) for each element of the last row of the determinant (7) and expand the result as a sum of n determinants, then all but one of these determinants have two rows proportional to one another and hence vanish. The remaining non-vanishing determinant is proportional to the original Wronskian, and (7) becomes

$$W'(t) = -\frac{p_{n-1}(t)}{p_n(t)} W(t).$$

This is a first-order differential equation for $W(t)$. Separating the variables and integrating from t_0 to t, we obtain

$$\log\left(\frac{W(t)}{W(t_0)}\right) = -\int_{t_0}^{t} \frac{p_{n-1}(t')}{p_n(t')} dt',$$

which is equivalent to the required result.

Abel's formula (6) shows that any basis for the solution space of a linear differential equation has the same Wronskian, apart from an overall multiplicative constant. In other words, the Wronskian is actually an intrinsic characteristic of the differential equation and not of the particular basis solutions in terms of which it was originally defined.

6.3 The method of variation of parameters

The method of *variation of parameters* is a systematic procedure for finding a particular solution of a non-homogeneous linear differential equation of order n, say $Lx = h$, when the general solution of the associated homogeneous differential equation $Lx = 0$ is known, say

$$x(t) = \sum_{i=1}^{n} \alpha_i u_i(t),$$

where the $u_i(t)$ are n linearly independent functions and the α_i are arbitrary constants (the 'parameters').

The method enables us to construct a particular solution $x = x_p(t)$ in the form

$$x_p(t) = \sum_{i=1}^{n} a_i(t) u_i(t) \tag{1}$$

for certain functions $a_i(t)$. These n functions can be determined by means of the following n conditions (suppressing the range of summation $i = 1, \ldots, n$ and the argument t for brevity):

$$\sum a_i' u_i^{(k)} = 0 \quad (k = 0, 1, \ldots, n-2), \tag{2}$$
$$L[\sum a_i u_i] = h,$$

the last condition being the original differential equation itself.

Let us assume from the outset that the differential equation is written in such a way that the differential operator has the form

$$L \equiv \frac{d^n}{dt^n} + \ldots + p_1(t)\frac{d}{dt} + p_0(t).$$

In particular, we are assuming that the coefficient of the highest derivative in the differential equation is normalized to unity. In this case, we shall say that the differential equation is written in *normal form*.

When the first $n-1$ of the n conditions (2) are taken into account, the last condition of the set reduces to a much simpler form. To see this, we note that

$$\frac{d}{dt}\sum a_i u_i = \sum a_i u_i'$$

by the first condition,

$$\frac{d^2}{dt^2}\sum a_i u_i = \sum a_i u_i''$$

by the second condition, etc; finally,

$$\frac{d^{n-1}}{dt^{n-1}}\sum a_i u_i = \sum a_i u_i^{(n-1)}.$$

But the next derivative is

$$\frac{d^n}{dt^n}\sum a_i u_i = \sum a_i u_i^{(n)} + \sum a_i' u_i^{(n-1)}.$$

Hence

$$L[\sum a_i u_i] = \sum a_i u_i^{(n)} + \sum a_i' u_i^{(n-1)} + p_{n-1}\sum a_i u_i^{(n-1)} + \ldots +$$
$$+ p_1 \sum a_i u_i' + p_0 \sum a_i u_i$$
$$= \sum a_i' u_i^{(n-1)} + \sum a_i(Lu_i) = \sum a_i' u_i^{(n-1)}.$$

We can therefore replace the original set of n conditions (2) by the set

$$\sum a_i' u_i^{(k)} = 0 \quad (k = 0, 1, \ldots, n-2), \tag{3}$$
$$\sum a_i' u_i^{(n-1)} = h.$$

For each value of t, the n equations (3) can be solved algebraically for the n quantities a_i'. A solution always exists, since the determinant of the coefficients in these equations is simply the Wronskian $W(t)$ of the n solutions $u_i(t)$, and $W(t) \neq 0$ because the functions $u_i(t)$ are linearly independent by hypothesis. According to Cramer's rule in linear algebra, the solution is in fact given by $a_i'(t) = H_i(t)/W(t)$, where $H_i(t)$ is the determinant formed from the determinant that defines $W(t)$ by replacing the elements in column i of the latter by the elements $0, \ldots, 0, h(t)$. The undetermined functions $a_i(t)$ are then determined by integration:

$$a_i(t) = \int_{t_0}^{t} \frac{H_i(t')}{W(t')} \, dt', \tag{4}$$

where t_0 is any fixed value of t, which may be different for each value of i. The expression (1) then provides a particular solution of the original differential equation $Lx = h$.

Note that a change in the value of the constant t_0 in the formula (4) for some particular function $a_i(t)$ merely results in the addition of some constant to this function, which in turn corresponds to the addition of some multiple of $u_i(t)$ to the expression (1) for the particular solution $x_p(t)$; since $u_i(t)$ is a solution of the homogeneous differential equation $Lx = 0$, this change merely leads to another particular solution of the differential equation $Lx = h$.

If all the functions $a_i(t)$ are calculated by means of (4) using the same value of t_0, then the particular solution $x_p(t)$ which is obtained is the one which satisfies the homogeneous initial conditions $x_p(t_0) = \ldots = x_p^{(n-1)}(t_0) = 0$. It is easy to verify this statement by evaluating the derivative of (1), making use of the first $n-1$ conditions in the set (2).

Example 1 Find a particular solution of the differential equation $x'' + x = \csc t$.

The general solution of the associated homogeneous differential equation $x'' + x = 0$ is $x(t) = \alpha_1 \sin t + \alpha_2 \cos t$. The Wronskian is $W(t) = -1$, while

$$H_1(t) = \begin{vmatrix} 0 & \cos t \\ \csc t & -\sin t \end{vmatrix} = -\frac{\cos t}{\sin t},$$

$$H_2(t) = \begin{vmatrix} \sin t & 0 \\ \cos t & \csc t \end{vmatrix} = 1.$$

Hence, omitting the constants of integration, which are immaterial here, we find

$$a_1(t) = \int^t \frac{H_1(t')}{W(t')} dt' = \int^t \frac{\cos t'}{\sin t'} \, dt' = \log |\sin t|,$$

$$a_2(t) = \int^t \frac{H_2(t')}{W(t')} dt' = -\int^t dt' = -t,$$

so that a particular solution is given by

$$x_p(t) = a_1(t) \sin t + a_2(t) \cos t$$

$$= \sin t \log |\sin t| - t \cos t.$$

We next consider a closely related technique known as the method of *reduction of order*. Suppose that we are given a linear differential equation $Lx = h$ of order n. If any one non-trivial solution $x = u(t)$ of the associated homogeneous differential equation $Lx = 0$ is known, this method enables us to reduce the problem of solving the original differential equation to one of solving another differential equation of order $n - 1$.

The essence of the method is to seek a solution of the differential equation $Lx = h$ in the product form $x(t) = u(t) v(t)$, where the function $v(t)$ is to be determined. If we substitute the expression $x = uv$ into the differential equation $Lx = h$, we obviously obtain a new differential equation of order n for the unknown function $v(t)$, say $L_1 v = h$, where L_1 is some differential operator. But we know that $x = u(t)$ is a solution of the differential equation $Lx = 0$, so that the constant function $v = 1$ is necessarily a solution of the differential equation $L_1 v = 0$. This means that the form of the differential equation $L_1 v = 0$ is such that it contains terms involving derivatives of v but not the function v itself. In other words, the differential equation $L_1 v = 0$ is actually a differential equation of order $n - 1$ for the variable $v'(t) \equiv dv/dt$.

Example 2 Find the general solution of the differential equation $x'' - 2ax' + a^2 x = 0$, given that one solution is $x(t) = e^{at}$.

We seek a solution in the form $x(t) = e^{at} v(t)$. Substituting this product form into the differential equation, we find $e^{at} v'' = 0$, i.e., $v'' = 0$ (which is the expected first-order differential equation for v'). This equation can be integrated to give $v(t) = \alpha + \beta t$, where α and β are arbitrary constants. Hence the general solution of the original differential equation is $x(t) = e^{at}(\alpha + \beta t)$.

6.4 Oscillation theorems

In this section we shall be concerned exclusively with linear differential equations of the form $Lx = 0$, where L is a second-order differential operator. The theorems derived here characterize the general properties of zeros of the solutions of such differential equations and are of importance in understanding the oscillatory behaviour of certain special functions.

THEOREM 1   All the zeros of a non-trivial solution of the differential equation $Lx = 0$ are *simple;* i.e., if the function itself is equal to zero at some point, then its derivative at that point is non-zero.

PROOF   Suppose that a solution $x = u(t)$ has a multiple zero at some point $t = t_0$. This means that $u(t_0) = u'(t_0) = 0$, so that the uniqueness theorem discussed in Sec. 6.1 implies that $u(t) = 0$ for all t.

THEOREM 2   A non-trivial solution $x = u(t)$ of the differential equation $Lx = 0$ has at most a finite number of zeros in any finite interval.

The main purpose of this theorem is to show that it is always meaningful to speak of *consecutive* zeros.

PROOF   Assume that some interval of t contains an infinite set of zeros of some non-trivial solution. Then some point $t = T$ is a limit point of distinct zeros in the interval, and there exists a sequence of zeros $\{t_1, t_2, \ldots\}$ such that $t_n \to T$ as $n \to \infty$. Without loss of generality, we may assume that $t_n \neq T$ for all n. It follows from the continuity of the function $u(t)$ that $u(T) = 0$. Moreover,

$$u'(T) = \lim_{n \to \infty} \left[\frac{u(t_n) - u(T)}{t_n - T} \right] = 0.$$

Since $u(T) = u'(T) = 0$, the uniqueness theorem implies that $u(t) = 0$ for all t, which is a contradiction.

THEOREM 3   *(the Sturm separation theorem)*   Let $x = u_1(t)$ and $x = u_2(t)$ be linearly independent non-trivial solutions of the differential equation $Lx = 0$. Then $u_2(t)$ has precisely one zero between any two successive zeros of $u_1(t)$ (and vice versa); i.e., the zeros of $u_1(t)$ and $u_2(t)$ alternate.

PROOF   If the given solutions are linearly independent on some interval, then

$$W(t) \equiv u_1(t) u'_2(t) - u_2(t) u'_1(t) \neq 0$$

on that interval. Suppose that $u_1(c) = u_1(d) = 0$, but that $u_1(t) \neq 0$ for all t in the interval $c < t < d$. Then $W(c) = -u_2(c) u_1'(c) \neq 0$ and $W(d) = -u_2(d) u_1'(d) \neq 0$, so that $u_2(c)$, $u_2(d)$, $u_1'(c)$ and $u_1'(d)$ are all non-zero. Now $u_1(t)$ must have the same sign for all $t \in (c, d)$ (otherwise the mean-value theorem would imply the existence of a zero in this interval, contradicting the hypothesis). Therefore $u_1'(c)$ and $u_1'(d)$ have opposite signs. But $W(c)$ and $W(d)$ must have the same sign (otherwise $W(t)$ would have a zero in the interval by the mean-value theorem). Hence $u_2(c)$ and $u_2(d)$ have opposite signs, and by the mean-value theorem we deduce that $u_2(t^*) = 0$ for some $t^* \in (c, d)$, as required.

Finally, we argue that this zero is *unique*. For suppose that $u_2(t^*) = u_2(t^{**}) = 0$, where t^* and t^{**} are consecutive zeros of the function $u_2(t)$ in the interval $c < t < d$. Then we can apply the preceding argument, but with the roles of the functions $u_1(t)$ and $u_2(t)$ interchanged, to show that $u_1(T) = 0$ for some number $T \in (c, d)$, which contradicts the hypothesis.

THEOREM 4 Any differential equation of the form $x'' + P(t)x' + Q(t)x = 0$ can be reduced to the form $v'' + R(t)v = 0$ by some change of variable $x(t) = u(t)v(t)$ for an appropriate choice of the function $u(t)$.

PROOF Putting $x = uv$, the differential equation becomes

$$uv'' + (2u' + Pu)v' + (u'' + Pu' + Qu)v = 0.$$

The function $u(t)$ can be chosen to ensure that $2u' + Pu = 0$, namely

$$u(t) = \exp\left[-\tfrac{1}{2} \int_{t_0}^{t} P(t')\,dt'\right].$$

The differential equation for $v(t)$ then has the required form.

Note that since $u(t) \neq 0$ for all t, the function $v(t)$ has exactly the same set of zeros as the function $x(t)$. It is therefore sufficient to discuss most of the oscillation theorems for normal differential equations in terms of the special type of equation $v'' + R(t)v = 0$.

THEOREM 5 (*the Sturm comparison theorem*) Let $x = u_1(t)$ and $x = u_2(t)$ be non-trivial solutions of the differential equations $u_1'' + R_1(t)u_1 = 0$ and $u_2'' + R_2(t)u_2 = 0$, where $R_2(t) > R_1(t)$ for all $t \in [a, b]$. Then the function $u_2(t)$ has at least one zero between any two zeros of the function $u_1(t)$.

PROOF Let $t = c$ and $t = d$ be consecutive zeros of the function $u_1(t)$, so that $u_1(c) = u_1(d) = 0$, while $u_1(t) \neq 0$ if $c < t < d$. We must prove that $u_2(t^*) = 0$ for some $t^* \in (c, d)$. Suppose that this were not the case. Without loss of generality, we may assume that $u_1(t) > 0$ and $u_2(t) > 0$ for all $t \in (c, d)$ [since the functions $-u_1(t)$ and $-u_2(t)$ satisfy the same differential equations and have the same zeros as the functions $u_1(t)$ and $u_2(t)$]. Let

$$W(t) \equiv u_1(t) u_2'(t) - u_2(t) u_1'(t).$$

Then

$$\frac{dW}{dt} = u_1 u_2'' - u_2 u_1'' = u_1(-R_2 u_2) - u_2(-R_1 u_1) = (R_1 - R_2) u_1 u_2 < 0$$

for all $t \in (c, d)$. Hence

$$W(d) - W(c) = \int_c^d W'(t)\, dt < 0.$$

But $W(c) = -u_2(c) u_1'(c) \leqslant 0$ and $W(d) = -u_2(d) u_1'(d) \geqslant 0$, so that $W(d) - W(c) \geqslant 0$, which is a contradiction.

6.5 Simultaneous differential equations

In this section we shall illustrate the application of methods of linear algebra to problems involving systems of simultaneous differential equations.

The discussion will be confined here to the case of systems of simultaneous homogeneous linear differential equations of first order with constant coefficients. Assuming that the equations have been solved algebraically for the derivatives of the unknown functions, such a system of n equations for n unknown functions can be written in the general form

$$\begin{cases} \dfrac{dx_1}{dt} = a_{11} x_1(t) + \ldots + a_{1n} x_n(t), \\ \qquad \cdots\cdots\cdots\cdots\cdots \\ \dfrac{dx_n}{dt} = a_{n1} x_1(t) + \ldots + a_{nn} x_n(t). \end{cases} \qquad (1)$$

As a first step in the analysis of this problem, we write the system of equations (1) in a more compact matrix notation. Introducing the column vectors

$$\mathbf{X}(t) = \begin{pmatrix} x_1(t) \\ \vdots \\ x_n(t) \end{pmatrix}, \qquad \mathbf{X}'(t) = \begin{pmatrix} x_1'(t) \\ \vdots \\ x_n'(t) \end{pmatrix}$$

consisting of the unknown functions and their derivatives, the system (1) becomes $\mathbf{X}'(t) = A\mathbf{X}(t)$, where A is the matrix of coefficients.

For simplicity, we shall consider only the case in which all the eigenvalues of the matrix A are distinct. In this case, we know that the matrix A can be brought to diagonal form $\overline{A}$ by a similarity transformation of the form $\overline{A} = N^{-1}AN$. Suppose that we have already solved the eigenvalue problem for the matrix A. Then the diagonal elements of $\overline{A}$ are simply the eigenvalues $\lambda_1, \ldots, \lambda_n$, and the matrix N can be constructed explicitly as the matrix whose columns contain the components of a corresponding set of eigenvectors. The normalization of these eigenvectors is unimportant for the present purposes.

Let $\mathbf{Y}(t)$ denote the new column vector

$$\mathbf{Y}(t) \equiv N^{-1}\mathbf{X}(t) \equiv \begin{pmatrix} y_1(t) \\ \vdots \\ y_n(t) \end{pmatrix},$$

each of whose components is some specific linear combination of the unknown functions $x_1(t), \ldots, x_n(t)$. Differentiating with respect to t, we find that

$$\mathbf{Y}'(t) = N^{-1}\mathbf{X}'(t) = N^{-1}A\mathbf{X}(t) = N^{-1}AN\mathbf{Y}(t) = \overline{A}\mathbf{Y}(t).$$

Now since the matrix $\overline{A}$ is diagonal, the equation $\mathbf{Y}'(t) = \overline{A}\,\mathbf{Y}(t)$ represents a system of n *uncoupled* equations for the n functions $y_i(t)$, namely $y_i'(t) = \lambda_i y_i(t)$ $(i = 1, \ldots, n)$. This means that each of these equations can be solved without reference to the others, and the general solution of this system of equations is $y_i(t) = C_i \exp(\lambda_i t)$, where the C_i are arbitrary constants.

Finally, since $\mathbf{X}(t) = N\mathbf{Y}(t)$, the general solution for the original set of functions $x_i(t)$ is given by

$$x_1(t) = N_{11}C_1 e^{\lambda_1 t} + \ldots + N_{1n}C_n e^{\lambda_n t},$$

$$\ldots\ldots\ldots\ldots\ldots\ldots\ldots$$

$$x_n(t) = N_{n1}C_1 e^{\lambda_1 t} + \ldots + N_{nn}C_n e^{\lambda_n t},$$

and this solution contains n arbitrary constants $C_1, \ldots, C_n$.

Example 1   Find the general solution of the system of simultaneous differential equations

$$\begin{cases} \dfrac{dx}{dt} = 3x + 5y + z, \\[2mm] \dfrac{dy}{dt} = 5x - 8y + 4z, \\[2mm] \dfrac{dz}{dt} = x + 4y. \end{cases}$$

Here it is easy to verify that the matrix of coefficients A has the distinct eigenvalues $\lambda_1 = 0$, $\lambda_2 = 6$ and $\lambda_3 = -11$, and a corresponding set of eigenvectors is

$$\mathbf{u}_1 = \begin{pmatrix} -4 \\ 1 \\ 7 \end{pmatrix}, \quad \mathbf{u}_2 = \begin{pmatrix} 2 \\ 1 \\ 1 \end{pmatrix}, \quad \mathbf{u}_3 = \begin{pmatrix} 1 \\ -3 \\ 1 \end{pmatrix}.$$

This means that a matrix N for which $N^{-1}AN$ is diagonal is given by

$$N = \begin{pmatrix} -4 & 2 & 1 \\ 1 & 1 & -3 \\ 7 & 1 & 1 \end{pmatrix},$$

and the general solution of the system of differential equations satisfies the condition

$$N^{-1} \begin{pmatrix} x(t) \\ y(t) \\ z(t) \end{pmatrix} = \begin{pmatrix} a \\ b\, e^{6t} \\ c\, e^{-11t} \end{pmatrix},$$

where a, b and c are arbitrary constants. Therefore

$$x(t) = -4a + 2b\, e^{6t} + c\, e^{-11t},$$
$$y(t) = a + b\, e^{6t} - 3c\, e^{-11t},$$
$$z(t) = 7a + b\, e^{6t} + c\, e^{-11t}.$$

As the following example illustrates, the method can be extended to the more general situation in which some of the eigenvalues are complex.

Example 2   Find the general solution of the system of simultaneous differential equations

$$\begin{cases} \dfrac{dx}{dt} = 5x - 4y, \\[2mm] \dfrac{dy}{dt} = 2x + y. \end{cases}$$

Here we find the complex eigenvalues $\lambda_1 = 3 + 2i$ and $\lambda_2 = 3 - 2i$, and the corresponding complex-valued eigenvectors

$$\mathbf{u}_1 = \begin{pmatrix} 2 \\ 1 - i \end{pmatrix}, \qquad \mathbf{u}_2 = \begin{pmatrix} 2 \\ 1 + i \end{pmatrix}.$$

Hence the general solution can be written in the form

$$x(t) = 2A\, e^{(3+2i)t} + 2B\, e^{(3-2i)t},$$

$$y(t) = (1 - i)\, A\, e^{(3+2i)t} + (1 + i)\, B\, e^{(3-2i)t},$$

where A and B are arbitrary constants.

It is more convenient for most purposes to re-express such a solution in a form which involves only real quantities. This can be done by noting that if the pair of complex-valued functions $x(t)$ and $y(t)$ provides a solution of the system of differential equations with real coefficients, then the real and imaginary parts of these functions must separately give solutions of the same system. Let us write $x(t) = x_R(t) + ix_I(t)$ and $y(t) = y_R(t) + iy_I(t)$, where $x_R(t)$, $x_I(t)$, $y_R(t)$ and $y_I(t)$ are all real. Then the two pairs of functions

$$x_R(t) = 2(A + B)\, e^{3t} \cos 2t,$$

$$y_R(t) = (A + B)\, e^{3t} (\cos 2t + \sin 2t)$$

and

$$x_I(t) = 2(A - B)\, e^{3t} \sin 2t,$$

$$y_I(t) = (A - B)\, e^{3t} (\sin 2t - \cos 2t)$$

are both solutions. Since the differential equations are linear, any linear combination of these two solutions is also a solution. But each of these two solutions already contains an overall arbitrary multiplicative constant. Therefore it is sufficient to represent the general solution in the form $x(t) = x_R(t) + x_I(t)$, $y(t) = y_R(t) + y_I(t)$. Writing for simplicity $C_1 \equiv A + B$ and $C_2 \equiv A - B$, this gives

$$x(t) = 2e^{3t} (C_1 \cos 2t + C_2 \sin 2t),$$

$$y(t) = e^{3t} [(C_1 - C_2) \cos 2t + (C_1 + C_2) \sin 2t].$$

Similar techniques can be used to study certain types of systems of simultaneous differential equations of higher order. Consider, for example, a linear system of the type $X''(t) = AX(t)$ involving the second, but not the first, derivatives of the unknown functions. Let us consider the special class of problems of this type in which all the eigenvalues of the matrix A are negative and distinct.

Such problems arise in many physical applications, for example in the description of undamped mechanical systems or electrical circuits. Under the assumptions which we have made, it can be shown that there exist certain special solutions in which, as a function of t (which is normally the time variable), all the dependent variables simultaneously undergo sinusoidal oscillations of the same frequency.

Let us denote the eigenvalues of the matrix A by $-\omega_1^2, \ldots, -\omega_n^2$. Introducing a matrix N such that $\bar{A} \equiv N^{-1}AN$ is diagonal and proceeding exactly as in the discussion of systems of first-order differential equations at the beginning of this section, it is easy to see that the vector $\mathbf{Y}(t) \equiv N^{-1}\mathbf{X}(t)$ satisfies the differential equation $\mathbf{Y}''(t) = \bar{A}\,\mathbf{Y}(t)$, which represents a set of *uncoupled* differential equations $y_i''(t) = -\omega_i^2 y_i(t)$ $(i = 1, \ldots, n)$. These equations describe simple harmonic motion of the variables $y_i(t)$ with frequencies ω_i. The amplitudes and phases of these oscillations can of course be determined uniquely if an appropriate set of initial conditions is prescribed.

It is of particular interest to consider the special type of solution in which only *one* of the variables $y_i(t)$ actually undergoes such oscillations, while all the others remain identically zero. Since $\mathbf{X}(t) = N\mathbf{Y}(t)$, in general such a solution corresponds to simultaneous oscillations of *all* the original variables $x_j(t)$ with the same frequency and phase, and it is easy to see that the relative amplitudes of oscillation of the variables $x_j(t)$ are determined by the elements in column i of the matrix N (i.e., by the components of the i-th eigenvector). Such a pattern of oscillation is known as a *normal mode*, and the possible frequencies of oscillation are called the *normal frequencies*. It is obvious that an arbitrary solution can be expressed as some linear combination of these fundamental normal modes.

Example 3   Find the normal modes for the system of simultaneous differential equations

$$\begin{cases} \dfrac{d^2x}{dt^2} = -5x + 2y, \\[2mm] \dfrac{d^2y}{dt^2} = 2x - 2y. \end{cases}$$

Here the eigenvalues of the matrix of coefficients are found to be $\lambda_1 = -1$ and $\lambda_2 = -6$, and a corresponding pair of eigenvectors is given by

$$\mathbf{u}_1 = \begin{pmatrix} 1 \\ 2 \end{pmatrix}, \qquad \mathbf{u}_2 = \begin{pmatrix} -2 \\ 1 \end{pmatrix}.$$

The normal frequencies are therefore $\omega_1 = 1$ and $\omega_2 = \sqrt{6}$. The most general solution corresponding to the first normal mode can be represented in the form

$$x(t) = a_1 \sin(t + \phi_1),$$

$$y(t) = 2a_1 \sin(t + \phi_1),$$

where a_1 and ϕ_1 are arbitrary constants. Similarly, the second normal mode corresponds to solutions of the form

$$x(t) = -2a_2 \sin(\sqrt{6}t + \phi_2),$$

$$y(t) = a_2 \sin(\sqrt{6}t + \phi_2),$$

where a_2 and ϕ_2 are arbitrary constants.

Appendix: Proof of Picard's theorem

The proof of Picard's theorem is divided into four stages. Using the notation of Sec. 6.1, we shall show that (i) there is some region R having the property that $\phi^* \in \Omega_R$ whenever $\phi \in \Omega_R$, (ii) in some neighbourhood of the point $t = t_0$ the sequence of functions $\{\phi_0, \phi_1, \ldots\}$ converges to a limiting function ϕ, (iii) this limiting function ϕ satisfies the relation $\phi = A\phi$, and (iv) this solution is unique.

(i) Let S be the region of the tx-plane mentioned in the hypothesis of Picard's theorem, and let $T \subset S$ be a rectangular region specified by inequalities of the form $|t - t_0| \le b$ and $|x - x_0| \le a$. We shall determine a number $r \le b$ such that if a region $R \subset T$ is defined by the inequalities $|t - t_0| \le r$ and $|x - x_0| \le a$, then $\phi^* \in \Omega_R$ whenever $\phi \in \Omega_R$. What we require is that $|\phi^*(t) - x_0| \le a$ whenever $|t - t_0| \le r$. But

$$|\phi^*(t) - x_0| = \left| \int_{t_0}^{t} f(t', \phi(t')) \, dt' \right| \le Mr,$$

where M is an upper bound for $|f(t, x)|$ in the region T (which is finite, since f is continuous on the closed bounded set T). It is therefore sufficient to choose any $r \le b$ such that $r \le a/M$.

(ii) To establish the convergence of the sequence $\{\phi_0, \phi_1, \ldots\}$, it is convenient to introduce the norm $\|\phi\|$, defined as the supremum of $|\phi(t)|$ in the interval $|t - t_0| \le r$. The quantity $\|\phi - \psi\|$ is a measure of the extent to which two functions $\phi(t)$ and $\psi(t)$ differ from each other within this interval. In particular, two continuous functions $\phi(t)$ and $\psi(t)$ are identical in the interval if and only if $\|\phi - \psi\| = 0$. A sequence of functions $\{\phi_0, \phi_1, \ldots\}$ converges uniformly to a function $\phi(t)$ in the interval if $\|\phi_n - \phi\| \to 0$ as $n \to \infty$.

The essence of the second stage of the proof is to show that if r is chosen sufficiently small, then $\|A\phi - A\psi\| \leqslant k\|\phi - \psi\|$ for all functions ϕ, $\psi \in \Omega_R$, for some fixed number k such that $0 < k < 1$. An operator A which has such a property is said to be a *contraction mapping*. Suppose for the moment that r has been chosen so that this condition is satisfied in addition to the previous condition imposed in part (i) of the proof. If we define ϕ_0 as the constant function $\phi_0(t) = x_0$, then the sequence of functions $\{\phi_0, \phi_1, \ldots\}$ ($\phi_n = A^n \phi_0$) has the property $\|\phi_{n+1} - \phi_n\| \leqslant k\|\phi_n - \phi_{n-1}\|$ and hence $\|\phi_{n+1} - \phi_n\| \leqslant k^n \|\phi_1 - \phi_0\| \leqslant k^n a$, where the last inequality follows from the fact that $\phi_1 \in \Omega_R$. Since $\|\phi_{n+1} - \phi_n\| \to 0$ as $n \to \infty$, the sequence $\{\phi_0, \phi_1, \ldots\}$ converges uniformly for $|t - t_0| \leqslant r$ to some function $\phi \in \Omega_R$.

It remains to show that r can indeed be chosen sufficiently small to ensure that A is a contraction mapping. For any functions ϕ, $\psi \in \Omega_R$, we have

$$|\phi^*(t) - \psi^*(t)| = \left| \int_{t_0}^{t} [f(t', \phi(t')) - f(t', \psi(t'))] \, dt' \right|$$

$$\leqslant \left| \int_{t_0}^{t} |f(t', \phi(t')) - f(t', \psi(t'))| \, dt' \right|.$$

By the mean-value theorem, the integrand is equal to

$$\left| \left[\frac{\partial f(t', x)}{\partial x} \right]_{x=X} [\phi(t') - \psi(t')] \right|$$

for some X between the values $\phi(t')$ and $\psi(t')$. Since the function $\partial f/\partial x$ is assumed to be continuous on a closed bounded set, $|\partial f/\partial x|$ has some upper bound K. This leads to the bound

$$\|A\phi - A\psi\| = \|\phi^* - \psi^*\| \leqslant Kr\|\phi - \psi\|.$$

Thus the operator A is a contraction mapping, provided that r is chosen so that $r < 1/K$.

(iii) We have shown that in some interval $|t - t_0| \leqslant r$ we have $\phi_n \to \phi$ as $n \to \infty$, where $\phi \in \Omega_R$. Since $\|A\phi_n - A\phi\| \leqslant k\|\phi_n - \phi\|$ for some fixed $k < 1$, we also have $A\phi_n \to A\phi$ as $n \to \infty$. Taking the limit as $n \to \infty$ in the relation $\phi_{n+1} = A\phi_n$, we therefore have $\phi = A\phi$ in the interval $|t - t_0| \leqslant r$, which shows that the function ϕ is indeed the required solution. This completes the proof of the existence theorem.

(iv) Next we prove that the solution is unique. Suppose that $x = \phi(t)$ and $x = \psi(t)$ are two solutions of the original differential equation in some interval $r_1 \leqslant t \leqslant r_2$, both satisfying the prescribed condition $x(t_0) = x_0$ at the point $t = t_0$ in this interval. Then $\phi = A\phi$ and $\psi = A\psi$. Let r be chosen sufficiently small so as to satisfy the two conditions imposed earlier in the proof of the existence theorem. In addition, since the functions $\phi(t)$ and $\psi(t)$ are continuous, we can choose r sufficiently small that $|\phi(t) - x_0| \leqslant a$ and $|\psi(t) - x_0| \leqslant a$ whenever $|t - t_0| \leqslant r$. Then $\phi, \psi \in \Omega_R$ and we have

$$\|\phi - \psi\| = \|A\phi - A\psi\| \leqslant k\|\phi - \psi\|$$

for some $k < 1$. This implies that $\|\phi - \psi\| = 0$, i.e., $\phi(t) = \psi(t)$ whenever $|t - t_0| \leqslant r$.

Finally, we show that $\phi(t) = \psi(t)$ on the entire interval $r_1 \leqslant t \leqslant r_2$. Suppose that, on the contrary, $\phi(t^*) \neq \psi(t^*)$ for some point $t^* \in [r_1, r_2]$. Then $t^* \neq t_0$, since by hypothesis $\phi(t_0) = \psi(t_0) = x_0$. For definiteness, suppose that $t^* > t_0$. Let N be the set of all points $t \in [t_0, t^*]$ for which $\phi(t) = \psi(t)$. If $\{t_1, t_2, \ldots\}$ is any sequence of points $t_i \in N$, with $t_i \to T$ as $i \to \infty$, then the continuity of the functions $\phi(t)$ and $\psi(t)$ implies that $\phi(t_i) \to \phi(T)$ and $\psi(t_i) \to \psi(T)$, so that $\phi(T) = \psi(T)$, i.e., $T \in N$. This means that the set N is closed. Let $\bar{t}$ be the supremum of the set N. Then $\bar{t} \in N$, since N is closed, and hence $\phi(\bar{t}) = \psi(\bar{t})$. Moreover, $\bar{t}$ is an interior point of the interval $[r_1, r_2]$, since $t_0 \leqslant \bar{t} < t^*$. We can therefore apply the first part of the uniqueness proof, with the role of t_0 played by $\bar{t}$, to show that $\phi(t) = \psi(t)$ in some neighbourhood of $\bar{t}$ and, in particular, for some values $t > \bar{t}$. However, this contradicts the definition of $\bar{t}$. We conclude that $\phi(t) = \psi(t)$ for *all* $t \in [r_1, r_2]$.

Problems

1 Use the iteration method of Picard's theorem to obtain solutions of the following initial-value problems:

   (i) $dx/dt = x - t$, $\quad x(0) = 2$;

   (ii) $dx/dt = x^2$, $\quad x(0) = 1$.

   Sum the resulting series and verify that the answers agree with the solutions obtained in closed form by elementary methods.

2 Use an iteration method analogous to that of Picard's theorem to solve the initial-value problem

$$\begin{cases} dx/dt = -y, & x(0) = 1, \\ dy/dt = x, & y(0) = 0. \end{cases}$$

   Sum the resulting series and compare the answer with the solution obtained in closed form by other means.

3 (i) Let $x = u_1(t)$ and $x = u_2(t)$ be two linearly independent solutions of the differential equation

$$x''(t) + P(t)x'(t) + Q(t)x(t) = 0.$$

By considering the Wronskian of the functions $x(t)$, $u_1(t)$ and $u_2(t)$, where $x(t)$ is an arbitrary solution of the differential equation, derive expressions for the coefficients $P(t)$ and $Q(t)$ in terms of the functions $u_1(t)$ and $\ddot{u}_2(t)$.

(ii) Use the results to construct a homogeneous second-order linear differential equation which has the two functions $x(t) = t$ and $x(t) = \log t$ as solutions for $t > 0$.

4 Find the general solutions of the following differential equations:

(i) $x'' + x = \sec t$;

(ii) $4x'' + 4x' + x = te^{-t/2} \sin t$.

5 Given that the function $x(t) = t^{-1/2} \sin t$ is a solution of the differential equation

$$t^2 x'' + tx' + (t^2 - \tfrac{1}{4})x = 0,$$

find a second linearly independent solution, and verify that the two solutions are actually linearly independent.

6 For each of the following differential equations, verify that the given function satisfies the associated homogeneous differential equation and then find a particular solution of the given equation:

(i) $t^2 x'' - 2tx' + 2x = t^3 \log t$ $(t > 0)$, $x(t) = at + bt^2$;

(ii) $(\cos^2 t)x'' - 2x = \cos^2 t \cot t$, $x(t) = \tan t$.

7 Find the general solution of the differential equation

$$x''(t) + P(t)x'(t) + Q(t)x(t) = (\cos t)/(1 + \sin^2 t),$$

given that the functions $x(t) = \cos t$ and $x(t) = \tan t$ are both solutions of the associated homogeneous differential equation.

8 With the help of the method of variation of parameters, find the general solution of the differential equation

$$tx'' - (1 + 2t^2)x' = t^5 \exp(t^2).$$

9 (i) Show that every non-trivial solution of the differential equation $x''(t) + (\sinh t)x(t) = 0$ has at most one zero in the range $-\infty < t < 0$

but has an infinite set of zeros in the range $0 < t < \infty$.

(ii) Show that the spacing between consecutive zeros of any non-trivial solution of this differential equation tends to zero as $t \to \infty$.

10 Use matrix methods to find the general solutions of the simultaneous differential equations

(i)
$$\begin{cases} \dfrac{dx}{dt} = x + 2y, \\[2mm] \dfrac{dy}{dt} = 3x + 2y; \end{cases}$$

(ii)
$$\begin{cases} 2\dfrac{dx}{dt} + \dfrac{dy}{dt} + 5x = 0, \\[2mm] \dfrac{dx}{dt} + \dfrac{dy}{dt} + 11x + 2y = 0. \end{cases}$$

11 Use matrix methods to find the general solution of the simultaneous differential equations

$$\begin{cases} \dfrac{dx}{dt} = y, \\[2mm] \dfrac{dy}{dt} = z, \\[2mm] \dfrac{dz}{dt} = x. \end{cases}$$

12 Find the normal modes for the system of simultaneous differential equations

$$\begin{cases} \dfrac{d^2x}{dt^2} = -4x + 2y, \\[2mm] \dfrac{d^2y}{dt^2} = 2x - 4y. \end{cases}$$

13 By means of a substitution of the type $x(t) = u(t)v(t)$, with an appropriate choice of the function $u(t)$, reduce the differential equation

$$t^2 x'' - tx' + x = 0$$

to an equation of the form $v'' + R(t)v = 0$.

14 (i) Bessel's differential equation of order n is

$$t^2 x'' + tx' + (t^2 - n^2)x = 0.$$

Reduce this equation to the form $v'' + R(t)v = 0$ by means of a substitution $x(t) = u(t)v(t)$ for an appropriate choice of the function $u(t)$.

(ii) Show that the spacing between consecutive positive zeros of any non-trivial solution of Bessel's differential equation with $|n| < \frac{1}{2}$ is always less than π.

(iii) Show that, for any value of n, the spacing between consecutive zeros of any non-trivial solution tends to π for asymptotically large t.

7 Power series solutions of ordinary differential equations

7.1 Solutions near an ordinary point

Although the methods which we shall develop in this chapter are applicable to linear differential equations of arbitrary order, we shall restrict the discussion to second-order equations. These are the equations that are most important for practical applications, and in fact most of the special functions which occur in applied mathematics can be defined as solutions of such equations.

Consider a normal differential equation of the type

$$\frac{d^2x}{dt^2} + P(t)\,\frac{dx}{dt} + Q(t)\,x = 0, \tag{1}$$

subject to initial conditions of the form $x(t_0) = a_0$ and $x'(t_0) = a_1$. From the results of the previous chapter, we know that if the coefficients $P(t)$ and $Q(t)$ are continuous in some neighbourhood of the point $t = t_0$, then there exists a unique solution of this initial-value problem in some neighbourhood of that point.

It is reasonable to expect that if the functions $P(t)$ and $Q(t)$ both have convergent power-series expansions about the point $t = t_0$ in some neighbourhood $|t - t_0| < R$ (which, in the language of complex-variable theory, means that these functions are analytic throughout the region $|t - t_0| < R$ of the complex t-plane), then any solution $x = x(t)$ of the differential equation also has a convergent power-series representation (i.e., it is analytic) in the same neighbourhood. A detailed analysis of the problem shows that this is indeed the case.

If the coefficients $P(t)$ and $Q(t)$ in (1) are both analytic in some neighbourhood of a point $t = t_0$, we say that this point is an *ordinary point* of the differential equation. Otherwise, the point $t = t_0$ is called a *singular point* of the differential equation. The result stated above tells us that the general solution (or indeed any particular solution) of the differential equation can be represented in the form of a power-series expansion in the neighbourhood of an ordinary point.

To develop the theory of power-series solutions, it will be convenient to consider expansions about the point $t = 0$. This entails no loss of generality, since if any other point $t = t_0$ is chosen instead, we can make the change of variable $t' = t - t_0$ in the differential equation and consider expansions about the point $t' = 0$ in the new differential equation.

We illustrate the basic method of obtaining power-series solutions by means of the following example.

Example   Legendre's differential equation of order n is

$$(1 - t^2)x'' - 2t\,x' + n(n + 1)\,x = 0. \tag{2}$$

When the differential equation (2) is written in normal form by dividing at by the coefficient of x'', the new coefficients $P(t) \equiv -2t/(1 - t^2)$ and $Q(t) \equiv n(n + 1)/(1 - t^2)$ are both analytic near $t = 0$, which is therefore an ordinary point of the differential equation. Since the only singularities of these coefficients in the complex t-plane are at $t = \pm1$, we expect that any solution of the differential equation in the neighbourhood of the origin can be represented in the form of a power series

$$x(t) = \sum_{k=0}^{\infty} a_k t^k \tag{3}$$

and that this series solution will be valid for $-1 < t < 1$.

Assuming that there exists a solution of the form (3), let us construct the corresponding series expansions for the various terms which appear in the differential equation (2), expressing each of them as a sum of terms involving t^k for $k = 0, 1, \ldots$. The first and second derivatives of (3) are

$$x'(t) = \sum_{r=0}^{\infty} a_r r t^{r-1} = \sum_{k=0}^{\infty} a_{k+1}\,(k + 1)t^k, \tag{4}$$

$$x''(t) = \sum_{r=0}^{\infty} a_r r(r - 1)t^{r-2} = \sum_{k=0}^{\infty} a_{k+2}\,(k + 2)\,(k + 1)t^k, \tag{5}$$

where in the second step of (4) we have put $k = r - 1$ and used the fact that the term with $k = -1$ vanishes and can therefore be omitted in the summation, while in (5) we have put $k = r - 2$ and used the fact that the terms with $k = -2$ and $k = -1$ both vanish. Multiplying the first series in (4) and (5) by t and t^2, respectively, and putting $k = r$, we obtain

$$t\,x'(t) = \sum_{k=0}^{\infty} a_k k t^k, \tag{6}$$

$$t^2\,x''(t) = \sum_{k=0}^{\infty} a_k k\,(k - 1)t^k. \tag{7}$$

If we now substitute the expressions (3) and (5)–(7) into the differential equation (2), we find

$$\sum_{k=0}^{\infty} \{(k+2)(k+1)a_{k+2} + [-k(k-1) - 2k + n(n+1)]a_k\}t^k = 0. \quad (8)$$

For the left-hand side of (8) to vanish identically as a function of t, the coefficient of t^k must vanish for each individual value of k. Thus the constants a_k must satisfy the recurrence relation

$$a_{k+2} = -\frac{n(n+1) - k(k+1)}{(k+2)(k+1)} a_k$$

$$= -\frac{(n-k)(n+k+1)}{(k+2)(k+1)} a_k \quad (k = 0, 1, \ldots). \quad (9)$$

By repeated application of this recurrence relation, it is easy to see that all the coefficients a_k for even (odd) values of k can be expressed in terms of a_0 (a_1) in the form

$$a_{2m} = \frac{(-1)^m}{(2m)!} [(n - 2m + 2)(n - 2m + 4) \ldots (n)]$$

$$[(n + 2m - 1)(n + 2m - 3) \ldots (n + 1)] a_0,$$

$$a_{2m+1} = \frac{(-1)^m}{(2m+1)!} [(n - 2m + 1)(n - 2m + 3) \ldots (n - 1)]$$

$$[(n + 2m)(n + 2m - 2) \ldots (n + 2)] a_1$$

$(m = 1, 2, \ldots)$. Since there are no restrictions on a_0 and a_1, we have the solution

$$x(t) = a_0 x_0(t) + a_1 x_1(t), \quad (10)$$

where

$$x_0(t) = 1 - \frac{n(n+1)}{2!} t^2 + \frac{(n-2)(n)(n+3)(n+1)}{4!} t^4 - \ldots,$$

$$x_1(t) = t - \frac{(n-1)(n+2)}{3!} t^3 + \frac{(n-3)(n-1)(n+4)(n+2)}{5!} t^5 - \ldots.$$

The two solutions $x_0(t)$ and $x_1(t)$ are linearly independent. Formally, this can be seen, for example, from the fact that they satisfy the conditions $x_0(0) = 1$, $x_0'(0) = 0$ and $x_1(0) = 0$, $x_1'(0) = 1$ (see Theorem 4 of Sec. 6.2). This means that (10) is indeed the general solution of the differential equation.

In this example, it is of special interest to note that the series expansion for one of the two solutions $x_0(t)$ or $x_1(t)$ terminates if the parameter n is equal to any non-negative integer, owing to the presence of the factor $(n - k)$ in the recurrence relation (9). Thus, if $n = 2m$ $(m = 0, 1, \ldots)$, then $a_{2m+2} = 0$, so that the series for $x_0(t)$ terminates with the term involving t^{2m}. Similarly, if $n = 2m + 1$ $(m = 0, 1, \ldots)$, then $a_{2m+3} = 0$ and the series for $x_1(t)$ terminates with the term involving t^{2m+1}. In other words, if n is any non-negative integer, the differential equation has one *polynomial solution* of degree n. These polynomials are proportional to the so-called Legendre polynomials, whose properties we shall study later in greater detail. The existence of these polynomial solutions shows, incidentally, that the radius of convergence of a particular power-series solution (which is infinite in the case of a polynomial solution) may sometimes be larger than what is expected purely on the basis of the domain of analyticity of the coefficients in the differential equation.

7.2 The Frobenius method

The method outlined in the preceding section does not necessarily enable us to find the general solution (or even any solution) in the neighbourhood of a singular point of a differential equation. It is instructive to consider an example in which the method fails and to analyze the reason for this failure.

Consider the differential equation

$$4tx'' + 2x' + x = 0, \tag{1}$$

which has a singular point at $t = 0$. If we assume the existence of a power-series solution of the form

$$x(t) = \sum_{n=0}^{\infty} a_n t^n \tag{2}$$

and substitute this expression into the differential equation, following the procedure of the preceding section, we find the condition

$$\sum_{n=0}^{\infty} \{[4n(n + 1) + 2(n + 1)]a_{n+1} + a_n\}t^n = 0,$$

which leads to the recurrence relation

$$a_{n+1} = -\frac{a_n}{(2n + 2)(2n + 1)} \qquad (n = 0, 1, \ldots).$$

Unlike the example considered in the preceding section, repeated application of this recurrence relation fixes *all* the coefficients a_n in the terms of a_0 alone:

$$a_n = \frac{(-1)^n}{(2n)!} a_0.$$

This leads to a series solution of the form (2), which in this particular case can be summed in closed form:

$$x(t) = a_0 \sum_{n=0}^{\infty} \frac{(-1)^n}{(2n)!} t^n = a_0 \cos \sqrt{t}.$$

However, since this solution contains only a single arbitrary constant a_0, it is obviously not the general solution.

It is easy to verify by straightforward substitution that a second independent solution of the differential equation (1) is $x(t) = \sin \sqrt{t}$. We can now see why the simple power-series method used above fails to give the general solution in this case. Since

$$\sin \sqrt{t} = \sum_{n=0}^{\infty} \frac{(-1)^n}{(2n+1)!} t^{(2n+1)/2} = t^{1/2} \sum_{n=0}^{\infty} \frac{(-1)^n}{(2n+1)!} t^n, \qquad (3)$$

this second solution behaves like $t^{1/2}$ near $t = 0$ and is therefore not analytic at the origin, so that it cannot be expressed in the form (2).

Nevertheless, the power series which multiplies $t^{1/2}$ in (3) does represent an analytic function. This suggests that the general solution of the differential equation can be found by assuming, instead of the simple power series (2), a more general series representation of the form

$$x(t) = \sum_{n=0}^{\infty} a_n t^{n+c}, \qquad (4)$$

where c is an additional (possibly non-integral) undetermined constant. This is the essence of the *Frobenius method*, which, as we shall show later, provides the general solution for a rather wide class of differential equations.

We now illustrate the use of the Frobenius method in obtaining the general solution of the differential equation (1) in the neighbourhood of the point $t = 0$. We assume a solution of the type (4), where, without loss of generality, we may suppose that $a_0 \neq 0$. Then the first two terms in the differential equation involve the series

$$x'(t) = \sum_{n=0}^{\infty} a_n (n+c)t^{n+c-1} = \sum_{n=-1}^{\infty} a_{n+1} (n+c+1)t^{n+c},$$

$$tx''(t) = \sum_{n=-1}^{\infty} a_{n+1} (n+c+1)(n+c)t^{n+c}.$$

Note in particular that these series begin with $n = -1$, whereas the series (4) for the third term in the differential equation begins with $n = 0$, so that the case $n = -1$ must be distinguished. The differential equation leads to the condition

$$\{[4c(c-1) + 2c]a_0\}t^{c-1}$$

$$+ \sum_{n=0}^{\infty} \{[4(n+c+1)(n+c) + 2(n+c+1)]a_{n+1} + a_n\}t^{n+c} = 0, \quad (5)$$

where the first term comes from the contributions with $n = -1$. As before, the coefficients of all the powers of t in (5) must be equal to zero.

Since $a_0 \neq 0$ by hypothesis, the vanishing of the coefficient of t^{c-1} implies that $4c^2 - 2c = 0$. Such an equation for the parameter c, which is deduced from the vanishing of the coefficient of the lowest power of t, is called the *indicial equation*. The roots of the indicial equation (in our case, $c = 0$ and $c = \frac{1}{2}$) give the possible values of c for which solutions may exist. These roots are called the *indices* of the differential equation at the point about which the expansion is made (here, $t = 0$).

The next step is to examine the possible solutions for each of the indices in turn. If we put $c = 0$, the condition that the coefficient of t^n in (5) vanishes for $n = 0, 1, \ldots$ leads directly to the same recurrence relation as that obtained earlier in the analysis of the problem by the simple power-series method. Thus we obtain the solution which was found earlier by that method. This is not surprising, since when $c = 0$ the assumed form of the series solution (4) reduces to a simple power series of the type considered previously.

We therefore turn to the second index $c = \frac{1}{2}$. The recurrence relation in this case takes the form

$$a_{n+1} = -\frac{a_n}{(2n+3)(2n+2)},$$

which gives

$$a_n = \frac{(-1)^n}{(2n+1)!} a_0.$$

Inserting these values of a_n in the assumed series solution (4), we recover the expected second solution (3), with an arbitrary multiplicative constant a_0. Thus the Frobenius method gives the general solution for this example.

It may be observed that the solution (3) becomes complex for $t < 0$ because of the factor $t^{1/2}$. However, if we remember that the constant a_0 is arbitrary and note that $t^{1/2} = \pm i|t|^{1/2}$ for $t < 0$, we can rewrite this solution in real form for $t < 0$ by simply replacing $t^{1/2}$ by $|t|^{1/2}$. Alternatively, we can obtain the solution directly in real form for $t < 0$ by making the change of variable $t = -t'$ in the differential equation and using the Frobenius method to construct the solution of the new differential equation for $t' > 0$. More generally, a Frobenius solution of the type (4) can always be written in real form for $t < 0$ by replacing the factor t^c by $|t|^c$.

It may not be obvious at first sight what advantage the Frobenius method offers over the simpler power-series method studied previously, since the latter always leads to the general solution in the neighbourhood of any ordinary point of the differential equation and the more powerful Frobenius method is required only if we insist on obtaining the solution in the neighbourhood of a singular point. However, the foregoing example shows clearly that the Frobenius method has two distinct advantages. First, the Frobenius solution in the neighbourhood of a singular point has a larger domain of validity, since it automatically incorporates the singular (fractional power) behaviour of the solution at the singular point. In the example considered above, the solution is valid for all $t \neq 0$, whereas a power-series solution about any ordinary point $t_0 \neq 0$ would have only a finite radius of convergence (equal to $|t_0|$).

Secondly, the Frobenius solution clearly exhibits the type of behaviour which the singular solution has near the singular point of the differential equation. For example, the solution (3) has the behaviour $x(t) = t^{1/2} + O(t^{3/2})$ near $t = 0$. This information cannot be obtained directly by examining a power-series expansion of the solution about any other point.

7.3 Solutions near a regular singular point

In this section we shall show by a general theoretical analysis of the Frobenius method that this method always leads to at least one formal series solution in the neighbourhood of a singular point, provided that suitable restrictions are imposed on the nature of the singular point.

A singular point $t = t_0$ of the differential equation

$$x'' + P(t)x' + Q(t)x = 0 \tag{1}$$

is said to be *regular* if the functions $(t - t_0)P(t)$ and $(t - t_0)^2 Q(t)$ are both analytic at $t = t_0$. In the language of complex-variable theory, this means that $P(t)$ may have a simple pole, while $Q(t)$ may have either a simple pole or a double pole at $t = t_0$. Any singular point which does not satisfy this criterion is said to be *irregular*.

Without loss of generality, we may consider solutions in the neighbourhood of the point $t = 0$. Suppose that $t = 0$ is a regular singular point of the differential equation (1). Then we can assume the validity of power-series expansions of the type

$$tP(t) = \sum_{n=0}^{\infty} p_n t^n, \tag{2}$$

$$t^2 Q(t) = \sum_{n=0}^{\infty} q_n t^n \tag{3}$$

in some neighbourhood of the origin. Let us seek a Frobenius-type solution

$$x(t) = \sum_{n=0}^{\infty} a_n t^{n+c}, \tag{4}$$

assuming as before that $a_0 \neq 0$. Then the three terms of the differential equation take the form

$$Q(t) x(t) = t^{c-2} \left[\sum_{n=0}^{\infty} q_n t^n \right] \left[\sum_{n=0}^{\infty} a_n t^n \right]$$

$$= t^{c-2} \sum_{n=0}^{\infty} \left[\sum_{k=0}^{n} q_{n-k} a_k \right] t^n,$$

$$P(t) x'(t) = t^{c-2} \left[\sum_{n=0}^{\infty} p_n t^n \right] \left[\sum_{n=0}^{\infty} a_n (n+c) t^n \right]$$

$$= t^{c-2} \sum_{n=0}^{\infty} \left[\sum_{k=0}^{n} p_{n-k} a_k (k+c) \right] t^n,$$

$$x''(t) = t^{c-2} \sum_{n=0}^{\infty} a_n (n+c)(n+c-1) t^n,$$

so that the differential equation leads to the condition

$$t^{c-2} \sum_{n=0}^{\infty} \{[(n+c)(n+c-1)+p_0(n+c)+q_0]a_n$$

$$+ \sum_{k=0}^{n-1} [p_{n-k}(k+c)+q_{n-k}]a_k\}t^n = 0, \tag{5}$$

where it is understood that the term containing the summation over k in (5) is absent for $n = 0$.

Now the indicial equation is the condition stating that the factor accompanying a_0 in the coefficient of t^n for $n = 0$ is equal to zero:

$$F(c) \equiv c(c-1)+p_0 c + q_0 = 0. \tag{6}$$

Let us suppose that the constant c is taken to be equal to one of the two roots of this equation, which we shall call c_1 and c_2. The condition that the coefficient of t^n in (5) vanishes for $n = 1, 2, \ldots$ leads to the recurrence relation

$$a_n F(n+c) = - \sum_{k=0}^{n-1} [p_{n-k}(k+c)+q_{n-k}]a_k, \tag{7}$$

where the function F is defined in (6). Equation (7) uniquely determines each coefficient a_n in terms of the preceding coefficients $a_0, \ldots, a_{n-1}$, except when $F(n+c) = 0$.

Under what conditions can it happen that $F(N+c) = 0$ for some integer $N \geqslant 1$? This is possible only if either $N+c = c_1$ or $N+c = c_2$, i.e. only if the indices c_1 and c_2 differ by the integer N. For definiteness, suppose that $c_2 - c_1 = N$. Then we have $F(N+c_1) = F(c_2) = 0$. In other words, $F(N+c)$ vanishes when c is taken to be equal to c_1, the *smaller* of the two (unequal) indices. In this situation, there are two distinct possibilities, depending on whether the right-hand side of the recurrence relation (7) is non-zero or zero when $n = N$.

Case 1 The right-hand side of the recurrence relation is non-zero when $n = N$. In this case, there is no value of a_N for which the recurrence relation is satisfied when $c = c_1$, so that no Frobenius solution exists for the smaller index c_1.

Case 2 The right-hand side of the recurrence relation vanishes when $n = N$. In this case, the recurrence relation is satisfied for *any* value of

a_N, so that we obtain the general solution of the differential equation (involving the two arbitrary constants a_0 and a_N).

To summarize the results of the foregoing discussion, we can say that the Frobenius method always leads to two independent solutions if the indices do not differ by an integer; it obviously gives only one solution (apart from the arbitrary multiplicative constant a_0) if the indices are equal; and it may give either one or two independent solutions if the indices differ by an integer.

Three further remarks are in order. First, the roots of the indicial equation may be complex. They are then complex conjugates, since the indicial equation is a quadratic equation with real coefficients, and the Frobenius method necessarily leads to the general solution. We shall not consider this case in further detail.

Secondly, it can be shown by a more detailed analysis that the formal power-series solutions obtained by the Frobenius method actually converge in the same neighbourhood as the original power series (2) and (3) for the functions $tP(t)$ and $t^2 Q(t)$.

Thirdly, we have not actually made use of the assumption that $t = 0$ is a singular point of the differential equation in our general analysis of the Frobenius method. This means that the discussion also applies to the case of an ordinary point. Let us consider what happens in this case. If $t = 0$ is an ordinary point, then the functions $P(t)$ and $Q(t)$ are analytic there, so that $p_0 = 0$ in (2) and $q_0 = q_1 = 0$ in (3). It can be seen from the general form of the indicial equation (6) that the indices in this case necessarily have the values $c = 0, 1$. To determine the number of independent Frobenius solutions, we must therefore examine the right-hand side of the recurrence relation (7) when $c = 0$ and $n = 1$; this is found to have the value $-q_1 a_0$, which is equal to zero. This means that we are dealing with 'case 2' considered above, and the Frobenius method leads to the general solution of the differential equation.

We conclude this section with an example of the exceptional case in which the Frobenius method does not give the general solution.

Example Find the Frobenius solutions of the differential equation $tx'' - x = 0$ near the regular singular point $t = 0$.

Substituting an assumed solution of the form (4) into the differential equation, we find

$$c(c - 1)a_0 t^{c-1} + \sum_{n=0}^{\infty} [(n + c + 1)(n + c)a_{n+1} - a_n] t^{n+c} = 0.$$

The indices are therefore $c = 0, 1$. For the larger index $c = 1$, we obtain the recurrence relation

$$a_{n+1} = \frac{a_n}{(n+2)(n+1)},$$

so that in general

$$a_n = \frac{a_0}{(n+1)!\,n!}.$$

Thus we obtain a solution which can be written

$$x(t) = a_0 \sum_{n=0}^{\infty} \frac{t^{n+1}}{(n+1)!\,n!}.$$

For the smaller index $c = 0$, we find instead the recurrence relation $(n+1)na_{n+1} - a_n = 0$. Since it is assumed that $a_0 \neq 0$, there is no value of a_1 satisfying this relation and hence no second Frobenius solution.

7.4 Extension of the Frobenius method

Here we shall find the general form of a second independent solution in those exceptional cases in which the Frobenius method developed so far leads to only one solution in the neighbourhood of a regular singular point. Suppose that $t = 0$ is a regular singular point of the differential equation

$$x'' + P(t)x' + Q(t)x = 0, \tag{1}$$

whose indices c_1 and c_2 ($c_1 \leqslant c_2$) differ by an integer. As we have seen, the larger index c_2 always leads to a Frobenius solution, which, for $t > 0$, can be written in the form

$$x(t) = t^{c_2} \sum_{n=0}^{\infty} a_n t^n \equiv u(t) \quad (a_0 \neq 0). \tag{2}$$

Knowing this solution $u(t)$, we can find another solution by the method of reduction of order. If we put $x(t) = u(t)v(t)$ in the differential equation, where the function $v(t)$ is to be determined, we find that $v(t)$ satisfies the differential equation

$$uv'' + (2u' + Pu)v' = 0,$$

which can readily be solved for $v'(t)$:

$$v'(t) = \frac{1}{[u(t)]^2} \exp[-\int^t P(t')\,dt'].$$

Using the series expansions for the functions $u(t)$ and $P(t)$, with the same notation as in the preceding section, this gives

$$v'(t) = t^{-2c_2}\left(\sum_{n=0}^{\infty} a_n t^n\right)^{-2} \exp\left[-\int^t \left(\frac{p_0}{t'} + p_1 + p_2\,t' + \ldots\right) dt'\right]$$

$$= t^{-2c_2 - p_0}\left(\sum_{n=0}^{\infty} a_n t^n\right)^{-2} \exp\left(-p_1 t - \tfrac{1}{2} p_2 t'^2 - \ldots\right). \quad (3)$$

As we saw in the preceding section, the indicial equation takes the form

$$c^2 + (p_0 - 1)c + q_0 = 0.$$

Comparing this with the same equation written in the form $(c - c_1)$ $(c - c_2) = 0$, we find that $p_0 - 1 = -(c_1 + c_2)$ and hence

$$2c_2 + p_0 = c_2 - c_1 + 1 \equiv k.$$

We can therefore write (3) in the form $v'(t) = t^{-k} f(t)$, where $f(t)$ is some function which is analytic at $t = 0$ and satisfies $f(0) = a_0^{-2} \neq 0$. This means that we can represent $f(t)$ in the form of a power series

$$f(t) = \sum_{n=0}^{\infty} b_n t^n \quad (b_0 \neq 0).$$

The resulting series expansion

$$v'(t) = b_0 t^{-k} + b_1 t^{-k+1} + \ldots + b_{k-2} t^{-2} + b_{k-1} t^{-1} + b_k + \ldots$$

can be integrated directly to give

$$v(t) = \frac{b_0 t^{-k+1}}{-k+1} + \ldots - b_{k-2} t^{-1} + b_{k-1} \log t + b_k t + \ldots$$

$$\equiv b_{k-1} \log t + t^{-k+1} g(t),$$

where the function $g(t)$ is analytic at $t = 0$. Now a second solution of the differential equation is given by $x(t) = u(t)v(t)$. Using the series expansions for $u(t)$ and $v(t)$ and recalling that $k = c_2 - c_1 + 1$, it can be seen that this solution must have the form

$$x(t) = b_{k-1} u(t) \log t + t^{c_1} h(t), \quad (4)$$

where $h(t)$ is some function which is analytic at $t = 0$. This is our final result.

If one Frobenius solution $x = u(t)$ is known, the general solution can therefore be found in practice by substituting an assumed solution of the form

$$x(t) = u(t) \log t + t^{c_1} \sum_{n=0}^{\infty} h_n t^n$$

into the differential equation and making use of the usual consistency requirements to determine the coefficients h_n. Note that an arbitrary multiplicative constant can be included in the function $u(t)$.

In the case in which the general solution is actually of the Frobenius type, the logarithmic term cannot occur, so that we must have $b_{k-1} = 0$ in (4). In the special case of equal indices ($c_1 = c_2$), we have $b_{k-1} = b_0 \neq 0$, so that the logarithmic term is necessarily present in the second solution.

Example   Consider the differential equation $tx'' - x = 0$. We saw in the example at the end of Sec. 7.3 that the indices of this equation at $t = 0$ have the values $c = 0, 1$ and that a Frobenius solution is obtained only for $c = 1$, namely

$$x(t) = a \sum_{n=0}^{\infty} \frac{t^{n+1}}{(n+1)! \, n!} \equiv u(t). \tag{5}$$

Consequently, there must exist a second solution of the form

$$x(t) = u(t) \log t + \sum_{n=0}^{\infty} h_n t^n.$$

Substitution of this expression into the differential equation gives

$$a\left[(tu'' - u) \log t + 2u' - \frac{u}{t} \right] + \sum_{n=0}^{\infty} \left[(n+1)nh_{n+1} - h_n \right] t^n = 0. \tag{6}$$

The coefficient of $\log t$ in (6) actually vanishes because $u(t)$ satisfies the original differential equation. Using the series representation (5) for the function $u(t)$, equation (6) becomes

$$\sum_{n=0}^{\infty} \left[\frac{2a}{(n!)^2} - \frac{a}{(n+1)! \, n!} + (n+1)nh_{n+1} - h_n \right] t^n = 0. \tag{7}$$

If in (7) we equate the coefficient of t^n for $n = 0$ to zero, we obtain the condition $h_0 = a$. The requirement that the coefficient of t^n vanishes for all positive integers n gives the recurrence relation

$$h_{n+1} = \frac{1}{n(n+1)} \left[h_n - \frac{2n+1}{(n+1)! \, n!} a \right] \qquad (n = 1, 2, \dots).$$

However, there is no restriction on h_1. Thus all the coefficients in the series solution are uniquely determined in terms of the two arbitrary parameters a and h_1, and we have indeed found the general solution. Note that this solution incorporates the previously determined Frobenius solution as a special case.

7.5 Homographic transformations on the independent variable

It is sometimes important to consider the asymptotic behaviour of solutions of a differential equation, say

$$x'' + P(t)x' + Q(t)x = 0, \tag{1}$$

as $t \to \infty$. In this case, we speak of the *point at infinity*. To study the large-t behaviour, it is convenient to make the change of variable $t = 1/s$ in the differential equation and to examine the transformed equation in the neighbourhood of the point $s = 0$.

A straightforward calculation shows that the differential equation for $x(s)$ corresponding to equation (1) is

$$x'' + \frac{1}{s}\left[2 - \frac{P(1/s)}{s}\right]x' + \frac{Q(1/s)}{s^4} \ x = 0, \tag{2}$$

where the primes now denote differentiation with respect to s. Thus solutions of the original differential equation (1) in the region of large t can be obtained by solving the transformed differential equation (2) in the neighbourhood of $s = 0$ and re-expressing the resulting solutions in terms of the original variable $t = 1/s$.

The nature of the point at infinity for the original differential equation (1) (ordinary, regular or irregular singular) is defined to be the same as the nature of the point $s = 0$ for the transformed differential equation (2). This means, in particular, that the point at infinity for the differential equation (1) is an ordinary point if the coefficients of x' and x in (2) are both analytic at $s = 0$. If the point at infinity for the differential equation (1) (or the point $s = 0$ for the transformed equation (2)) is a singular point, then this point is classified as regular if the functions $[2 - P(1/s)/s]$ and $Q(1/s)/s^2$ are both analytic at $s = 0$.

In the case of a regular singular point, we also define the indices of the original differential equation (1) at infinity to be equal to the indices of the transformed differential equation (2) at $s = 0$.

Example   Legendre's differential equation of order n is

$$(1 - t^2)x'' - 2tx' + n(n + 1)x = 0. \tag{3}$$

Writing this equation in the normal form (1), it can be seen from (2) that the corresponding differential equation for the function $x(s)$, where $s = 1/t$, is

$$x'' + \frac{1}{s}\left[2 + \frac{2}{s^2 - 1}\right]x' + \frac{1}{s^2}\left[\frac{n(n+1)}{s^2 - 1}\right]x = 0. \qquad (4)$$

Now both of the functions in square brackets in (4) are analytic at $s = 0$. The first square bracket has a double zero at $s = 0$, so that the overall coefficient of x' is analytic there, but the second square bracket is non-zero at $s = 0$ when $n(n+1) \neq 0$. Consequently, Legendre's differential equation (3) has a regular singular point at infinity, except when either $n = 0$ or $n = -1$, when this point is an ordinary point. In general, since the coefficients of the differential equation (4) are analytic in the region $0 < |s| < 1$, we expect any series solutions about the point $s = 0$ obtained by the Frobenius method to be valid for $0 < |s| < 1$ or, when expressed in terms of the original variable $t = 1/s$, for $|t| > 1$.

We have defined the nature of the point at infinity for a given differential equation, and its indices at that point in the case of a regular singular point, to be the same as the corresponding characteristics at $s = 0$ for the new differential equation obtained by making the substitution $t = 1/s$. More generally, it can be verified by direct calculation that the transformation $t = 1/s$ also leaves these characteristics invariant for any other point $s \neq 0$.

Suppose, for example, that the original differential equation has a regular singular point at $t = a \neq 0$, so that it can be written in the form

$$x'' + \frac{p(t)}{t - a}x' + \frac{q(t)}{(t-a)^2}x = 0, \qquad (5)$$

where the functions $p(t)$ and $q(t)$ are both analytic at $t = a$. It is easy to check that the differential equation obtained from (5) by putting $t = 1/s$ can be written

$$x'' + \frac{A(s)}{s - \frac{1}{a}}x' + \frac{B(s)}{(s - \frac{1}{a})^2}x = 0, \qquad (6)$$

where the functions

$$A(s) \equiv 2 + \frac{p(1/s) - 2}{as}, \qquad B(s) \equiv \frac{q(1/s)}{(as)^2}$$

are both analytic at $s = 1/a$ and have the same behaviour at that point as the functions $p(t)$ and $q(t)$, respectively, at the point $t = a$. Therefore the transformed differential equation (6) has a regular singular point at $s = 1/a$.

Next consider the indices. The indicial equation at the point $t = a$ for the original differential equation (5) is

$$c(c - 1) + p(a) c + q(a) = 0$$

(see equation (6) of Sec. 7.3). Similarly, the indicial equation of the transformed differential equation (6) at the point $s = 1/a$ is

$$c(c - 1) + A \frac{1}{a} c + B \frac{1}{a} = 0.$$

But $A(1/a) = p(a)$ and $B(1/a) = q(a)$. Therefore these two indicial equations have the same roots.

These ideas can be extended to the more general class of *homographic* (or *bilinear*) transformations

$$s = \frac{at + b}{ct + 1}, \tag{7}$$

where the condition $a - bc \neq 0$ must be imposed to ensure that s is not simply a constant. Provided that $c \neq 0$, equation (7) can be written in the form

$$s = \frac{b - a/c}{ct + 1} + \frac{a}{c}.$$

Thus, when $c \neq 0$, the general homographic transformation (7) can be generated by the chain of simpler transformations $t_1 = ct$, $t_2 = t_1 + 1$, $t_3 = 1/t_2$, $t_4 = (b - a/c)t_3$, $s = t_4 + a/c$. The special case $c = 0$ corresponds to the transformation $s = at + b$, which can be decomposed into a composition of the two simpler transformations $t' = at$ and $s = t' + b$. In either case, these simpler transformations are of three basic types: multiplication by a constant, addition of a constant, and inversion. It is easy to show (as we have already done above in the case of the inversion transformation) that the nature of a particular point of a given differential equation, as well as its indices in the case of a regular singular point, are invariant under each of these basic types of transformation. Consequently, these characteristics also remain invariant under general homographic transformations of the independent variable. This fact will be of great importance in the remainder of this chapter.

7.6 Fuchsian equations and their classification

We shall consider here differential equations of the type

$$x'' + P(t)x' + Q(t)x = 0 \tag{1}$$

which have no irregular singular points throughout the entire complex *t*-plane. Such differential equations are known as *Fuchsian equations.* Many of the special differential equations which arise in practice are of this type, and the number of singular points seldom exceeds three.

First of all, it can be shown that a differential equation of the form (1) must always possess at least one singular point. For suppose that there are no singular points for finite *t*. This means that the coefficients $P(t)$ and $Q(t)$ are analytic for all finite *t*. To avoid an irregular singular point at infinity, we require, according to the results of the preceding section, that (i) $P(1/s)$ and $Q(1/s)$ are both analytic at $s = 0$ and (ii) $P(1/s) = O(s)$ and $Q(1/s) = O(s^2)$ as $s \to 0$.

Condition (i) implies that $P(t) = \text{const}$ and $Q(t) = \text{const}$, since, by Liouville's theorem of complex-variable theory, a function of *t* which is analytic for all *t*, including the point at infinity, must be a constant. Condition (ii) then requires that $P(t) = Q(t) = 0$, so that the differential equation is simply $x'' = 0$. Putting $t = 1/s$, we find that the corresponding differential equation for $x(s)$ is $x'' + (2/s)x' = 0$, which has a regular singular point at $s = 0$. The original differential equation must therefore have a regular singular point at infinity.

We turn now to the classification of Fuchsian equations with up to three regular singular points.

Case 1: One regular singular point

By means of a suitable homographic transformation $s = s(t)$, the singular point can always be mapped onto the point at infinity in the variable *s*. It follows from the foregoing discussion that the transformed differential equation then takes the 'standard form' $x''(s) = 0$, and its general solution is $x(s) = \alpha s + \beta$ (i.e., $x(t) = \alpha s(t) + \beta$), where α and β are arbitrary constants.

Example   The differential equation

$$(t - a)x'' + 2x' = 0$$

has precisely one regular singular point, namely the point $t = a$. In particular, there is no singular point at infinity, since the substitution $t = 1/u$ gives, after simplification,

$$x'' + \frac{2a}{au - 1} \, x' = 0,$$

where the coefficient of x' is analytic at $u = 0$. The singular point of the original differential equation at $t = a$ can be mapped onto the point at infinity by means of the homographic transformation $s(t) = 1/(t - a)$. As is easily checked by direct calculation, the differential equation in the new variable s is $x'' = 0$. The general solution of the original differential equation is therefore

$$x(t) = \alpha s(t) + \beta = \frac{\alpha}{t - a} + \beta.$$

Case 2: Two regular singular points

Suppose that the differential equation (1) has regular singular points at $t = a, b$. By means of the homographic transformation

$$s(t) = \frac{t - a}{t - b},$$
(2)

we can transform this differential equation into a new differential equation with regular singular points at $s = 0, \infty$ (the 'standard form').

To find the form of this new differential equation, we first observe that since $s = 0$ is the only singular point for finite s, it must have the general structure

$$x'' + \frac{P(s)}{s} x' + \frac{Q(s)}{s^2} x = 0,$$

where $P(s)$ and $Q(s)$ are both analytic for all finite s. To fix the nature of the point at infinity, we put $s = 1/u$, which gives, according to the first two equations of the preceding section,

$$x'' + \frac{1}{u} [2 - P(1/u)] x' + \frac{1}{u^2} Q(1/u)x = 0.$$

Since $s = \infty$ and hence $u = 0$ is a regular singular point, the functions $P(1/u)$ and $Q(1/u)$ must both be analytic at $u = 0$. As in the analysis of Case 1 above, we conclude that $P(s) = p$ and $Q(s) = q$, where p and q are certain constants. Consequently, the most general differential equation with exactly two regular singular points at $s = 0, \infty$ can be written in the two-parameter form

$$s^2 x'' + psx' + qx = 0.$$
(3)

It is easy to obtain the general solution of the differential equation (3). First, let us rewrite this differential equation by expressing its parameters p and q in terms of the indices c_1 and c_2 at $s = 0$. Recalling that the indicial equation takes the form $c^2 + (p - 1) c + q = 0$ and comparing the coefficients in this equation with the corresponding coefficients in the equation $(c - c_1)(c - c_2) = 0$, we have $p - 1 = -(c_1 + c_2)$ and $q = c_1 c_2$. Therefore (3) can be written

$$s^2 x'' + (1 - c_1 - c_2)sx' + c_1 c_2 x = 0.$$
(4)

As is easily verified, the general solution of (4) is

$$x(s) = \begin{cases} \alpha s^{c_1} + \beta s^{c_2}, & c_1 \neq c_2, \\ s^{c_1}(\alpha + \beta \log s), & c_1 = c_2. \end{cases} \tag{5}$$

Knowing the homographic transformation $s = s(t)$, equation (2), which brought the original differential equation into the 'standard form' (3), the general solution of the original equation can then be written down by simply re-expressing (5) as a function of t.

Case 3: Three regular singular points

Suppose that the singular points are at $t = t_1, t_2, t_3$. By means of the homographic transformation

$$z(t) = \frac{(t_2 - t_3)(t - t_1)}{(t_2 - t_1)(t - t_3)},$$

which has the properties $z(t_1) = 0$, $z(t_2) = 1$ and $z(t_3) = \infty$, we can obtain a new differential equation with regular singular points at $z = 0, 1, \infty$ (the 'standard form').

Clearly, such a differential equation must have the general structure

$$x'' + \frac{P(z)}{z(z-1)} x' + \frac{Q(z)}{z^2(z-1)^2} x = 0, \tag{6}$$

where $P(z)$ and $Q(z)$ are both analytic for all finite z. Let us examine the point at infinity. Putting $z = 1/u$ in (6), we find the following differential equation for $x(u)$:

$$x'' + \frac{1}{u}\left[2 - \frac{uP(1/u)}{1-u}\right]x' + \frac{1}{u^2}\left[\frac{u^2 Q(1/u)}{(1-u)^2}\right]x = 0.$$

For $z = \infty$ and hence $u = 0$ to be a regular singular point, the functions $uP(1/u)$ and $u^2 Q(1/u)$ must both be analytic at $u = 0$; i.e., $P(z)$ is analytic everywhere except possibly for a simple pole at $z = \infty$, and $Q(z)$ is analytic everywhere except possibly for a simple or double pole at $z = \infty$. The most general form for these functions is therefore $P(z) = P_0 + P_1 z$ and $Q(z) = Q_0 + Q_1 z + Q_2 z^2$.

Our next step is to further simplify the differential equation by means of a certain transformation on the dependent variable. Suppose that the differential equation (6) has indices α and α' at $z = 0$ and indices β and β' at $z = 1$. It can be verified by straightforward, albeit rather tedious, calculations that if we change the dependent variable by means of the substitution

$$x(z) = z^{\alpha'}(z-1)^{\beta'} y(z), \tag{7}$$

then the new variable $y(z)$ satisfies a differential equation with indices 0 and $\alpha - \alpha'$ at $z = 0$ and indices 0 and $\beta - \beta'$ at $z = 1$. In other words, the transformation (7) reduces the indices at $z = 0$ by an amount α' and the indices at $z = 1$ by an amount β'. Although the indices are changed, the new differential equation has regular singular points at the same positions as the original one.

Before carrying out the transformation (7) in the differential equation (6), we indicate briefly how these facts can be established. Consider the more general situation in which a given differential equation for $x(z)$ has a regular singular point at $z = a$ with indices c_1 and c_2. We shall show that the substitution

$$x(z) = (z - a)^\lambda \, y(z) \qquad (8)$$

leads to a differential equation for the function $y(z)$ which has a regular singular point at $z = a$ with indices $c_1 - \lambda$ and $c_2 - \lambda$.

We first note that the given differential equation for $x(z)$ can be written in the form

$$(z - a)^2 \, x'' + (z - a)A(z)x' + B(z)x = 0,$$

where $A(z)$ and $B(z)$ are analytic at $z = a$. The indicial equation at $z = a$,

$$c(c - 1) + A(a)c + B(a) = 0, \qquad (9)$$

must have the roots $c = c_1, c_2$. On making the change of variable (8), the new differential equation for $y(z)$ is found to be

$$(z - a)^2 y'' + (z - a)[2\lambda + A(z)] y'$$
$$+ [\lambda(\lambda - 1) + \lambda A(z) + B(z)] y = 0. \qquad (10)$$

The functions in square brackets in (10) are analytic at $z = a$, and this shows that (10) has a regular singular point there. The new indicial equation is

$$c(c - 1) + [2\lambda + A(a)]c + [\lambda(\lambda - 1) + \lambda A(a) + B(a)] = 0. \qquad (11)$$

Now since the original indicial equation (9) has the roots $c = c_1, c_2$, we know (by the argument given in the analysis of Case 2) that $A(a) = 1 - c_1 - c_2$ and $B(a) = c_1 c_2$. Using these values, (11) becomes

$$c(c - 1) + [1 - (c_1 - \lambda) - (c_2 - \lambda)] c + (c_1 - \lambda)(c_2 - \lambda) = 0,$$

so that the indices of the transformed differential equation are indeed $c_1 - \lambda$ and $c_2 - \lambda$.

Suppose now that we have carried out the transformation (7) in the differential equation (6). By virtue of what we have said above, this leads to a differential equation for $y(z)$ which can be written in the form

$$z^2(z-1)^2 y'' + z(z-1)p(z)y' + q(z)y = 0, \qquad (12)$$

where, for the same reasons as in the case of the differential equation (6), the functions $p(z)$ and $q(z)$ in (12) must have the form $p(z) = p_0 + p_1 z$ and $q(z) = q_0 + q_1 z + q_2 z^2$. However, since one index at $z = 0$ is now 0, it follows from the form of the indicial equation

$$c(c-1) - p(0)c + q(0) = 0$$

that $q(0) = 0$, i.e., $q_0 = 0$. Thus, $q(z) = q_1 z + q_2 z^2$. Similarly, the existence of the index 0 at $z = 1$ implies that $q(1) = 0$ and hence $q_1 + q_2 = 0$, so that $q(z) = q_2 z(z-1)$. Consequently, the differential equation (12) can be written in terms of only three parameters in the form

$$z(z-1)y'' + (p_0 + p_1 z)y' + q_2 y = 0. \qquad (13)$$

Finally, we shall express the parameters p_0, p_1 and q_2 in terms of the second index at $z = 0$ (which we shall represent in the form $1 - d$) and the two indices at $z = \infty$ (which we denote by a and b). Since the indicial equation at $z = 0$ is $c(c-1) - p_0 c = 0$, the indices there have the values 0 and $p_0 + 1$, so that $p_0 = -d$. To relate the other two parameters to the indices at $z = \infty$, we put $z = 1/u$ in (13) and consider the point $u = 0$. The transformed equation is

$$y'' + \frac{1}{u}\left[2 - \frac{p_0 u + p_1}{1-u}\right]y' + \frac{1}{u^2}\left[\frac{q_2}{1-u}\right]y = 0.$$

Thus the indicial equation at $u = 0$ (and hence at $z = \infty$) is

$$c(c-1) + (2 - p_1)c + q_2 = 0.$$

If the roots of this equation are $c = a, b$, then we must have $1 - p_1 = -(a+b)$ and $q_2 = ab$. These are the required relations for p_1 and q_2 in terms of a and b. Using the expressions obtained for p_0, p_1 and q_2, we can finally write (13) as

$$z(1-z)y'' + [d - (a+b+1)z]y' - aby = 0. \qquad (14)$$

The differential equation (14), containing three parameters, is known as the *hypergeometric equation*. We shall occasionally write the hypergeometric equation with different expressions in place of the parameters a, b and d. To distinguish the original form of this equation given in (14) from these other variants, we shall sometimes refer to (14) as the 'standard hypergeometric equation'.

The special significance of the hypergeometric equation lies in the fact that, as we have seen, any Fuchsian equation with precisely three regular singular points can be transformed to the form (14) by appropriate changes of both the independent and dependent variables. Unlike the standard forms of the differential equations with only one or two regular singular points, the solutions of the hypergeometric equation cannot in general be expressed in closed form in terms of elementary functions. We shall study these solutions using power-series methods in the next section.

7.7 The hypergeometric function

The hypergeometric equation has regular singular points at $z = 0, 1, \infty$. As we have seen, the standard form of this equation is completely determined once we stipulate that its indices at $z = 0$ are 0 and $1 - d$, its indices at $z = \infty$ are a and b, and one of its indices at $z = 1$ is 0. It is easy to verify that the second index at $z = 1$ has the value $d - a - b$. Thus the sum of all six indices is always equal to 1.

Series solutions of the hypergeometric equation can be obtained by the Frobenius method. Assuming a series solution of the form

$$y(z) = \sum_{n=0}^{\infty} a_n z^{n+c},$$

the usual procedure leads to the expected indices 0 and $1 - d$ at $z = 0$ and a recurrence relation which, for $c = 0$, takes the form

$$a_{n+1} = \frac{(n + a)(n + b)}{(n + 1)(n + d)} a_n \qquad (n = 0, 1, \dots).$$

We shall assume throughout this section that the parameter d is not equal to zero or a negative integer. In this case, the recurrence relation uniquely determines all the coefficients a_n in terms of a_0, and we obtain the solution

$$y(z) = a_0 \left[1 + \sum_{n=1}^{\infty} \frac{[(a + n - 1) \dots (a + 1)a] [(b + n - 1) \dots (b + 1)b]}{n!(d + n - 1) \dots (d + 1)d} z^n \right]$$

$$\equiv a_0 F(a, b; d; z). \tag{1}$$

The function $F(a, b; d; z)$ defined by (1) is called the *hypergeometric function* and its series expansion, valid for $|z| < 1$, is called the *hypergeometric series.*

Two elementary properties of the hypergeometric function should be noted. First, the special case

$$F(1, b; b; z) = \sum_{n=0}^{\infty} z^n$$

reduces to a simple geometric series; this is the origin of the name 'hypergeometric series'. Secondly, we have the symmetry property

$$F(a, b; b; z) = F(b, a; d; z),$$

which means that the order of the first two parameters is immaterial.

Next we invoke a simple argument to deduce the form of the second solution of the standard hypergeometric equation near $z = 0$. For any of the admissible values of the parameter d (excluding $d = 1$), the general theory of the Frobenius method tells us that there must exist a solution corresponding to the second index $(1 - d)$ having the form

$$y(z) = z^{1-d} g(z), \tag{2}$$

where $g(z)$ is analytic at $z = 0$. If we make the transformation (2) in the hypergeometric equation, we obtain a new differential equation for $g(z)$ which has regular singular points at the same positions as those of the hypergeometric equation.

Let us consider the indices of this new differential equation. Since the hypergeometric equation for $y(z)$ has indices 0 and $1 - d$ at $z = 0$, we know from the results of the preceding section that the function $g(z)$ must satisfy a differential equation with indices $d - 1$ and 0 at $z = 0$. Consider next the indices at $z = \infty$. We know that the differential equation for $y(z)$ has indices a and b at $z = \infty$, which are also the indices at $u = 0$ of the differential equation for $y(u)$ obtained by putting $z = 1/u$. But $y(u) = u^{d-1} g(u)$, so that the differential equation for $g(u)$ has indices $a - (d - 1)$ and $b - (d - 1)$ at $u = 0$, and these in turn must agree with the indices of the differential equation for the function $g(z)$ at $z = \infty$.

To summarize these arguments, the function $g(z)$ satisfies a differential equation with regular singular points at $z = 0, 1, \infty$, with indices $d - 1$ and 0 at $z = 0$ and indices $a - d + 1$ and $b - d + 1$ at $z = \infty$. Knowing these indices, we can identify the function $g(z)$ with the solution of the hypergeometric equation (for certain values of its three parameters) which is analytic at $z = 0$:

$$g(z) = F(a - d + 1, \quad b - d + 1; \quad 2 - d; z).$$

Note that we have deduced this solution without actually carrying out the transformation (2) in the hypergeometric equation.

Thus, for the admissible values of d, the general solution of the standard hypergeometric equation near $z = 0$ is

$$y(z) = \alpha F(a, b; d; z) + \beta z^{1-d} F(a - d + 1, \quad b - d + 1; \quad 2 - d; z),$$

where α and β are arbitrary constants.

Next we determine the solutions of the standard hypergeometric equation in the neighbourhood of its other singular points. To study the solutions near $z = 1$, we make the substitution $u = 1 - z$. This gives the equation

$$u(1 - u)y'' + [(a + b - d + 1) - (a + b + 1)u]y' - aby = 0,$$

which is identical in form with the original hypergeometric equation, but with the replacements $z \to u = 1 - z$ and $d \to a + b - d + 1$. Consequently, the general solution of the standard hypergeometric equation near $z = 1$ is

$$y(z) = \alpha F(a, b; a + b - d + 1; 1 - z)$$
$$+ \beta(1 - z)^{d-a-b} F(d - b, \ d - a; \ d - a - b + 1; \ 1 - z),$$

provided that $d - a - b$ is not an integer.

Finally, to find the solution of the standard hypergeometric equation for large z, we make the substitution $z = 1/u$. This gives, after simplification,

$$u(1 - u)y'' + [2(1 - u) + du - a - b - 1]y' + \frac{1}{u} aby = 0.$$

As it stands, this differential equation cannot be identified with the hypergeometric equation, although its singular points are at the required positions.

We know that the indices at $z = \infty$ (i.e., at $u = 0$) are a and b. We therefore make the substitution $y(u) = u^a v(u)$, so that the corresponding differential equation satisfied by $v(u)$ will have one index 0 at $u = 0$. After simplification, this differential equation is found to be

$$u(1 - u)v'' + [(a - b + 1) + (d - 2a - 2)u]v' + a(d - a - 1)v = 0,$$

which can be identified with the original hypergeometric equation, but with the replacements $z \to u = 1/z$, $y \to v = u^{-a}y$, $b \to a - d + 1$ and $d \to a - b + 1$. This gives the general solution

$$v(u) = \alpha F(a, a - d + 1; a - b + 1; u) + \beta u^{b-a} F(b, b - d + 1; b - a + 1; u)$$

near $u = 0$ and hence

$$y(z) = \alpha z^{-a} F(a, a - d + 1; a - b + 1; 1/z)$$
$$+ \beta z^{-b} F(b, b - d + 1; b - a + 1; 1/z)$$

for large z. Note that the final form of this solution is completely symmetric in a and b. This is not surprising, since the parameters a and b occur in a symmetric way in the original hypergeometric equation.

Using the techniques developed here, the solution of any differential equation with three regular singular points in the neighbourhood of any one of these singular points can always be expressed in terms of the hypergeometric function. This means that it is possible to express many of the familiar special functions in terms of the hypergeometric function.

Example Express the solution of Legendre's differential equation of order n,

$$(1 - x^2)y'' - 2xy' + n(n + 1)y = 0,$$

which is analytic at $x = 1$ in terms of the hypergeometric function.

This differential equation has regular singular points at $x = \pm 1$, ∞ (see the example of Sec. 7.5). To study the solutions near $x = 1$, it is convenient to make a homographic transformation $z = z(x)$ such that $z(-1) = 1$, $z(1) = 0$ and $z(\infty) = \infty$, namely $z = \frac{1}{2}(1 - x)$. (Note that the points $\pm\infty$ are both identified as the same 'point at infinity'.) We must determine the indices of the differential equation at its singular points. The indices of the original differential equation at $x = 1$ are readily found to be 0 and 0, while the indices at $x = \infty$ (which can be determined by making the transformation $x = 1/u$) are $-n$ and $n + 1$. In other words, the corresponding differential equation for $y(z)$, which has its regular singular points at the standard positions $z = 0, 1, \infty$, has indices 0 and 0 at $z = 0$ and indices $-n$ and $n + 1$ at infinity, Its solutions can therefore be identified with the solutions of the hypergeometric equation with appropriate values of the parameters. In particular, the solution which is analytic at $z = 0$ is

$$y(z) = F(-n,\ n + 1;\ 1;\ z).$$

Accordingly, the solution of Legendre's differential equation which is analytic at $x = 1$ is

$$y(x) = F(-n,\ n + 1;\ 1;\ \tfrac{1}{2}(1 - x)).$$

We conclude this section by considering briefly an important limiting form of the hypergeometric equation. Let us make the substitution $z = t/b$ in the standard hypergeometric equation. This gives the differential equation

$$t\left(1 - \frac{t}{b}\right)y'' + \left(d - t - \frac{a + 1}{b}t\right)y' - ay = 0,$$

which has regular singular points at $t = 0, b, \infty$. If we now take the formal limit $b \rightarrow \infty$, we obtain the differential equation

$$ty'' + (d - t)y' - ay = 0, \tag{3}$$

which is known as the *confluent hypergeometric equation*. As can easily be verified, this differential equation has one regular singular point at $t = 0$ and one *irregular* singular point at infinity (the latter having been produced by the 'confluence' of two regular singular points).

Like the ordinary hypergeometric equation, the confluent hypergeometric equation (3) has indices 0 and $1 - d$ at $t = 0$. Therefore it possesses a solution $y = y(t)$ which is analytic at $t = 0$. This solution, when normalized by the condition $y(0) = 1$, is called the *confluent hypergeometric function* and is denoted by $F(a; d; t)$. A straightforward application of the Frobenius method gives its series representation

$$F(a; d; t) = 1 + \sum_{n=1}^{\infty} \frac{(a + n - 1) \ldots (a + 1) a}{n! \, (d + n - 1) \ldots (d + 1)d} \, t^n \tag{4}$$

(assuming, as before, that the parameter d is not equal to zero or a negative integer). This series converges for all finite t, as we expect from the fact that the differential equation has no singular points for finite t apart from $t = 0$. A second linearly independent solution (corresponding to the index $1 - d$) is found to be

$$y(t) = t^{1-d} \, F(a - d + 1; \, 2 - d; t).$$

As one might expect from the relation between the ordinary hypergeometric equation and the confluent hypergeometric equation, the ordinary and the confluent hypergeometric functions are related by the equation

$$F(a; \, d; \, t) = \lim_{b \to \infty} F(a, \, b; \, d; \, t/b),$$

which can be verified directly from their series representations.

The importance of the confluent hypergeometric equation is that, as for the ordinary hypergeometric equation, many differential equations which arise in practice can be reduced to this form by appropriate transformations of the variables. Accordingly, many of the familiar special functions can be expressed in terms of the confluent hypergeometric function.

Problems

1 Use power-series methods to find the general solutions of the following differential equations near $t = 0$:

(i) $x'' - tx = 0$;

(ii) $t^2 x'' - 6tx' + 10x = 0$;

(iii) $3t^2 x'' + tx' - (t + 1)x = 0$.

2 Use power-series methods to find the general solutions of the following differential equations near $t = 0$:

(i) $x'' - tx' - x = 0$;

(ii) $(t^2 + 1)x'' - 6x = 0$.

3 Find the values of the integer m for which the differential equation

$$t^2x'' - mtx' - t^2x = 0$$

possesses two linearly independent Frobenius solutions. Write down the general solution in the case $m = 2$.

4 Use power-series methods to find the general solutions of the following differential equations near $t = 0$ (for $t > 0$):

(i) $t^2x'' + (t^2 - t)x' + (1 - t)x = 0$;

(ii) $tx'' + tx' + x = 0$;

(iii) $tx'' + (1 - t)x' + 3x = 0$;

(iv) $tx'' + x_t' - x = 0$.

5 Hermite's differential equation of order n is

$$x'' - 2tx' + 2nx = 0.$$

(i) Use power-series methods to find its general solution.

(ii) Show that there exists a polynomial solution $x = H_n(t)$ of degree n if n is a non-negative integer. (These polynomial solutions are proportional to the so-called Hermite polynomials.)

(iii) Write down the explicit forms of the Hermite polynomials $H_n(t)$ for $n = 0, 1, 2, 3$, the normalization being such that $H_n(t)$ contains a term $2^n t^n$.

6 The Laguerre polynomial $L_n(t)$ may be defined as the polynomial of degree n which satisfies the differential equation

$$tL_n''(t) + (1 - t)L_n'(t) + nL_n(t) = 0$$

and is normalized so that the coefficient of t^n in $L_n(t)$ has the value $(-1)^n$. Prove that such polynomials exist for all non-negative integers n, and write down the explicit forms of $L_0(t)$, $L_1(t)$ and $L_2(t)$.

7 Prove that Chebyshev's differential equation of order n,

$$(1 - t^2)x'' - tx' + n^2x = 0,$$

possesses a polynomial solution of degree n if n is any non-negative integer. (These solutions are proportional to the so-called Chebyshev polynomials.)

8 Show that the differential equation

$$(1 - t^2)x'' - tx' + \lambda x = 0$$

possesses a polynomial solution for certain values of the constant λ and find all such values of λ.

9 Show that the differential equation

$$t^3 x'' + x = 0$$

has no non-trivial Frobenius solutions near $t = 0$.

10 Show that the differential equation

$$t^4 x'' + 2t^3 x' + x = 0$$

has no non-trivial Frobenius solutions near $t = 0$. By making the substitution $t = 1/u$, solve this equation by means of power-series methods, and sum the resulting series in closed form.

11 (i) Use power-series methods to find the general solution of the differential equation

$$(1 - t^2)x'' - 2tx' + 2x = 0$$

in the region $|t| < 1$.

(ii) Use the transformation $t = 1/u$ to obtain the solution in the region $|t| > 1$.

12 Show that Bessel's differential equation of order n,

$$t^2 x'' + tx' + (t^2 - n^2)x = 0,$$

has an irregular singular point at infinity.

13 Show that each of the following differential equations has a total of three singular points, all of which are regular, and express its general solution $y = y(x)$ near the indicated singular point in terms of the hypergeometric function:

(i) $(2x^2 + 2x)y'' + (5x + 1)y' + y = 0$ $(x = 0)$;

(ii) $(x^2 - 1)y'' + (5x + 4)y' + 4y = 0$ $(x = -1)$.

14 Show that the differential equation

$$(x^2 - x - 6)y'' + (3x + 5)y' + y = 0$$

has a total of three singular points, all of which are regular, and express the solution of this equation which satisfies $y(3) = 1$ in terms of the hypergeometric function.

15 Using the argument outlined in the text (Sec. 7.5), prove that the classification of a particular point of a differential equation (as an ordinary, regular or irregular singular point), as well as its indices in the case of a regular singular point, remain invariant under arbitrary homographic transformations of the independent variable.

16 Derive the power-series representation of the hypergeometric function [equation (1) of Sec. 7.7].

17 Derive the power-series representation of the confluent hypergeometric function [equation (4) of Sec. 7.7].

18 Establish the following identities for the hypergeometric function:

(i) $(1 - x)^{-a} = F(a, \ b; \ b; \ x)$;

(ii) $\log(1 - x) = xF(1, \ 1; \ 2; \ x)$;

(iii) $\sin^{-1}x = xF(\frac{1}{2}, \ \frac{1}{2}; \ \frac{3}{2}; \ x^2)$.

19 The Chebyshev polynomial $T_n(x)$ is a solution of the differential equation

$$(1 - x^2)y'' - xy' + n^2 y = 0$$

and is normalized so that $T_n(1) = 1$. By considering an appropriate transformation $z = z(x)$, show that the Chebyshev polynomials can be expressed in terms of the hypergeometric function in the form

$$T_n(x) = F(n, \ -n; \ \tfrac{1}{2}; \ \tfrac{1}{2}(1 - x)).$$

8 Boundary value problems for ordinary differential equations

8.1 The Sturm-Liouville problem

In solving boundary-value problems for partial differential equations by the method of separation of variables, we were led to the problem of finding solutions of second-order ordinary differential equations satisfying prescribed homogeneous boundary conditions at each end-point of an interval.

For instance, Example 1 of Sec. 4.5 led to the problem of solving the differential equation $X''(x) + \lambda^2 X(x) = 0$ subject to the boundary conditions $X(0) = X(L) = 0$, where λ is an adjustable parameter. Non-trivial solutions were found for the discrete set of values $\lambda = n\pi/L$ ($n = 1, 2, \ldots$), namely $X(x) = C \sin(n\pi x/L)$, where C is an arbitrary constant.

Our use of Fourier series in solving the original boundary-value problem in terms of a superposition of such functions was effectively based on the orthogonality property of these solutions,

$$\int_0^L \sin\left(\frac{m\pi x}{L}\right) \sin\left(\frac{n\pi x}{L}\right) dx = 0 \quad (m \neq n)$$

and the fact that these solutions form a 'complete' set of functions on the interval $0 \leqslant x \leqslant L$, in the sense that any function in a certain general class of functions can be represented in the mean as an expansion in terms of these basic trigonometric functions.

Other boundary-value problems for partial differential equations lead naturally to different two-point boundary-value problems for ordinary differential equations. It turns out that the characteristic features of the solutions of the boundary-value problem discussed above are not peculiar to that particular problem, but are typical of a large class of boundary-value problems.

Consider the general second-order linear ordinary differential equation

$$My(x) \equiv p_2(x) y''(x) + p_1(x) y'(x) + p_0(x) y(x) = h(x).$$

We shall assume that this differential equation is normal on the interval $a < x < b$, i.e. that $p_2(x) \neq 0$ on this interval. Let us define the functions

$$p(x) \equiv \exp\left[\int^x \frac{p_1(x')}{p_2(x')} \, dx'\right],$$

$$q(x) \equiv \frac{p_0(x)}{p_2(x)}\ p(x),$$

as well as another differential operator

$$L \equiv \frac{d}{dx}\left[p(x)\frac{d}{dx}\right] + q(x). \tag{1}$$

Then

$$Ly(x) = \frac{d}{dx}[p(x)y'(x)] + q(x)y(x)$$

$$= p(x)y''(x) + \frac{p_1(x)}{p_2(x)}\ p(x)y'(x) + \frac{p_0(x)}{p_2(x)}\ p(x)y(x) = \frac{p(x)}{p_2(x)}\ My(x).$$

This shows that the original differential equation $My(x) = h(x)$ is equivalent to the differential equation $Ly(x) = H(x)$, where $H(x) \equiv [p(x)/p_2(x)]\ h(x)$ is some non-homogeneous term. A differential equation of the type

$$Ly(x) \equiv \frac{d}{dx}\left[p(x)\frac{dy}{dx}\right] + q(x)y(x) = H(x) \tag{2}$$

is said to be in *self-adjoint form*, and the linear operator L is said to be a self-adjoint operator. Thus we have shown that any second-order normal linear differential equation can be written in self-adjoint form.

The general class of problems known as the *Sturm-Liouville problem* is defined as follows. We are given a self-adjoint operator L having the form (1), where the functions $p(x)$, $p'(x)$ and $q(x)$ are real and continuous for $a \leqslant x \leqslant b$, and $p(x) \neq 0$ for $a < x < b$. We seek all non-trivial (i.e., non-zero) solutions of the 'eigenvalue equation' $Ly(x) = \lambda r(x)y(x)$ in the interval $a \leqslant x \leqslant b$, where λ is an undetermined parameter and $r(x)$ is a given real function, subject to appropriate boundary conditions at the end-points $x = a, b$. The specific types of boundary conditions which are admitted will be specified later. The solution of this problem consists of the set of all non-trivial functions $y(x)$ satisfying the differential equation (the *eigenfunctions*), together with the associated values of λ (the *eigenvalues*).

Let us consider the general properties of the eigenfunctions. Suppose that λ_1 and λ_2 are distinct eigenvalues ($\lambda_1 \neq \lambda_2$), so that $Ly_1(x) = \lambda_1 r(x)y_1(x)$ and $Ly_2(x) = \lambda_2 r(x)y_2(x)$ for some functions $y_1(x)$ and $y_2(x)$. Then

$$y_2(x)Ly_1(x) - y_1(x)Ly_2(x) = (\lambda_1 - \lambda_2)r(x)y_1(x)y_2(x). \tag{3}$$

The left-hand side of (3) has the value

$$y_2(x)[p(x)y''_1(x) + p'(x)\,y'_1(x)] - y_1(x)[p(x)y''_2(x) + p'(x)y'_2(x)]$$

$$= \frac{d}{dx}\left\{p(x)[y_2(x)y'_1(x) - y_1(x)\,y'_2(x)]\right\}.$$

Therefore, integrating (3) over the interval $a \leqslant x \leqslant b$, we have

$$(\lambda_1 - \lambda_2)\int_a^b r(x)y_1(x)y_2(x)\,dx$$

$$= \left\{p(x)[y_2(x)y'_1(x) - y_1(x)y'_2(x)]\right\}_{x=a}^b. \tag{4}$$

Now if the functions $y_1(x)$ and $y_2(x)$ satisfy some set of boundary conditions at $x = a$, b which ensure that the right-hand side of (4) vanishes, then we obtain the relation

$$\int_a^b r(x)y_1(x)\,y_2(x)\,dx = 0. \tag{5}$$

Two functions $y_1(x)$ and $y_2(x)$ which satisfy a relation of the form (5) are said to be orthogonal with respect to the 'weight function' $r(x)$ over the interval $a \leqslant x \leqslant b$. Thus we have shown that this orthogonality relation is satisfied by any two eigenfunctions corresponding to distinct eigenvalues, provided that the boundary conditions are such that the right-hand side of (4) vanishes.

We can now specify a general class of two-point boundary conditions ('Sturm-Liouville boundary conditions') which have the property that the right-hand side of (4) vanishes whenever $y_1(x)$ and $y_2(x)$ are eigenfunctions satisfying identical boundary conditions from this class. We shall distinguish three particular types of Sturm-Liouville boundary conditions.

(i) At each end-point, a particular linear combination of the function and its first derivative vanishes:

$$\alpha_1\,y(a) + \alpha_2\,y'(a) = 0, \tag{6}$$

where α_1 and α_2 are given real constants, not both zero, and

$$\beta_1\,y(b) + \beta_2\,y'(b) = 0, \tag{7}$$

where β_1 and β_2 are given real constants, not both zero. For example, if $\alpha_1 = 0$, then the boundary condition (6) states that $y'_1(a) = y'_2(a) = 0$, and we see directly that the part of the right-hand side of (4) which is evaluated at $x = a$ vanishes. If, on the other hand, $\alpha_1 \neq 0$, then we can write

$$y_2(x)y_1'(x) - y_1(x)y_2'(x)$$

$$= \frac{1}{\alpha_1}\{y_1'(x)[\alpha_1 \, y_2(x) + \alpha_2 \, y_2'(x)] - y_2'(x)[\alpha_1 \, y_1(x) + \alpha_2 \, y_1'(x)]\},$$

and again we see that this quantity vanishes when $x = a$.

(ii) If the function $p(x)$ is such that $p(a) = 0$, then no further boundary condition is required at $x = a$, provided that the solutions $y_1(x)$ and $y_2(x)$ are such that $p(x)y_2(x)y_1'(x)$ and $p(x)y_1(x)y_2'(x)$ both have finite limits as $x \to a$. An exactly analogous statement can be made about the point $x = b$. Note that if $p(a) = 0$, for example, then $x = a$ is a singular point of the differential equation, so that the condition formulated here is not necessarily satisfied by a given solution and is therefore a non-trivial restriction.

(iii) If the function $p(x)$ is such that $p(a) = p(b)$, then we may impose the so-called 'periodic boundary conditions' $y(a) = y(b)$ and $y'(a) = y'(b)$.

All three types of boundary conditions lead to the same orthogonality relation (5) between eigenfunctions belonging to distinct eigenvalues.

This orthogonality property can also be discussed in a natural way in the framework of a vector-space (function-space) approach. We define the scalar product of two functions $u(x)$ and $v(x)$ to be the integral

$$\langle u|v \rangle \equiv \int_a^b u^*(x)\,v(x)\,dx. \tag{8}$$

Note that this definition involves the complex conjugate of $u(x)$, implying that the functions are allowed to be complex; this possibility is left open here in order to prove later that all the eigenfunctions of a Sturm-Liouville boundary-value problem can always be taken to be real.

THEOREM 1   If L is the self-adjoint operator (1) (with the restrictions on the real functions $p(x)$ and $q(x)$ mentioned in the statement of the Sturm-Liouville problem), then $\langle u|Lv \rangle = \langle v|Lu \rangle^*$ for any functions $u(x)$ and $v(x)$ in the space of twice-differentiable functions satisfying a given set of Sturm-Liouville boundary conditions at $x = a, \, b$.

PROOF   We have

$$\langle u|Lv \rangle - \langle v|Lu \rangle^* = \int_a^b [u^*(x)\,Lv(x) - v(x)\,Lu^*(x)]\,dx$$

$$= \int_a^b \left\{ u^*(x)\frac{d}{dx}[p(x)\,v'(x)] - v(x)\frac{d}{dx}[p(x)\,u^{*\prime}(x)] \right\}dx$$

$$= \int_a^b \frac{d}{dx} \left[p(x) u^*(x) v'(x) - p(x) v(x) u^{*\prime}(x) \right] dx$$

$$= \left[p(x) u^*(x) v'(x) - p(x) v(x) u^{*\prime}(x) \right] \Big|_{x=a}^b = 0,$$

where we have made use of the boundary conditions and their complex conjugates in the last step.

The orthogonality relation (5) is a direct consequence of Theorem 1. For suppose that $Ly_1(x) = \lambda_1 r(x) y_1(x)$ and $Ly_2(x) = \lambda_2 r(x) y_2(x)$, where L is a self-adjoint operator and $y_1(x)$ and $y_2(x)$ satisfy identical Sturm-Liouville boundary conditions at $x = a, b$. Then

$$(\lambda_1 - \lambda_2) \int_a^b r(x) y_1(x) y_2(x) \, dx = \int_a^b \left[y_2(x) Ly_1(x) - y_1(x) Ly_2(x) \right] dx$$

$$= \langle y_2^* | Ly_1 \rangle - \langle y_1^* | Ly_2 \rangle = \langle y_2^* | Ly_1 \rangle - \langle y_2 | Ly_1^* \rangle^*$$

$$= \langle y_2^* | Ly_1 \rangle - \langle y_2^* | Ly_1 \rangle = 0.$$

Thus, if $\lambda_1 \neq \lambda_2$, then

$$\int_a^b r(x) y_1(x) y_2(x) \, dx = 0.$$

Example 1   Legendre's differential equation of order n is

$$(1 - x^2) y'' - 2xy' + n(n+1)y = 0$$

or, in self-adjoint form,

$$\frac{d}{dx} \left[(1 - x^2) \frac{dy}{dx} \right] + n(n+1)y = 0.$$

Since the function $p(x) \equiv 1 - x^2$ vanishes when $x = \pm 1$, it is appropriate to apply Sturm-Liouville boundary conditions of type (ii) at both of the points $x = \pm 1$. Now we have already seen (Sec. 7.1) that if n is any non-negative integer, then Legendre's differential equation of order n possesses a polynomial solution of degree n. These polynomial solutions, when appropriately normalized, are the Legendre polynomials $P_n(x)$ ($n = 0, 1, \dots$). Any two Legendre polynomials $P_m(x)$ and $P_n(x)$, with $m \neq n$, therefore satisfy the orthogonality relation

$$\int_{-1}^1 P_m(x) P_n(x) \, dx = 0.$$

Example 2   Laguerre's differential equation of order n is

$$xy'' + (1 - x)y' + ny = 0.$$

We have previously shown that there exist polynomial solutions of degree
n, the Laguerre polynomials $L_n(x)$, for $n = 0, 1, \ldots$ (see Example 3 in Sec.
5.5; this can also be done by the more direct method used for Legendre
polynomials in Sec. 7.1). Do these polynomials satisfy an orthogonality
property?

In order to apply the Sturm-Liouville theory, we first bring the
differential equation into self-adjoint form by dividing by the coefficient
of y'' (namely, x) and then multiplying by

$$p(x) = \exp\left(\int^x \frac{1-x'}{x'} \, dx'\right) = \exp(\log x - x) = xe^{-x}.$$

This gives

$$\frac{d}{dx}\left(xe^{-x} \frac{dy}{dx}\right) + ne^{-x} y = 0.$$

Now the function $p(x) \equiv xe^{-x}$, when multiplied by an arbitrary polynomial,
vanishes at $x = 0$ and $x = +\infty$ (more precisely, in the limit as $x \to +\infty$).
Therefore the polynomial solutions $L_n(x)$ satisfy Sturm-Liouville boundary
conditions of type (ii) at $x = 0, +\infty$. Consequently, any two distinct
Laguerre polynomials $L_m(x)$ and $L_n(x)$ $(m \neq n)$ satisfy the orthogonality
relation

$$\int_0^\infty e^{-x} L_m(x) L_n(x) \, dx = 0.$$

Finally, we consider some further properties of the eigenvalues and
eigenfunctions of a Sturm-Liouville boundary-value problem.

THEOREM 2   All the eigenvalues of a Sturm-Liouville boundary-value
problem are real.

PROOF   Suppose that $Ly(x) = \lambda r(x)y(x)$, where $y(x)$ satisfies a given
set of Sturm-Liouville boundary conditions at $x = a, b$. Then $y^*(x) Ly(x)$
$= \lambda r(x)|y(x)|^2$, so that

$$\lambda \int_a^b r(x)|y(x)|^2 \, dx = \langle y|Ly \rangle = \langle y|Ly \rangle^*, \tag{9}$$

where we have made use of Theorem 1 in the last step. The integral on
the left-hand side of (9) is obviously real, and the right-hand side, being
equal to its own complex conjugate, is also real. Hence λ is real.

As a consequence of this theorem, the eigenfunctions can also be chosen to be real.

THEOREM 3   If a Sturm-Liouville boundary-value problem involves boundary conditions of types (i) or (ii), then each eigenvalue corresponds to a unique eigenfunction, apart from an arbitrary multiplicative constant; in other words, the space of eigenfunctions corresponding to each eigenvalue is one-dimensional.

PROOF   Let L be the self-adjoint operator (1) and suppose that $Lu(x) = \lambda r(x)u(x)$ and $Lv(x) = \lambda r(x)v(x)$, where $u(x)$ and $v(x)$ satisfy identical boundary conditions at $x = a, b$. Then $u(x)Lv(x) - v(x)Lu(x) = 0$, i.e.,

$$u(x) \frac{d}{dx}[p(x)v'(x)] - v(x) \frac{d}{dx}[p(x)u'(x)] = 0.$$

This condition can be written

$$\frac{d}{dx}\{p(x)[u(x)v'(x) - v(x)u'(x)]\} = 0.$$

Hence $p(x)[u(x)v'(x) - v(x)u'(x)] = K$, where K is some constant. But $K = 0$ by the boundary conditions at $x = a, b$, provided that these boundary conditions are of type (i) or (ii). Since $p(x)$ is not identically zero, we conclude that $u'(x)/u(x) = v'(x)/v(x)$. Integrating, we get $\log u(x) = \log v(x) + \log C$, where C is some constant, so that $u(x) = Cv(x)$, as required.

It can be seen from a simple counterexample that the result of Theorem 3 does not necessarily apply to problems involving periodic boundary conditions, i.e. boundary conditions of type (iii). For example, consider the differential equation $y''(x) = \lambda y(x)$, with periodic boundary conditions at $x = 0, 2\pi$. It is readily verified that the eigenvalues here are $\lambda = -n^2$ $(n = 0, 1, \ldots)$ and that each non-zero eigenvalue has the two linearly independent eigenfunctions $\sin nx$ and $\cos nx$.

8.2   Green's functions for boundary-value problems

Consider the differential equation $Ly(x) = h(x)$, with given homogeneous boundary conditions at $x = a, b,$ where L is the second-order self-adjoint operator.

$$L \equiv \frac{d}{dx}\left[p(x) \frac{d}{dx}\right] + q(x).$$

The *Green's function* for this problem is the function $G(x; x')$ satisfying the differential equation

$$LG(x; x') = \delta(x - x') \tag{1}$$

and the given boundary conditions at $x = a, b$; here x' is a parameter which can take any value in the range $a < x' < b$.

The non-homogeneous term $h(x)$ can always be written as a formal superposition of δ-functions in the form

$$h(x) = \int_a^b h(x') \delta(x - x') \, dx'.$$

Since the differential equation is linear, the solution of the original boundary-value problem can accordingly be expressed in terms of the Green's function as a similar superposition:

$$y(x) = \int_a^b h(x') G(x; x') \, dx'. \tag{2}$$

It is easy to verify formally that the function (2) is indeed a solution of the original differential equation. Thus

$$Ly(x) = \int_a^b h(x') LG(x; x') \, dx' = \int_a^b h(x') \delta(x - x') \, dx' = h(x).$$

Moreover, since $G(x; x')$ satisfies the given (homogeneous) boundary conditions at $x = a, b$ for any fixed value of x', the solution $y(x)$ constructed in (2) will also satisfy these boundary conditions.

We now consider some of the general properties of the Green's function $G(x; x')$. The differential equation for $G(x; x')$ can be written

$$\frac{d}{dx}\left[p(x)\frac{dG}{dx}\right] + q(x)G = \delta(x - x'). \tag{3}$$

Let us integrate this equation from the lower end-point $x = a$ to an arbitrary point x in the range $a \leqslant x \leqslant b$. The properties of the δ-function on the right-hand side are such that

$$\int_a^z \delta(x - x') \, dx = \begin{cases} 0, & z < x', \\ 1, & z > x'. \end{cases}$$

It is convenient here to introduce the so-called *Heaviside step function*

$$H(x) = \begin{cases} 0, & x < 0, \\ 1, & x > 0, \end{cases} \tag{4}$$

having the property

$$\int_a^z \delta(x) \, dx = H(z)$$

for any $a < 0$ or, equivalently, $H'(x) = \delta(x)$. Then, on integrating (3) from the fixed point $x = a$ to a general point x, we obtain

$$p(x) \frac{dG}{dx} = H(x - x') - \int_a^x q(x'') G(x''; \ x') \, dx'' + C, \tag{5}$$

where C is some constant. The right-hand side of (5) is continuous for all $x \neq x'$, but the term $H(x - x')$ has the discontinuous behaviour

$$[H(x - x')]_{x = x'+} - [H(x - x')]_{x = x'-} = 1.$$

Since the function $p(x)$ on the left-hand side of (5) is assumed to be continuous, we have

$$\left[\frac{dG}{dx}\right]_{x = x'+} - \left[\frac{dG}{dx}\right]_{x = x'-} = \frac{1}{p(x')} . \tag{6}$$

We shall refer to equation (6) as the discontinuity condition on dG/dx.

By integrating the expression for dG/dx obtained from (5) once more, we see that the Green's function $G(x; \ x')$ itself is always continuous, even at $x = x'$:

$$G(x'^+; \ x') = G(x'^-; \ x'). \tag{7}$$

We shall refer to equation (7) as the continuity condition on G.

We have not yet made use here of the fact that the operator L is self-adjoint. This means that

$$\langle u | Lv \rangle = \langle v | Lu \rangle \tag{8}$$

for any functions $u(x)$ and $v(x)$ satisfying the given boundary conditions at $x = a, b$. Choosing $v(x) = G(x; \ x_1)$ and $u(x) = G(x; \ x_2)$, the condition (8) gives

$$\int_a^b G(x; \ x_2) \delta(x - x_1) \, dx = \int_a^b G(x; \ x_1) \delta(x - x_2) \, dx$$

and hence

$$G(x_1; \ x_2) = G(x_2; \ x_1). \tag{9}$$

We shall refer to equation (9) as the symmetry property of the Green's function.

The Green's function for any particular problem can be constructed by making use of its general properties discussed above. For $x \neq x'$ (i.e. in each of the two regions $a < x < x'$ and $x' < x < b$), $G(x; \ x')$ satisfies the homogeneous differential equation $Ly(x) = 0$. Suppose that we know the general solution of this equation, say $y(x) = \alpha u_1(x) + \beta u_2(x)$, where α and β are arbitrary constants. Then we can write

$$G(x; x') = \begin{cases} Au_1(x) + Bu_2(x), & a < x < x', \\ Cu_1(x) + Du_2(x), & x' < x < b, \end{cases}$$

where the coefficients A, B, C and D may depend on x' but not on x. These four coefficients can be determined from the following four conditions: the two boundary conditions at $x = a$, b, the continuity condition on G, and the discontinuity condition on dG/dx.

Example Find the Green's function for the boundary-value problem

$$y'' + k^2 y = h(x), \qquad y(0) = y(a) = 0.$$

The solution of the associated homogeneous differential equation is $y(x) = \alpha \sin kx + \beta \cos kx$. Therefore

$$G(x; x') = \begin{cases} A \sin kx + B \cos kx, & 0 < x < x', \\ C \sin kx + D \cos kx, & x' < x < a, \end{cases}$$

where $A \equiv A(x')$, etc. The boundary conditions give the two relations

$$G(0; x') = B = 0,$$
$$G(a; x') = C \sin ka + D \cos ka = 0.$$

The continuity condition on G gives

$$A \sin kx' = C \sin kx' + D \cos kx',$$

and the discontinuity condition on dG/dx gives

$$(Ck \cos kx' - Dk \sin kx') - Ak \cos kx' = 1.$$

Solving these four equations simultaneously for A, B, C and D and substituting the results back into the general expression for $G(x; x')$, we obtain

$$G(x; x') = \begin{cases} \dfrac{\sin kx \sin [k(x' - a)]}{k \sin ka}, & 0 < x < x', \\[4mm] \dfrac{\sin kx' \sin [k(x - a)]}{k \sin ka}, & x' < x < a. \end{cases} \qquad (10)$$

As a check, we observe that the result (10) has the required symmetry property $G(x; x') = G(x'; x)$. This symmetry property can in fact be useful as an aid in constructing the Green's function. For example, if we already know the coefficients A and B and hence the form of $G(x; x')$ for $x < x'$, then this symmetry property directly determines $G(x; x')$ for $x > x'$.

It should be pointed out that the expression (10) for the Green's function is not valid if it happens that $\sin ka = 0$. This is precisely the case in which the homogeneous differential equation $y'' + k^2y = 0$ (without the δ-function non-homogeneous term which is present in the differential equation for the Green's function) has a non-trivial solution satisfying the given boundary conditions. In that case, imposition of the boundary conditions alone is sufficient to determine this solution uniquely, and it is found to be impossible to satisfy the discontinuity condition on dG/dx at the same time. In other words, no Green's function exists in this case. This is true more generally whenever the boundary conditions are such that there is a solution of the corresponding homogeneous differential equation. The nonexistence of the Green's function in this case will be seen in a different way in the following section.

8.3 The eigenfunction expansion of the Green's function

Let us consider again the boundary-value problem $Ly(x) = h(x)$ in the interval $a \leqslant x \leqslant b$, with suitable boundary conditions at the end-points $x = a, b$, where L is a second-order self-adjoint operator. It may happen that the general solution of the associated homogeneous differential equation $Ly(x) = 0$ cannot readily be obtained. In this case, the method of constructing the Green's function which we developed in the preceding section is impractical. However, we shall see that it is still possible to construct the Green's function by means of an alternative procedure, provided that we know the complete set of eigenvalues λ_n and eigenfunctions $u_n(x)$ ($n = 1, 2, \dots$) of the Sturm-Liouville boundary-value problem $Lu_n(x) = \lambda_n u_n(x)$ subject to the same boundary conditions as in the original boundary-value problem.

We know from the general theory of the Sturm-Liouville problem that the eigenfunctions $u_n(x)$ must be mutually orthogonal (with respect to the constant weight function 1) over the interval $a \leqslant x \leqslant b$. For definiteness, let us choose these functions to be orthonormal:

$$\int_a^b u_m(x)\, u_n(x)\, dx = \delta_{mn} . \tag{1}$$

We shall assume without further discussion that the set of eigenfunctions $u_n(x)$ is *complete* in the interval $a \leqslant x \leqslant b$, in the sense that an arbitrary function from some sufficiently general class of functions in this interval can be expanded in terms of these eigenfunctions. Such completeness properties have in fact been rigorously established for a large class of Sturm-Liouville boundary-value problems.

If the eigenfunctions are indeed complete, then the required Green's function can be represented in the form of an expansion

$$G(x; x') = \sum_n a_n(x') u_n(x), \tag{2}$$

where the $a_n(x')$ are certain coefficients which do not depend on x. Substituting (2) into the differential equation satisfied by the Green's function,

$$LG(x; x') = \delta(x - x'),$$

we find

$$\sum_n a_n(x') \lambda_n u_n(x) = \delta(x - x'). \tag{3}$$

If we now multiply (3) by $u_m(x)$ and integrate both sides of the resulting equation over the range $a \leqslant x \leqslant b$, making use of the orthogonality relation (1), we obtain $a_m(x') \lambda_m = u_m(x')$. This determines the coefficients $a_n(x')$ in the series expansion (2) for the Green's function, which becomes

$$G(x; x') = \sum_n \frac{u_n(x) u_n(x')}{\lambda_n}. \tag{4}$$

Equation (4) is the *eigenfunction expansion* of the Green's function. It provides a means of constructing the Green's function in terms of the complete set of eigenvalues and eigenfunctions of the Sturm-Liouville boundary-value problem associated with the original boundary-value problem.

Note that the eigenfunction expansion (4) exhibits the expected symmetry property $G(x; x') = G(x'; x)$. It should also be observed that this expansion breaks down if there is an eigenvalue equal to zero; this is precisely the case in which there exists a non-trivial solution of the associated homogeneous differential equation $Ly(x) = 0$ subject to the same boundary conditions as in the original boundary-value problem, as discussed in the preceding section, and no Green's function exists in this case.

Example   Use the eigenfunction expansion to construct the Green's function for the problem $y'' + k^2 y = h(x)$, $0 \leqslant x \leqslant a$, subject to the boundary conditions $y(0) = y(a) = 0$.

The Sturm-Liouville problem $y'' + k^2 y = \lambda y$ with the boundary conditions $y(0) = y(a) = 0$ has the complete orthonormal set of eigenfunctions

$$u_n(x) \equiv \sqrt{\frac{2}{a}} \sin \frac{n\pi x}{a} \qquad (n = 1, 2, \ldots)$$

with corresponding eigenvalues $\lambda_n = k^2 - (n\pi/a)^2$; the completeness of the eigenfunctions in this case is guaranteed by the theory of Fourier series. The Green's function is therefore given by

$$G(x; x') = \frac{2}{a} \sum_{n=1}^{\infty} \frac{\sin\dfrac{n\pi x}{a}\,\sin\dfrac{n\pi x'}{a}}{k^2 - \left(\dfrac{n\pi}{a}\right)^2},$$

provided that the denominator is non-zero for all n. If $k = n\pi/a$ for some integer n, then $\sin ka = 0$; this is precisely the case when, as discussed in the preceding section, no Green's function exists.

Problems

1 Find the eigenvalues and eigenfunctions for each of the following boundary-value problems, and find an orthogonality relation satisfied by any two distinct eigenfunctions:

(i) $y'' + \lambda y = 0$, $y'(0) = y'(\pi) = 0$;

(ii) $y'' + (2 + \lambda)y = 0$, $y(0) = y(\pi) = 0$;

(iii) $y'' + 2y' + (1 - \lambda)y = 0$, $y(0) = y(\pi) = 0$;

(iv) $y'' + 2y' + (1 - \lambda)y = 0$, $y'(0) = y'(\pi) = 0$.

2 (i) Find a self-adjoint differential equation satisfied by the first derivatives of the Legendre polynomials, $P_n'(x) \equiv dP_n(x)/dx$.

(ii) Find an orthogonality relation satisfied by two distinct functions $P_m'(x)$ and $P_n'(x)$.

3 The Hermite polynomials $H_n(x)$ ($n = 0, 1, \ldots$) are solutions of the differential equation

$$y'' - 2xy' + 2ny = 0.$$

Find an orthogonality relation satisfied by any two distinct Hermite polynomials.

4 The Chebyshev polynomials $T_n(x)$ ($n = 0, 1, \ldots$) are solutions of the differential equation

$$(1 - x^2)y'' - xy' + n^2 y = 0.$$

Find an orthogonality relation satisfied by any two distinct Chebyshev polynomials.

5 The Chebyshev polynomials of type II, $C_n(x)$ $(n = 0, 1, \ldots)$ are polynomials of degree n which satisfy the differential equation

$$(1 - x^2)y'' - 3xy' + n(n + 2)y = 0.$$

Find an orthogonality relation satisfied by any two distinct Chebyshev polynomials of type II.

6 Obtain expressions in closed form for the Green's functions associated with the following boundary-value problems:

(i) $y''(x) = f(x)$, $\quad y(0) = y(1) = 0$;

(ii) $y''(x) = f(x)$, $\quad y(0) = y'(1) = 0$.

7 Use the Green's functions determined in Problem 6 to solve the following boundary-value problems:

(i) $y''(x) = x^2$, $\quad y(0) = y(1) = 0$;

(ii) $y''(x) = \sin x$, $\quad y(0) = y'(1) = 0$.

8 Obtain an expression in closed form for the Green's function associated with the boundary-value problem

$$y''(x) = f(x), \quad y(0) - y'(0) = 0, \quad y(1) + y'(1) = 0.$$

9 Find the eigenfunction expansions of the Green's functions for the following boundary-value problems:

(i) $y''(x) = f(x)$, $\quad y(0) = y(1) = 0$;

(ii) $y''(x) = f(x)$, $\quad y(0) = y'(1) = 0$.

10 By considering the eigenfunction expansion of the Green's function for an appropriate boundary-value problem, show that the Dirac δ-function has the formal representation

$$\delta(x - x') = \frac{2}{\pi} \sum_{n=1}^{\infty} \sin nx \, \sin nx'.$$

11 Solve the eigenvalue problem

$$y'' + \lambda^2 y = 0, \quad y(0) = 0, \quad 2y'(L) + y(L) = 0,$$

expressing the eigenvalues as the roots of a certain transcendental equation. Write down an orthogonality relation satisfied by any two distinct eigenfunctions.

9 Special functions

9.1 Bessel's differential equation and its solutions

In this chapter we shall consider some of the more important special functions which arise in a natural way in the solution of boundary-value problems for partial differential equations.

Let us begin with Laplace's equation in three dimensions:

$$\frac{\partial^2 U}{\partial x^2} + \frac{\partial^2 U}{\partial y^2} + \frac{\partial^2 U}{\partial z^2} = 0. \tag{1}$$

When solutions of Laplace's equation are to be found in a region of space bounded by a circular cylinder, it is more convenient to transform (1) to cylindrical polar coordinates (r, θ, z), which are related to the Cartesian coordinates (x, y, z) by the equations $x = r \cos \theta$, $y = r \sin \theta$, $z = z$. This gives

$$\frac{\partial^2 U}{\partial r^2} + \frac{1}{r} \frac{\partial U}{\partial r} + \frac{1}{r^2} \frac{\partial^2 U}{\partial \theta^2} + \frac{\partial^2 U}{\partial z^2} = 0. \tag{2}$$

Let us apply the method of separation of variables to find product solutions of (2) having the form

$$U(r, \theta, z) = R(r) H(\theta) Z(z). \tag{3}$$

Substituting (3) into (2) and dividing by U, we can write

$$\frac{R''}{R} + \frac{1}{r} \frac{R'}{R} + \frac{1}{r^2} \frac{H''}{H} = -\frac{Z''}{Z} = -m^2, \tag{4}$$

where we have set both sides of the equality equal to a common separation constant $-m^2$, since the left-hand side is independent of z, while the right-hand side is independent of r and θ. It can be seen that the ordinary differential equation for the function $Z(z)$ obtained from (4) has solutions

$$Z(z) = C e^{\pm mz}.$$

If we now separate the variables in the relation obtained by equating the left-hand side of (4) to the constant $-m^2$, we can write

$$r^2 \frac{R''}{R} + r \frac{R'}{R} + m^2 r^2 = -\frac{H''}{H} = n^2,$$

where n^2 is another separation constant. Therefore the function $H(\theta)$ has the form

$$H(\theta) = A \cos n\theta + B \sin n\theta,$$

while the function $R(r)$ must be a solution of the differential equation

$$r^2 R'' + rR' + (m^2 r^2 - n^2) R = 0. \qquad (5)$$

Equation (5), unlike the differential equations for the functions $H(\theta)$ and $Z(z)$, cannot in general be solved in closed form in terms of elementary functions and must therefore be the subject of a special analysis.

We remark that certain special types of boundary-value problems lead to important restrictions on the admissible product solutions. If the region in which Laplace's equation is to be solved completely encloses the z-axis, then single-valued solutions $U(r, \theta, z)$ can be obtained only by imposing the periodicity condition $H(\theta + 2\pi) = H(\theta)$, which in turn restricts n to the integral values $n = 0, 1, \ldots$.

In addition, if the region includes any part of the z-axis, then it is necessary to stipulate that $R(0)$ is finite; this is a non-trivial restriction, since the point $r = 0$ is a singular point of the differential equation (5), so that the solutions of (5) do not necessarily have finite limits at the origin.

The differential equation (5) contains two parameters m and n. However, the dependence on the parameter m is of a fairly trivial nature. If $m = 0$ in (5) (in which case this differential equation becomes an Euler equation), it is easy to verify that the general solution is given by

$$R(r) = \begin{cases} \alpha r^n + \beta r^{-n}, & n \neq 0, \\ \alpha + \beta \log r, & n = 0, \end{cases}$$

where α and β are arbitrary constants. On the other hand, if $m \neq 0$, the change of variables $x = mr$ and $y = R$ in (5) yields the one-parameter differential equation

$$x^2 y'' + xy' + (x^2 - n^2)y = 0. \qquad (6)$$

Equation (6) is known as *Bessel's differential equation* of order n. Clearly, we can assume that $n \geq 0$ without loss of generality. It is obviously sufficient to find solutions of equation (6), since if $y = f(x)$ is a solution of (6), then $R = f(mr)$ is a solution of (5).

Series solutions of Bessel's differential equation (6) can be obtained by a straightforward application of the Frobenius method. It is found that the indices of this differential equation at $x = 0$ have the values $\pm n$, and a solution corresponding to the larger index n is found to be

$$y(x) = a \left[x^n + \sum_{k=1}^{\infty} \frac{(-1)^k x^{2k+n}}{2^{2k} k! (k+n) \dots (2+n)(1+n)} \right]. \tag{7}$$

The solution (7) is conventionally written in a more compact form by re-expressing the factors in the denominator in terms of the Γ-function (see Sec. A.9 for the definition and important properties of the Γ-function). By repeated application of the identity $\Gamma(z+1) = z\Gamma(z)$, we have

$$\Gamma(k+n+1) = (k+n) \dots (2+n)(1+n) \Gamma(1+n).$$

Therefore (7) can be written in the form

$$y(x) = a \left[x^n + \Gamma(1+n) \sum_{k=1}^{\infty} \frac{(-1)^k x^{2k+n}}{2^{2k} k! \Gamma(k+n+1)} \right]$$

$$= a \Gamma(1+n) \sum_{k=0}^{\infty} \frac{(-1)^k x^{2k+n}}{2^{2k} k! \Gamma(k+n+1)}$$

$$= a \Gamma(1+n) 2^n J_n(x),$$

where

$$J_n(x) \equiv \sum_{k=0}^{\infty} \frac{(-1)^k (\frac{1}{2}x)^{2k+n}}{k! \Gamma(k+n+1)}. \tag{8}$$

The function $J_n(x)$ defined by (8) is called the *Bessel function* of order n (or, more precisely, the Bessel function of order n of the first kind).

If n is not an integer, then another linearly independent solution of Bessel's differential equation (6) can be obtained from the second index $-n$, and this solution is found to be proportional to the function

$$J_{-n}(x) = \sum_{k=0}^{\infty} \frac{(-1)^k (\frac{1}{2}x)^{2k-n}}{k! \Gamma(k-n+1)}, \tag{9}$$

as we would expect from the fact that Bessel's differential equation depends only on n^2. However, no second Frobenius solution is obtained when n is an integer. Indeed, the expression (9) is identical to (8) when $n = 0$ and is undefined when n is a positive integer, since in that case $\Gamma(k-n+1)$ is undefined for $k = 0, \dots, n-1$. As we would expect from the general theory of the Frobenius method, the second solution in these cases (the so-called Bessel function of the second kind) contains a logarithmic term. The explicit form of this solution is rather complicated and will not be considered here. In any case, it is important to note that the only solutions of Bessel's differential equation which are analytic at the origin are the Bessel functions $J_n(x)$.

The Bessel functions have many important special properties and satisfy a large number of interesting identities. We shall consider here only a few of the most useful properties of Bessel functions.

Some idea of the general character of the Bessel functions can be obtained by inspecting their graphs. In Fig. 9.1 we show graphs of the functions $J_0(x)$ and $J_1(x)$. One of the most conspicuous features of the Bessel functions is their oscillatory behaviour. This can be understood in terms of the oscillation theorems which we studied earlier (see, e.g., Problem 14 of Chapter 6).

It can be seen from the series (8) that $J_n(x) = O(x^n)$ for small x. It is also easy to understand the asymptotic behaviour of the Bessel functions as $x \to \infty$. If we make the substitution $y(x) = x^{-1/2} v(x)$ in Bessel's differential equation (6), we obtain the differential equation

$$v'' + \left(1 + \frac{1 - 4n^2}{4x^2}\right) v = 0.$$

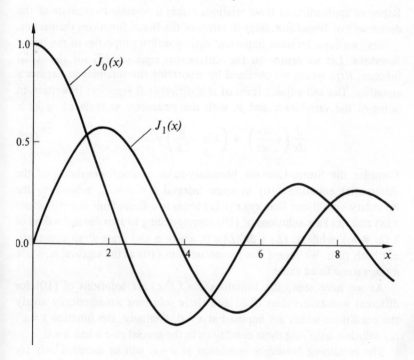

Fig. 9.1

It is natural to expect that at large x the function $v(x)$ behaves like a solution of the differential equation $v'' + v = 0$, namely $v(x) \sim C \sin(x + \phi)$ for some constants C and ϕ. This means that any solution of Bessel's differential equation should have the damped oscillatory behaviour $y(x) \sim Cx^{-1/2} \sin(x + \phi)$ as $x \to \infty$.

There are a number of simple recurrence relations between Bessel functions of different orders. For example, it can be verified directly from the series representation (8) that

$$J_{n+1}(x) = \frac{2n}{x} J_n(x) - J_{n-1}(x).$$

This relation is of particular importance, since it can be used, for example, to evaluate Bessel functions of arbitrary integral order in terms of only the two functions $J_0(x)$ and $J_1(x)$.

Similarly, it can be shown directly from the series for $J_n(x)$ that

$$J_n'(x) = J_{n-1}(x) - \frac{n}{x} J_n(x)$$

$$= \frac{n}{x} J_n(x) - J_{n+1}(x).$$

Repeated application of these relations makes it possible to evaluate all the derivatives of Bessel functions in terms of the Bessel functions themselves.

Next we consider some important orthogonality properties of the Bessel functions. Let us return to the differential equation (5) for the radial function $R(r)$ which we obtained by separating the variables in Laplace's equation. The self-adjoint form of this differential equation (rewritten in terms of the variables x and y, with the parameter m replaced by λ) is

$$\frac{d}{dx}\left(x \frac{dy}{dx}\right) + \left(\lambda^2 x - \frac{n^2}{x}\right) y = 0. \tag{10}$$

Consider the Sturm-Liouville boundary-value problem consisting of the differential equation (10) in some interval $0 \le x \le L$, subject to the boundary conditions that $xy_i(x)y_j'(x)$ tends to a finite limit as $x \to 0$, where $y_i(x)$ and $y_j(x)$ are solutions of (10) corresponding to two distinct values of λ ($\lambda_i \ne \lambda_j$), while $\alpha y(L) + \beta y'(L) = 0$, where α and β are given constants, not both zero. We regard the parameter λ in (10) as the eigenvalue, while n takes some fixed value.

As we have seen, the functions $y = J_n(\lambda x)$ are solutions of (10) for different non-zero values of λ, and these solutions automatically satisfy the conditions which are imposed at $x = 0$. Similarly, the function $y = x^n$ is a solution satisfying these conditions in the special case when $\lambda = 0$.

The remaining boundary condition at $x = L$ will be satisfied only for certain discrete values of λ, say $\lambda_1, \lambda_2, \ldots$. Thus we obtain a set of eigenvalues λ_i with corresponding eigenfunctions $J_n(\lambda_i x)$, plus one additional eigenfunction x^n in the special case of an eigenvalue (if any) equal to zero.

The general theory of the Sturm-Liouville problem considered in the preceding chapter leads to the orthogonality relation

$$\int_0^L x J_n(\lambda_i x) J_n(\lambda_j x)\,dx = 0 \qquad (\lambda_i \neq \lambda_j) \tag{11}$$

among these eigenfunctions. In other words, if λ_i and λ_j are any two distinct roots of the equation $\alpha J_n(\lambda L) + \beta J_n'(\lambda L) = 0$, then the functions $J_n(\lambda_i x)$ and $J_n(\lambda_j x)$ are mutually orthogonal over the interval $0 \leqslant x \leqslant L$ with respect to the weight function x.

In certain cases, there is an additional eigenfunction x^n corresponding to the eigenvalue $\lambda = 0$. The presence or absence of a zero eigenvalue depends on the form of the boundary condition at $x = L$. If, for example, this boundary condition is $y(L) = 0$, then $\lambda = 0$ cannot be an eigenvalue, since the function x^n is always non-zero for $x \neq 0$. But if the boundary condition is $y'(L) = 0$, then the function $y = x^n$ satisfies this condition when $n = 0$, so that we have an additional eigenfunction $y = \text{const}$. In this case, in addition to (11), we have the orthogonality relation

$$\int_0^L x J_0(\lambda_i x)\,dx = 0,$$

where λ_i is any non-zero eigenvalue.

9.2 Expansions in Bessel functions

We mentioned in the previous chapter that the sets of eigenfunctions obtained from many Sturm-Liouville boundary-value problems can be shown to be complete, so that given functions can be expanded in terms of them. This is true in particular for the sets of Bessel functions discussed in the preceding section.

Once we accept that a given function can be expressed as a series of Bessel functions of the type $J_n(\lambda_i x)$, where the λ_i are eigenfunctions of some Sturm-Liouville boundary-value problem, the expansion coefficients can be determined by exploiting the appropriate orthogonality relation among the eigenfunctions. However, for this purpose we shall require the value of the integral

$$\int_0^L x J_n^2(\lambda x)\,dx \tag{1}$$

for specified L, n and λ. This is the problem to which we now direct our attention.

It was shown in Sec. 8.1 that if

$$
\begin{aligned}
Ly_1(x) &= \lambda_1\, r(x)\, y_1(x), \\
Ly_2(x) &= \lambda_2\, r(x)\, y_2(x)
\end{aligned} \tag{2}
$$

for some self-adjoint operator

$$
L \equiv \frac{d}{dx}\left[p(x)\,\frac{d}{dx} \right] + q(x),
$$

then

$$
\begin{aligned}
(\lambda_1 - \lambda_2)\int_a^b r(x)\,y_1(x)\,y_2(x)\,dx \\
= \{p(x)\,[y_2(x)\,y_1'(x) - y_1(x)\,y_2'(x)]\}\Big|_{x=a}^{b}.
\end{aligned} \tag{3}
$$

The derivation of (3) required no specific assumption about any boundary conditions satisfied by the functions $y_1(x)$ and $y_2(x)$.

If we make the specific choice $p(x) = x$, $q(x) = -n^2/x$, $r(x) = x$, $\lambda_1 = -\lambda^2$ and $\lambda_2 = -\mu^2$, then the differential equations (2) have the solutions $y_1(x) = J_n(\lambda x)$ and $y_2(x) = J_n(\mu x)$. Thus, if $\lambda \neq \mu$, (3) yields the identity

$$
\int_0^L x\, J_n(\lambda x)\, J_n(\mu x)\, dx = \frac{L\,[J_n(\mu L)\,\lambda\, J_n'(\lambda L) - J_n(\lambda L)\,\mu\, J_n'(\mu L)]}{\mu^2 - \lambda^2}, \tag{4}
$$

where the primes denote differentiation with respect to the argument of the function J_n.

We are interested in the limit as $\mu \to \lambda$, with fixed λ. The right-hand side of (4) becomes indeterminate in this limit, and the integral (1) whose value we require can be calculated by applying L'Hospital's rule (with μ as the variable) to (4):

$$
\int_0^L x\, J_n^2(\lambda x)\, dx = \frac{L\,\{\lambda L\,[J_n'(\lambda L)]^2 - J_n(\lambda L)\,J_n'(\lambda L) - \lambda L\, J_n(\lambda L)\,J_n''(\lambda L)\}}{2\lambda}.
$$

This result can be simplified if we remember that the function $J_n(x)$ is a solution of Bessel's differential equation of order n, so that $J_n''(\lambda L)$ can be expressed by means of this equation in terms of $J_n(\lambda L)$ and $J_n'(\lambda L)$. This substitution gives

$$
\int_0^L x\, J_n^2(\lambda x)\, dx = \tfrac{1}{2} L^2\,[J_n'(\lambda L)]^2 + \frac{\lambda^2 L^2 - n^2}{2\lambda^2}\, J_n^2(\lambda L). \tag{5}
$$

Equation (5) is an identity which is valid for arbitrary λ, and no specific boundary condition at $x = L$ has been assumed.

Let us now consider some special cases. First, suppose that λ is chosen so that $J_n(\lambda L) = 0$. (There are infinitely many such values of λ because of the oscillatory behaviour of the Bessel functions.) Then (5) reduces to

$$\int_0^L x J_n^2(\lambda x)\, dx = \tfrac{1}{2} L^2\, [J_n'(\lambda L)]^2. \tag{6}$$

It is convenient for practical purposes to rewrite the right-hand side of (6) in terms of a Bessel function itself (instead of a derivative of such a function) by applying the identity

$$J_n'(x) = \frac{n}{x}\, J_n(x) - J_{n+1}(x)$$

mentioned in the preceding section. Recalling also the orthogonality relation between distinct eigenfunctions, we obtain the result that if λ_i ($i = 1, 2, \ldots$) are the positive roots of the equation $J_n(\lambda L) = 0$, then

$$\int_0^L x J_n(\lambda_i x) J_n(\lambda_j x)\, dx = \tfrac{1}{2} L^2\, J_{n+1}^2(\lambda_i L)\, \delta_{ij}. \tag{7}$$

The orthogonality property (7) can now be used to determine the coefficients in the expansion of a given function $F(x)$ in terms of the complete set of Bessel functions $J_n(\lambda_i x)$. Suppose that $F(x)$ is represented (in the mean) as an expansion

$$F(x) = \sum_{i=1}^{\infty} a_i J_n(\lambda_i x) \tag{8}$$

within the interval $0 \leqslant x \leqslant L$. Multiplying (8) by $x J_n(\lambda_j x)$ and integrating over the range $0 \leqslant x \leqslant L$, applying the orthogonality relation (7), we obtain

$$\int_0^L x J_n(\lambda_j x)\, F(x)\, dx = \tfrac{1}{2} L^2\, a_j J_{n+1}^2(\lambda_j L). \tag{9}$$

This determines the coefficient a_j in the expansion (8).

An expansion of the form (8) is called a *Fourier-Bessel series* (or a *Bessel series of the first kind*). Note that such a series can be written for any fixed value of n, and each value of n gives a distinct series.

Different series expansions can be constructed in terms of the eigenfunctions of other Sturm-Liouville boundary-value problems. Suppose, for example, that μ_i ($i = 1, 2, \ldots$) are the positive roots of the equation $J_n'(\mu L) = 0$. Then the functions $J_n(\mu_i x)$, together with the constant function 1 in the special case $n = 0$, again form a complete set of functions over the interval $0 \leqslant x \leqslant L$, and the corresponding expansion for a given function $F(x)$ takes the form

$$
F(x) = \begin{cases} \displaystyle\sum_{i=1}^{\infty} b_i J_n(\mu_i x) & (n \neq 0), \\[4mm] \displaystyle b_0 + \sum_{i=1}^{\infty} b_i J_0(\mu_i x) & (n = 0). \end{cases} \tag{10}
$$

An expansion of the form (10) is called a *Dini series* (or a *Bessel series of the second kind*). The coefficients in such a series can be determined by means of an orthogonality relation in exactly the same way as in the case of a Fourier-Bessel series. In the present case, we find from (5) that the orthogonality relation analogous to (7) takes the form

$$
\int_0^L x J_n(\mu_i x) J_n(\mu_j x)\, dx = \frac{\mu_i^2 L^2 - n^2}{2\mu_i^2}\, J_n^2(\mu_i L)\, \delta_{ij}. \tag{11}
$$

To illustrate these techniques, we give a specific example of the development of a Fourier-Bessel series.

Example 1   Find the Fourier-Bessel series with $n = 0$ for the constant function $F(x) = 1$ over the interval $0 < x < 1$.

The required series has the form

$$
1 = \sum_{i=1}^{\infty} a_i J_0(\lambda_i x),
$$

where λ_i are the positive roots of the equation $J_0(\lambda) = 0$. According to (9), the coefficients of this series are given by

$$
a_j = \frac{2}{J_1^2(\lambda_j)} \int_0^1 x J_0(\lambda_j x)\, dx.
$$

This integral can be evaluated as follows. The identity

$$
J_n'(x) = J_{n-1}(x) - \frac{n}{x} J_n(x)
$$

mentioned in the preceding section implies that

$$
\frac{d}{dx}[x J_1(x)] = x J_0(x).
$$

Thus, making the change of variable $u = \lambda_j x$ in the integral, we have

$$a_j = \frac{2}{\lambda_j^2 J_1^2(\lambda_j)} \int_0^{\lambda_j} u J_0(u)\, du$$

$$= \frac{2}{\lambda_j^2 J_1^2(\lambda_j)} \Big[u J_1(u) \Big]_{u=0}^{\lambda_j} = \frac{2}{\lambda_j J_1(\lambda_j)}.$$

The required expansion is therefore

$$1 = 2 \sum_{i=1}^{\infty} \frac{J_0(\lambda_i x)}{\lambda_i J_1(\lambda_i)} \qquad (0 < x < 1).$$

The following example illustrates a typical application of these ideas to a boundary-value problem for a partial differential equation.

Example 2 Find a solution $U = U(r, \theta, z)$ of Laplace's equation in the cylindrical region $0 \leqslant r \leqslant R$, $0 \leqslant z \leqslant c$, satisfying the boundary conditions $U(R, \theta, z) = 0$, $U(r, \theta, 0) = 0$ and $U(r, \theta, c) = F(r)$, where $F(r)$ is a given function.

As we have seen, the acceptable product solutions are

$$U(r, \theta, z) = J_n(\lambda r)(A \cos n\theta + B \sin n\theta)\, e^{\pm \lambda z}.$$

It is obvious from the nature of the problem that the solution must be axially symmetric about the z-axis, and this can be achieved only by taking $n = 0$. To satisfy the boundary condition at $r = R$, we must choose λ to be one of the positive roots $\lambda_1, \lambda_2, \ldots$ of the equation $J_0(\lambda R) = 0$. The remaining homogeneous boundary condition at $z = 0$ can be satisfied only by choosing the z-dependence in the form $\sinh \lambda z$. Combining all these restrictions, the most general superposition of admissible product solutions is

$$U(r, \theta, z) = \sum_{i=1}^{\infty} a_i J_0(\lambda_i r) \sinh (\lambda_i z).$$

Finally, the boundary condition at $z = c$ requires that

$$F(r) = \sum_{i=1}^{\infty} [a_i \sinh (\lambda_i c)] J_0(\lambda_i r)$$

for $0 < r < R$. We recognize this condition as a Fourier-Bessel series for the function $F(r)$, whose coefficients are given by

$$a_i \sinh(\lambda_i c) = \frac{2}{R^2 J_1^2(\lambda_i R)} \int_0^R r J_0(\lambda_i r) F(r)\, dr.$$

This determines the coefficients a_i in the series solution.

9.3 Legendre's differential equation and its polynomial solutions

In spherical coordinates (r, θ, ϕ), which are related to the Cartesian coordinates (x, y, z) by the equations $x = r \sin \theta \cos \phi$, $y = r \sin \theta \sin \phi$, $z = r \cos \theta$, Laplace's equation takes the form

$$\frac{1}{r^2} \frac{\partial}{\partial r}\left(r^2 \frac{\partial U}{\partial r}\right) + \frac{1}{r^2 \sin \theta} \frac{\partial}{\partial \theta}\left(\sin \theta \frac{\partial U}{\partial \theta}\right) + \frac{1}{r^2 \sin^2\theta} \frac{\partial^2 U}{\partial \phi^2} = 0. \quad (1)$$

Let us seek product solutions of this equation by the method of separation of variables. As a first step, we put $U(r, \theta, \phi) = R(r) Y(\theta, \phi)$ in (1) and multiply by r^2/U. This gives

$$\frac{1}{R} \frac{d}{dr}\left(r^2 \frac{dR}{dr}\right) = -\frac{1}{Y}\left[\frac{1}{\sin \theta} \frac{\partial}{\partial \theta}\left(\sin \theta \frac{\partial Y}{\partial \theta}\right) + \frac{1}{\sin^2\theta} \frac{\partial^2 Y}{\partial \phi^2}\right] = \lambda, \quad (2)$$

where λ is the separation constant. The ordinary differential equation for $R(r)$ obtained from (2) is an Euler equation, which, as is easily verified, has the general solution

$$R(r) = A r^n + B r^{-n-1}, \quad (3)$$

where n is related to λ by the equation $n(n + 1) = \lambda$.

Next we separate the variables in the partial differential equation for $Y(\theta, \phi)$ obtained from (2). Putting $Y(\theta, \phi) = H(\theta)\, \Phi(\phi)$ in this equation and multiplying by $\sin^2 \theta$, we can write

$$\frac{\sin \theta}{H} \frac{d}{d\theta}\left(\sin \theta \frac{dH}{d\theta}\right) + n(n + 1) \sin^2\theta = -\frac{1}{\Phi} \frac{d^2\Phi}{d\phi^2} = m^2, \quad (4)$$

where m^2 is another separation constant. The ordinary differential equation for $\Phi(\phi)$ obtained from (4) clearly has the solutions

$$\Phi(\phi) = \begin{cases} C \cos m\phi + D \sin m\phi, & m \neq 0, \\ C + D\phi, & m = 0. \end{cases} \quad (5)$$

It remains only to analyze the differential equation for $H(\theta)$ obtained from (4).

At this point, it is appropriate to mention some important restrictions on the admissible product solutions in certain types of boundary-value problems. First, if the region in which a solution of Laplace's equation is sought completely encloses the z-axis, we must impose the periodicity condition $\Phi(\phi + 2\pi) = \Phi(\phi)$ in order to ensure that the solution is single-valued. In this case, the constant m must be an integer, and it is obviously sufficient to consider only the values $m = 0, 1, \ldots$. Moreover, in the special case in which $m = 0$, the solution (5) must be restricted to $\Phi = $ const. Secondly, if the problem has axial symmetry about the z-axis, so that the solution is independent of ϕ, we must take $m = 0$, with $\Phi = $ const.

Next we turn to the ordinary differential equation for $H(\theta)$ obtained from (4). We first simplify this equation somewhat by making the change of variable $u = \cos\theta$. This gives

$$\frac{d}{du}\left[(1 - u^2)\frac{dH}{du}\right] + \left[n(n + 1) - \frac{m^2}{1 - u^2}\right]H = 0. \tag{6}$$

For the reasons discussed above, the case when $m = 0$ is of particular importance, and we shall examine this case in detail. The differential equation

$$\frac{d}{du}\left[(1 - u^2)\frac{dH}{du}\right] + n(n + 1)H = 0 \tag{7}$$

is *Legendre's differential equation* of order n. Although n can take arbitrary values, it is sufficient to consider only values in the range $n \geqslant -\frac{1}{2}$, since the quantity $n(n + 1)$ which appears in (7) is unchanged if n is replaced by $-(n + 1)$.

Now if the original boundary-value problem for Laplace's equation is to be solved in a region of space which includes the z-axis, where $u = \cos\theta = \pm 1$, we must confine ourselves to solutions $H(\theta)$ which are finite at the singular points $u = \pm 1$ of the differential equation (7). As we have already seen (see Sec. 7.1), such solutions exist when n is any non-negative integer. These solutions, $H(u) = P_n(u)$, are polynomials of degree n. When normalized by the condition $P_n(1) = 1$, they define the *Legendre polynomials*.

The Legendre polynomials $P_n(u)$, like the other special functions, obey a number of important relations. One of their most useful properties is the fact that they are mutually orthogonal over the interval $-1 \leqslant u \leqslant 1$ (see Example 1 in Sec. 8.1):

$$\int_{-1}^{1} P_m(u) P_n(u)\, du = 0 \qquad (m \neq n). \tag{8}$$

The individual Legendre polynomials can be constructed explicitly either by means of the Gram-Schmidt orthogonalization process, using the orthogonality property (8) and the normalization condition $P_n(1) = 1$ (see Problem 3 in Chapter 1), or by examining the appropriate (terminating) series solution of Legendre's differential equation (see Sec. 7.1). The first few Legendre polynomials are as follows:

$$P_0(u) = 1, \qquad\qquad P_1(u) = u,$$

$$P_2(u) = \tfrac{1}{2}(3u^2 - 1), \qquad P_3(u) = \tfrac{1}{2}(5u^3 - 3u),$$

$$P_4(u) = \tfrac{1}{8}(35u^4 - 30u^2 + 3), \qquad P_5(u) = \tfrac{1}{8}(63u^5 - 70u^3 + 15u).$$

It can be seen from the series solutions of Legendre's differential equation that each of the Legendre polynomials is either an even or an odd function; in particular, $P_n(-u) = (-1)^n P_n(u)$.

Another important property of the Legendre polynomials is expressed by the formula

$$P_n(u) = \frac{1}{2^n n!} \frac{d^n}{du^n} (u^2 - 1)^n, \tag{9}$$

by means of which these polynomials can be constructed directly. Equation (9) is known as *Rodrigues' formula.*

Let us now establish the property (9). Defining the function $y(u) \equiv (u^2 - 1)^n$, it is easy to see that $y(u)$ satisfies the first-order differential equation $(u^2 - 1)y' - 2nuy = 0$. Differentiating this equation n times with respect to u, using Leibnitz's rule, we find

$$(1 - u^2) \frac{d^{n+1} y}{du^{n+1}} + n(n+1) \frac{d^{n-1} y}{du^{n-1}} = 0.$$

The result of one further differentiation can be written in the form

$$\frac{d}{du}\left[(1 - u^2) \frac{dy^{(n)}}{du} \right] + n(n+1)y^{(n)} = 0,$$

where $y^{(n)} \equiv d^n y/du^n$. Thus the function $y^{(n)}(u)$ satisfies Legendre's differential equation of order n. Since by construction this function is a polynomial of degree n, it must be proportional to the Legendre polynomial $P_n(u)$:

$$\frac{d^n}{du^n} (u^2 - 1)^n = CP_n(u). \tag{10}$$

Thus our proof will be complete if we can show that $C = 2^n n!$ This can be done by comparing the values of both sides of (10) at $u = 1$. On the one hand, we have $P_n(1) = 1$. On the other hand,

$$\frac{d^n}{du^n} \left[(u-1)^n (u+1)^n \right]$$

$$= (u-1)^n \frac{d^n}{du^n} (u+1)^n + \ldots + (u+1)^n \frac{d^n}{du^n} (u-1)^n$$

by Leibnitz's rule, and only the last term in this expression contributes at $u = 1$, where it has the value $2^n n!$ This completes the proof of Rodrigues' formula.

Like the eigenfunctions of many other Sturm-Liouville boundary-value problems, the Legendre polynomials $P_n(u)$ form a complete set of functions (over the interval $-1 \leqslant u \leqslant 1$). This means that they can be used as a basis for expansions of a wide class of functions over this interval, and the expansion coefficients can be determined with the help of the orthogonality property (8). For this purpose, however, we also require the value of the integral

$$\int_{-1}^{1} P_n^2(u)\, du,$$

for exactly the same reasons that we required the value of the integral (5) of the preceding section in the case of Bessel functions.

If we replace each of the two factors $P_n(u)$ in this integral by its expression according to Rodrigues' formula and integrate by parts n times, noting that the term which does not involve an integral vanishes each time, we obtain

$$\int_{-1}^{1} P_n^2(u)\, du = \frac{(-1)^n}{2^{2n} (n!)^2} \int_{-1}^{1} (u^2-1)^n \frac{d^{2n}}{du^{2n}} \left[(u^2-1)^n \right] du$$

$$= \frac{(-1)^n (2n)!}{2^{2n} (n!)^2} \int_{-1}^{1} (u^2-1)^n\, du.$$

By integrating by parts in the remaining integral, it is not difficult to obtain the reduction formula

$$I_n \equiv \int_{-1}^{1} (u^2-1)^n\, du = -\frac{2n}{2n+1}\, I_{n-1} \qquad (n = 1, 2, \ldots).$$

Using the elementary result $I_0 = 2$, we find in general

$$I_n = \frac{(-1)^n\, 2^{2n+1}\, (n!)^2}{(2n+1)\,(2n)!}.$$

and hence

$$\int_{-1}^{1} P_n^2(u)\, du = \frac{2}{2n+1}.$$

Combining this result with the fact that any two distinct Legendre poly-nomials are mutually orthogonal over the interval $-1 \leqslant u \leqslant 1$, we finally obtain

$$\int_{-1}^{1} P_m(u)\, P_n(u)\, du = \frac{2}{2n+1}\, \delta_{mn}. \tag{11}$$

The orthogonality relation (11) enables us to determine the coefficients in the expansion of a given function in terms of Legendre polynomials. Thus, if a function $F(u)$ in the interval $-1 \leqslant u \leqslant 1$ is represented in the form

$$F(u) = \sum_{n=0}^{\infty} a_n P_n(u), \tag{12}$$

we can determine any particular coefficient a_m by multiplying (12) by $P_m(u)$ and integrating over the range $-1 \leqslant u \leqslant 1$, using the orthogonality property (11). This gives

$$\int_{-1}^{1} F(u)\, P_m(u)\, du = \frac{2a_m}{2m+1}.$$

In connection with boundary-value problems for partial differential equations involving the polar angle θ, as in the case of Laplace's equation in spherical coordinates, it is useful to rewrite the orthogonality property (11) in terms of the variable θ given by $u = \cos\theta$. Making this substitution, we obtain

$$\int_{0}^{\pi} P_m(\cos\theta)\, P_n(\cos\theta)\, \sin\theta\, d\theta = \frac{2}{2n+1}\, \delta_{mn}. \tag{13}$$

In other words, the various functions $P_n(\cos\theta)$ are mutually orthogonal with respect to the weight function $\sin\theta$ over the interval $0 \leqslant \theta \leqslant \pi$.

9.4 The classical orthogonal polynomials

In addition to the Legendre polynomials, we have encountered several other families of polynomials in various contexts: Laguerre polynomials, Chebyshev polynomials and Hermite polynomials. These are some of the more important special functions known collectively as the classical orthogonal polynomials, and all of them have many properties which are closely analogous to those of the Legendre polynomials studied in detail in the preceding section.

Each family of polynomials constitutes the complete set of eigenfunctions of some Sturm-Liouville boundary-value problem and therefore satisfies a certain orthogonality relation. In addition, the various types of polynomials can be generated from formulae analogous to Rodrigues' formula for the Legendre polynomials (see Example 4 of Sec. 5.4 for the case of the Laguerre polynomials).

For completeness, we summarize here the corresponding properties of the above-mentioned types of polynomials. It should be pointed out that there are no universally accepted conventions about the definitions of some of these types of polynomials. In particular, different normalizations are frequently encountered in the literature.

The *Legendre polynomials,* given by Rodrigues' formula

$$P_n(x) = \frac{1}{2^n\, n!}\ \frac{d^n}{dx^n}\ (x^2 - 1)^n,$$

satisfy the differential equation

$$(1 - x^2)y'' - 2xy' + n(n + 1)y = 0$$

and the orthogonality relation

$$\int_{-1}^{1} P_m(x)\, P_n(x)\, dx = \frac{2}{2n + 1}\ \delta_{mn} .$$

The *Laguerre polynomials* may be defined by

$$L_n(x) = \frac{e^x}{n!}\ \frac{d^n}{dx^n}\ (x^n\, e^{-x}).$$

They satisfy the differential equation

$$xy'' + (1 - x)y' + ny = 0$$

and the orthogonality relation

$$\int_{0}^{\infty} e^{-x}\, L_m(x)\, L_n(x)\, dx = \delta_{mn} .$$

The *Chebyshev polynomials* may be defined by

$$T_n(x) = \frac{(-1)^n 2^n\, n!}{(2n)!}\ (1 - x^2)^{1/2}\ \frac{d^n}{dx^n}\ \left[(1 - x^2)^{n - \frac{1}{2}}\right].$$

They satisfy the differential equation

$$(1 - x^2)y'' - xy' + n^2 y = 0$$

and the orthogonality relation

$$\int_{-1}^{1} \frac{T_m(x) T_n(x)}{\sqrt{1-x^2}} \, dx = \begin{cases} \pi, & m = n = 0, \\ \frac{1}{2} \pi \delta_{mn}, & \text{otherwise.} \end{cases}$$

The *Hermite polynomials* may be defined by

$$H_n(x) = (-1)^n \, e^{x^2} \, \frac{d^n}{dx^n} \, (e^{-x^2}).$$

They satisfy the differential equation

$$y'' - 2xy' + 2ny = 0$$

and the orthogonality relation

$$\int_{-\infty}^{\infty} e^{-x^2} H_m(x) H_n(x) \, dx = 2^n \, \pi^{1/2} \, n! \, \delta_{mn}.$$

Appendix: The gamma function and its properties

For $z > 0$, the Γ-function is defined by the integral

$$\Gamma(z) = \int_0^{\infty} e^{-x} x^{z-1} \, dx. \tag{1}$$

An integration by parts gives

$$\Gamma(z+1) = \int_0^{\infty} e^{-x} x^z \, dx = \left[-x^z \, e^{-x} \right]_0^{\infty} + z \int_0^{\infty} e^{-x} x^{z-1} \, dx$$

and hence

$$\Gamma(z+1) = z \Gamma(z). \tag{2}$$

The recurrence relation (2) can be used to define $\Gamma(z)$ for all negative non-integral values of z, for which the original integral (1) does not converge. It can also be used in practice to evaluate $\Gamma(z)$ for any real value in its domain of definition, once $\Gamma(z)$ has been determined numerically in the range $0 < z \leqslant 1$.

Since $\Gamma(1) = 1$ by direct integration of (1), repeated application of the recurrence relation (2) shows that

$$\Gamma(n+1) = n! \qquad (n = 0, 1, \dots).$$

Thus the Γ-function can be regarded as a generalization of the factorial function.

The Γ-function can also be evaluated exactly for half-integral values of its argument. Consider the integral

$$\Gamma(\tfrac{1}{2}) = \int_0^\infty e^{-x} x^{-1/2} \, dx = 2 \int_0^\infty e^{-z^2} \, dz,$$

where we have made the change of variable $x = z^2$ in the last step. In Sec. 5.2 it was shown that

$$\int_{-\infty}^\infty e^{-z^2} \, dz = \sqrt{\pi}.$$

Therefore we have

$$\Gamma(\tfrac{1}{2}) = \sqrt{\pi}.$$

By repeated application of the recurrence relation (2), we have more generally

$$\Gamma(n + \tfrac{1}{2}) = (n - \tfrac{1}{2})(n - \tfrac{3}{2}) \ldots (\tfrac{1}{2})\sqrt{\pi} \qquad (n = 1, 2, \ldots).$$

A graph of the Γ-function is given in Fig. 9.2.

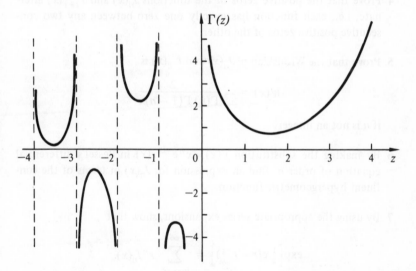

Fig. 9.2

Problems

1 Derive the power-series solution of Bessel's differential equation of order n (equation (7) of Sec. 9.1).

2 Show that the Bessel functions and their derivatives obey the following recurrence relations:

(i) $J_{n+1}(x) = (2n/x)J_n(x) - J_{n-1}(x)$;

(ii) $J_n'(x) = J_{n-1}(x) - (n/x)J_n(x)$;

(iii) $J_n'(x) = (n/x)J_n(x) - J_{n+1}(x)$.

3 Show that

(i) $\int_0^x y J_0(y)\,dy = x J_1(x)$;

(ii) $\int_0^x y^3 J_0(y)\,dy = 2x^2 J_0(x) + (x^3 - 4x)J_1(x)$.

4 Prove that the positive zeros of the functions $J_n(x)$ and $J_{n+1}(x)$ alternate, i.e., each function has exactly one zero between any two consecutive positive zeros of the other.

5 Prove that the Wronskian of $J_n(x)$ and $J_{-n}(x)$ is

$$W(x) = -\frac{2}{\Gamma(n)\,\Gamma(1-n)x}$$

if n is not an integer.

6 By making the substitution $y(x) = x^n e^{-ix} v(x)$ in Bessel's differential equation of order n, find an expression for $J_n(x)$ in terms of the confluent hypergeometric function.

7 By using the appropriate series expansions, show that

$$\exp\left[\tfrac{1}{2}x(r - r^{-1})\right] = \sum_{n=-\infty}^{\infty} r^n J_n(x).$$

(The function on the left-hand side of this identity is known as the 'generating function' for the Bessel functions $J_n(x)$.)

8 Expand the function $F(x) = x^2$, $0 < x < 1$, in terms of Bessel functions of order $n = 2$: (i) as a Fourier-Bessel series; (ii) as a Dini series.

9 Show that

$$\sum_k \frac{J_0(\lambda_k x)}{\lambda_k^3 J_1(\lambda_k)} = \tfrac{1}{8}(1 - x^2), \quad 0 < x < 1,$$

where λ_k are the positive zeros of the function $J_0(x)$.

10 The temperature $U(r, \theta, z, t)$ in a medium (in cylindrical polar coordinates) satisfies the heat equation

$$\frac{\partial^2 U}{\partial r^2} + \frac{1}{r}\frac{\partial U}{\partial r} + \frac{1}{r^2}\frac{\partial^2 U}{\partial \theta^2} + \frac{\partial^2 U}{\partial z^2} = \frac{1}{k}\frac{\partial U}{\partial t},$$

where k is a positive constant. Find the temperature $U(r, \theta, z, t)$ in the cylindrical region $0 \leqslant r \leqslant a$ when the initial temperature is $U(r, \theta, z, 0) = f(r)$, where $f(r)$ is a given function, and the surface $r = a$ is maintained at zero temperature.

11 Small-amplitude oscillations of a suspended string of length L are described by a partial differential equation of the form

$$\frac{\partial}{\partial x}\left(x\frac{\partial U}{\partial x}\right) = \frac{1}{a^2}\frac{\partial^2 U}{\partial t^2}$$

and the boundary condition $U(L, t) = 0$. Obtain a solution for arbitrary initial conditions

$$U(x, 0) = f(x), \quad \left[\frac{\partial U(x, t)}{\partial t}\right]_{t=0} = g(x) \quad (0 < x < L)$$

by first making the change of variable $x = y^2$.

12 By making the substitution $y(x) = x^{-1/2} v(x)$ in Bessel's differential equation of order $\tfrac{1}{2}$, show that this differential equation can be solved in closed form in terms of elementary functions. Show in particular that

$$J_{1/2}(x) = \sqrt{\frac{2}{\pi x}}\ \sin x, \quad J_{-1/2}(x) = \sqrt{\frac{2}{\pi x}}\ \cos x$$

and show how these results can be used to express the Bessel function of any half-integral order in terms of elementary functions.

13 By making the change of variables $y(x) = x^{1/2} v(x)$ and $t = \tfrac{2}{3} x^{3/2}$, show that the so-called Airy differential equation $y'' + xy = 0$ can be reduced to Bessel's differential equation of order $\frac{1}{3}$. Hence show that the function $y(x) = x^{1/2} J_{1/3}(\frac{2}{3}x^{3/2})$ is a solution of the Airy differential equation.

14 Show that the function $y(x) = x^2 J_2(x)$ is a solution of the differential equation $xy'' - 3y' + xy = 0$.

15 Assuming that the function

$$F(x) = \begin{cases} -1, & -1 < x < 0, \\ 1, & 0 < x < 1 \end{cases}$$

can be represented by an expansion in Legendre polynomials, determine the first two non-vanishing terms in this expansion.

16 If a function $f(x)$ is represented by an expansion in Chebyshev polynomials of the form

$$f(x) = \sum_{n=0}^{\infty} a_n T_n(x)$$

in the range $-1 \leqslant x \leqslant 1$, find an expression for the first coefficient a_0.

17 A function $U(r, \theta, \phi)$ (in spherical coordinates) satisfies Laplace's equation inside the sphere $r < R$ and the boundary condition

$$\left[\frac{\partial U(r, \theta, \phi)}{\partial r} \right]_{r=R} = -k\left[U(R, \theta, \phi) - f(\theta) \right]$$

on the surface, where k is a constant and

$$f(\theta) = \begin{cases} \cos\theta, & 0 \leqslant \theta \leqslant \frac{1}{2}\pi, \\ 0, & \frac{1}{2}\pi \leqslant \theta \leqslant \pi. \end{cases}$$

Obtain the function $U(r, \theta, \phi)$ in the form

$$U(r, \theta, \phi) = \sum_{n=0}^{\infty} a_n (r/R)^n P_n(\cos\theta) \qquad (r \leqslant R)$$

and find the numerical values of the first three coefficients a_0, a_1 and a_2.

Bibliography

1 G. Arfken, *Mathematical Methods for Physicists*, 2nd ed., Academic Press, New York, 1970.

2 J.C. Burkhill, *The Theory of Ordinary Differential Equations*, Oliver & Boyd, Edinburgh, 1962.

3 J.C. Clegg, *Calculus of Variations*, Oliver & Boyd, Edinburgh, 1968.

4 J.T. Cushing, *Applied Analytical Mathematics for Physical Scientists*, Wiley, New York, 1975.

5 P. Dennery and A. Krzywicki, *Mathematics for Physicists*, Harper & Row, New York, 1967.

6 J.W. Dettman, *Mathematical Methods in Physics and Engineering*, 2nd ed., McGraw-Hill, New York, 1962.

7 J.W. Dettman, *Introduction to Linear Algebra and Differential Equations*, McGraw-Hill, New York, 1974.

8 D.L. Kreider, R.G. Kuller, D.R. Ostberg and F.W. Perkins, *An Introduction to Linear Analysis*, Addison-Wesley, Reading, Mass., 1966.

9 G.F. Simmons, *Differential Equations with Applications and Historical Notes*, McGraw-Hill, New York, 1972.

Answers to the problems

Chapter 1

3 $P_0(x) = 1$, $P_1(x) = x$, $P_2(x) = \frac{1}{2}(3x^2 - 1)$, $P_3(x) = \frac{1}{2}(5x^3 - 3x)$.

4 $b = -1, c = 2$. $\lambda = 1 : (1\ 1\ 1)^T$; $\lambda = 2 : (1\ 0\ -1)^T$;
$\lambda = 4 : (1\ -2\ 1)^T$.

5 (a) $\lambda = 1,\ 3$,

$$R = \begin{pmatrix} 1/\sqrt{2} & 1/\sqrt{2} \\ -1/\sqrt{2} & 1/\sqrt{2} \end{pmatrix}.$$

The normalized eigenvectors form the columns of R. $f(x, y) = \bar{x}^2 + 3\bar{y}^2$, where $\bar{x} = (x - y)/\sqrt{2}, \bar{y} = (x + y)/\sqrt{2}$. The curve is an ellipse.

(b) $\lambda = 3,\ 6,\ -9$,

$$R = \begin{pmatrix} -\frac{2}{3} & \frac{2}{3} & \frac{1}{3} \\ \frac{2}{3} & \frac{1}{3} & \frac{2}{3} \\ \frac{1}{3} & \frac{2}{3} & -\frac{2}{3} \end{pmatrix}.$$

$g(x, y, z) = 3\bar{x}^2 + 6\bar{y}^2 - 9\bar{z}^2$, where $\bar{x} = \frac{1}{3}(-2x + 2y + z)$,
$\bar{y} = \frac{1}{3}(2x + y + 2z)$, $\bar{z} = \frac{1}{3}(x + 2y - 2z)$. The surface is a hyperboloid of one sheet.

(c) $\lambda = -1,\ -1,\ 2$,

$$R = \begin{pmatrix} 1/\sqrt{2} & 1/\sqrt{6} & 1/\sqrt{3} \\ 0 & -2/\sqrt{6} & 1/\sqrt{3} \\ -1/\sqrt{2} & 1/\sqrt{6} & 1/\sqrt{3} \end{pmatrix}.$$

Other distinct solutions are possible, since $\lambda = -1$ is a double eigenvalue. For this solution, $h(x, y, z) = -\bar{x}^2 - \bar{y}^2 + 2\bar{z}^2$, where $\bar{x} = (x - z)/\sqrt{2}, \bar{y} = (x - 2y + z)/\sqrt{6}, \bar{z} = (x + y + z)/\sqrt{3}$. The surface is a hyperboloid of two sheets.

7 (i) Not definite. (ii) Positive definite.

14 The principal axes are along the lines $y = x$ (length $\frac{1}{4}\sqrt{8}$) and $y = -x$ (length $\sqrt{2}$).

Chapter 2

3 Saddle point at $(0, 0)$, relative minimum at $(2, -4)$.

4 18, 45.

6 Relative minima at $(\pm\frac{1}{2}\sqrt{2}, \pm\frac{1}{2}\sqrt{2}, 0)$, relative maxima at $(\pm\frac{1}{2}\sqrt{2}, \mp\frac{1}{2}\sqrt{2}, 0)$, and stationary points at $(0, 0, \pm1)$ which are neither minima nor maxima.

7 $2 \pm \frac{1}{3}\sqrt{3}$.

9 $(\frac{1}{3}, \frac{2}{3}, 0)$, $(1, 0, 0)$.

11 $\frac{1}{3}\sqrt{21}$.

12 $(1/7, 2/7, 3/7)$.

13 $d_{min} = \sqrt{2} - 1$, $d_{max} = \sqrt{20/3}$.

Chapter 3

1 $y = Ax^{1-n} + B$ if $n \neq 1$, $y = A \log |x| + B$ if $n = 1$. Conditions: $x < 1$ or $A = 0$.

2 $(x + b)^2 + (y/a)^2 = (c/a^2)^2$.

3 $y = a(\sin kx)/(\sin k)$.

4 There is an infinite family of extremals $y = \pm(a/n\pi)\sin(n\pi x/a)$ $(n = 1, 2, \ldots)$, giving an integral $I = \pm(a^2/2n\pi)$. The extreme values are $\pm\frac{1}{2}a^2/\pi$.

5 $y = C \sin x$, where $C = (2 - X)^{1/3}/(\sin X)$, and the value $X \approx 1.83$ must be obtained numerically by solving a transcendental equation.

6 $(x + a)^2 + y^2 = b^2$.

7 Extremals are hyperbolas $(x + b)^2 - y^2 + c = 0$ $(c \neq 0)$ and the lines $y = 0$ and $y' = \pm1$. Corners can occur only on the x-axis, on extremals consisting of line segments on which $y = 0$ or $y' = \pm1$.

8 $y = \pm\sin n\pi x$ $(n = 1, 2, \ldots)$.

10 Extremal is $\sqrt{L/\pi} \sin \theta$, which is a circle with centre at $(x, y) = (0, \frac{1}{2}\sqrt{L/\pi})$. Corners cannot occur.

11 $y = \frac{1}{2}(x^2 + 1)$, $I_{min} = \frac{2}{3}\sqrt{2}$.

12 $y = \frac{1}{2}(x^2 - 3x + 1)$.

Chapter 4

1 (i) $\dfrac{4}{\pi} \displaystyle\sum_{k=0}^{\infty} \dfrac{\sin[(2k + 1)x]}{2k + 1}$.   (ii) $\dfrac{1}{2}\pi - \dfrac{4}{\pi} \displaystyle\sum_{k=0}^{\infty} \dfrac{\cos[(2k + 1)x]}{(2k + 1)^2}$.

(iii) $\dfrac{1}{\pi} + \dfrac{1}{2} \sin x - \dfrac{2}{\pi} \displaystyle\sum_{k=1}^{\infty} \dfrac{\cos 2kx}{4k^2 - 1}$.

2 $\dfrac{2}{\pi} \displaystyle\sum_{n=1}^{\infty} \dfrac{n[1 - (-1)^n e^\pi] \sin nx}{n^2 + 1}$.

The series represents $-e^{-x}$ for $-\pi < x < 0$ and $-e^{-(x - 2\pi)}$ for $\pi < x < 2\pi$.

3 $\dfrac{\sinh \pi}{\pi} \left[1 + 2 \displaystyle\sum_{n=1}^{\infty} \dfrac{(-1)^n (\cos nx - n \sin nx)}{n^2 + 1} \right]$.

4 $1 + \dfrac{3}{\pi} \displaystyle\sum_{n} \dfrac{\sin (2\pi nx/3)}{n}$,

where the summation is over all positive integers n not divisible by 3.

5 $\dfrac{\sin \lambda\pi}{\pi} \left[\dfrac{1}{\lambda} - 2\lambda \displaystyle\sum_{n=1}^{\infty} \dfrac{(-1)^n \cos nx}{n^2 - \lambda^2} \right]$;

(a) $\dfrac{1}{2\lambda} \left[\dfrac{1}{\lambda} - \pi \cot \lambda\pi \right]$;   (b) $\dfrac{1}{2\lambda} \left[\dfrac{1}{\lambda} - \pi \csc \lambda\pi \right]$.

7 (i) $a_n = 0$ for odd n, and $b_n = 0$ for all n.

(ii) $a_n = 0$ for even n, and $b_n = 0$ for all n.

8 $U(x, y) = \displaystyle\sum_{m=0}^{\infty} b_m \sin \left[\dfrac{(2m + 1)\pi x}{a} \right] \sinh \left[\dfrac{(2m + 1)\pi y}{a} \right]$,

where $b_m = \dfrac{4U_0 \cos [(2m + 1)\pi/3]}{(2m + 1) \pi \sinh [(2m + 1)\pi]}$.

9 $U(x, t) = \displaystyle\sum_{n=0}^{\infty} a_n \cos \frac{n\pi x}{L} \exp[-(n\pi a/L)^2 t],$

where $a_0 = \dfrac{1}{L} \displaystyle\int_0^L H(x)\, dx,\quad a_n = \dfrac{2}{L} \displaystyle\int_0^L H(x) \cos \frac{n\pi x}{L}\, dx \quad (n \neq 0).$

10 $U(x, t) = \frac{3}{4} \sin \pi x \cos [(\pi^2 - 1)^{1/2} t] - \frac{1}{4} \sin 3\pi x \cos [(9\pi^2 - 1)^{1/2} t].$

11 $U(r, \theta) = \displaystyle\sum_{n=0}^{\infty} r^{\pm n}(a_n \cos n\theta + b_n \sin n\theta)$ (with the upper and lower

signs for cases (i) and (ii), respectively), where $a_0 = \frac{1}{4} C$, and $a_n = 0$ if n is even $(n \neq 0)$, $a_n = (C/\pi n)(-1)^{(n-1)/2}$ if n is odd; $b_n = -(C/\pi n)$ $[(-1)^{n/2} - 1]$ if n is even, $b_n = C/\pi n$ if n is odd.

12 $U(r, \theta) = \dfrac{2C\alpha}{\pi} \displaystyle\sum_{n=1}^{\infty} \dfrac{(-1)^{n+1}\left(\dfrac{r}{R}\right)^{n\pi/\alpha} \sin \dfrac{n\pi\theta}{\alpha}}{n}.$

13 $U(x, t) = \dfrac{2}{\pi} - \dfrac{4}{\pi} \displaystyle\sum_{m=1}^{\infty} \dfrac{\cos \dfrac{2m\pi x}{L} \cos \dfrac{2m\pi at}{L}}{4m^2 - 1}.$

14 $\dfrac{2}{\pi} - \dfrac{4}{\pi} \displaystyle\sum_{m=1}^{\infty} \dfrac{\cos 2mx}{4m^2 - 1}\ ;\quad S = \frac{1}{8}\pi.$

15 $U(x, t) = \dfrac{4U_0}{\pi} \displaystyle\sum_{m=0}^{\infty} (2m + 1)^{-1} \exp\{-[k(2m + 1)^2 \pi^2/L^2 + c]\, t\}$

$\sin[(2m + 1)\pi x/L].$

16 $U(r, \theta) = \dfrac{2U_0}{\pi} + \dfrac{4U_0}{\pi} \displaystyle\sum_{m=1}^{\infty} \dfrac{(r/R)^{2m} \cos 2m\theta}{1 - 4m^2}.$

Chapter 5

1 $\widetilde{F}(\omega) = \dfrac{1}{\sqrt{2\pi}}\left(\dfrac{e^{i\omega a} - 1}{i\omega}\right),\quad \widetilde{F}_c(\omega) = \dfrac{1}{\omega}\sqrt{\dfrac{2}{\pi}} \sin \omega a,$

$\widetilde{F}_s(\omega) = \dfrac{1}{\omega}\sqrt{\dfrac{2}{\pi}} (1 - \cos \omega a).$

The integral has the value $\frac{1}{2}\pi$ if $|b| < a$, $\frac{1}{4}\pi$ if $|b| = a$, and 0 if $|b| > a$.

2 $U(x, y) = \dfrac{2}{\pi} \displaystyle\int_0^\infty d\lambda\, e^{-\lambda y} \sin \lambda x \int_0^\infty dx'\, f(x') \sin \lambda x'$.

3 $U(x, y) = \dfrac{1}{\pi} \displaystyle\int_0^\infty d\lambda\, e^{-\lambda y} \int_{-\infty}^\infty dx'\, f(x') \cos[\lambda(x - x')]$.

4 $U(x, y) = \dfrac{2}{\pi} \displaystyle\int_0^\infty d\lambda\, \dfrac{\sin \lambda x\, \sinh \lambda y}{\sinh \lambda a} \int_0^\infty dx'\, f(x') \sin \lambda x'$.

5 $\frac{1}{3}\{e^t - e^{-t/2}[\cos(\frac{1}{2}\sqrt{3}t) + \sqrt{3}\sin(\frac{1}{2}\sqrt{3}t)]\}$.

6 (i) $x(t) = e^{-t} \cos t$. (ii) $x(t) = \frac{1}{3}e^{2t} + \frac{7}{6}e^{-t} - \frac{1}{2}e^t$.

(iii) $x(t) = \frac{1}{5}(11 \sin t - 2 \cos t + e^{-t} \sin t + 2e^{-t} \cos t)$.

(iv) $x(t) = 1 - e^{-t}(\frac{1}{2}t^2 + t + 1)$. (v) $x(t) = \frac{1}{4}(3e^{-2t} - 4e^{-t} + 1)$.

(vi) $x(t) = \frac{1}{4}[e^t(2t + 1) - 4e^{2t}(t + 1) + 3e^{3t}]$.

7 $x(t) = 5e^{-t} + 3e^{4t}, y(t) = 5e^{-t} - 2e^{4t}$.

8 $x(t) = \frac{1}{2}(6 \sin t - \cos t - t \cos t + e^t)$,

$y(t) = \frac{1}{2}(\sin t + 5 \cos t + t \sin t - e^{-t})$.

9 $x(t) = e^t \sin 3t + 1, y(t) = \frac{1}{2}[e^t(3 \cos 3t - 5 \sin 3t) - 11]$.

11 (i) $x(t) = 1 + \sin t - \cos t$. (ii) $x(t) = \frac{1}{6}(7e^{-t} + 2e^{2t} - 3e^t)$.

12 (i) $G(t) = \frac{1}{2}(e^t - e^{-t})$, $x(t) = \displaystyle\int_0^t h(t')G(t - t')dt'$.

(ii) $x(t) = \frac{1}{5}[e^{-t}(2 \cos t - \sin t - 5) + 8e^t]$.

13 $2s(s^2 + 1)^{-1}(s + 1)^{-3}$.

14 (i) $\cot^{-1}(s/a)$. (ii) $2a^2 s/(s^4 + 4a^4)$. (iii) $\log[s/(s + 1)]$.

15 (i) $e^{-t}(\sin t)/t$. (ii) $(2a^3)^{-1}(\sinh at - \sin at)$.

19 $U(x, y) = x(1 - e^{-y})$.

20 (i) $y(x) = \frac{1}{2}(e^x - e^{-x})$. (ii) $y(x) = \cos x$.

Chapter 6

1 (i) $x(t) = e^t + t + 1$. (ii) $x(t) = 1/(1 - t)$ $(|t| < 1)$.

2 $x(t) = \cos t, y(t) = \sin t$.

3 (i) $P(t) = [u_2(t)u_1''(t) - u_1(t)u_2''(t)]/W(t)$ and

$\qquad Q(t) = [u_1'(t)u_2''(t) - u_2'(t)u_1''(t)]/W(t)$,

$\qquad$ where $W(t) = u_1(t)u_2'(t) - u_2(t)u_1'(t)$.

$\quad$ (ii) $t^2(1 - \log t)x''(t) + tx'(t) - x(t) = 0$.

4 (i) $x(t) = a \sin t + b \cos t + t \sin t + \cos t \log|\cos t|$.

$\quad$ (ii) $x(t) = \frac{1}{4}e^{-t/2}(a + bt - t \sin t - 2 \cos t)$.

5 $x(t) = t^{-1/2} \cos t$.

6 (i) $x_p(t) = \frac{1}{2}t^3 \log t - \frac{3}{4}t^3$.

$\quad$ (ii) $x_p(t) = \tan t \log|\sin t| - \frac{1}{2}t^2 \tan t - t$.

7 $x(t) = a \cos t + b \tan t + \frac{1}{2} \sec t$.

8 $x(t) = ae^{t^2} + b + \frac{1}{8}e^{t^2}(t^4 - 2t^2 + 2)$.

10 (i) $x(t) = c_1 e^{-t} + \frac{2}{3}c_2 e^{4t}$, $y(t) = -c_1 e^{-t} + c_2 e^{4t}$.

$\quad$ (ii) $x(t) = e^t[a \cos 3t + b \sin 3t]$,

$\qquad y(t) = \frac{1}{2}e^t[(3b - 5a) \cos 3t - (3a + 5b) \sin 3t]$.

11 $x(t) = ae^t + e^{-t/2}[b \cos(\frac{1}{2}\sqrt{3}t) + c \sin(\frac{1}{2}\sqrt{3}t)]$,

$\qquad y(t) = ae^t + \frac{1}{2}e^{-t/2}[(-b + \sqrt{3}c)\cos(\frac{1}{2}\sqrt{3}t) + (-\sqrt{3}b - c)\sin(\frac{1}{2}\sqrt{3}t)]$,

$\qquad z(t) = ae^t + \frac{1}{2}e^{-t/2}[(-b - \sqrt{3}c)\cos(\frac{1}{2}\sqrt{3}t) + (\sqrt{3}b - c)\sin(\frac{1}{2}\sqrt{3}t)]$.

12 $x(t) = a_1 \sin(\sqrt{2}t + \phi_1)$, $y(t) = a_1 \sin(\sqrt{2}t + \phi_1)$; and

$\qquad x(t) = a_2 \sin(\sqrt{6}t + \phi_2)$, $y(t) = -a_2 \sin(\sqrt{6}t + \phi_2)$.

13 $u(t) = t^{1/2}$, $R(t) = \frac{1}{4}t^{-2}$.

14 (i) $u(t) = t^{-1/2}$, $R(t) = (t^2 - n^2 + \frac{1}{4})/t^2$.

Chapter 7

1 (i) $x(t) = a\left[1 + \sum_{n=1}^{\infty} \frac{(3n - 2)(3n - 5) \dots (1)}{(3n)!} t^{3n}\right] +$

$\qquad b\left[t + \sum_{n=1}^{\infty} \frac{(3n - 1)(3n - 4) \dots (2)}{(3n + 1)!} t^{3n+1}\right]$.

$\quad$ (ii) $x(t) = at^2 + bt^5$.

(iii) $x(t) = a\left\{t + \sum_{n=1}^{\infty} [(7)(10)\ldots(3n+4)n!]^{-1}t^{n+1}\right\} +$

$bt^{-1/3}\left\{1 + \sum_{n=1}^{\infty} [(-1)(2)\ldots(3n-4)n!]^{-1}t^{n}\right\}.$

2 (i) $x(t) = a\sum_{n=0}^{\infty} [n!2^{n}]^{-1}t^{2n} + b\sum_{n=0}^{\infty} [(1)(3)\ldots(2n+1)]^{-1}t^{2n+1}.$

(ii) $x(t) = a(t + t^{3}) + b\sum_{n=0}^{\infty} (-1)^{n}[(2n-1)(2n-3)]^{-1}t^{2n}.$

3 $m = 0, \pm2, \pm4, \ldots;\ x(t) = a\sum_{n=0}^{\infty} \frac{2n-1}{(2n)!}t^{2n} + b\sum_{n=1}^{\infty} \frac{n}{(2n+1)!}t^{2n+1}.$

4 (i) $x(t) = at + b\left[t\log t + \sum_{n=1}^{\infty} (-1)^{n}(nn!)^{-1}t^{n+1}\right].$

(ii) $x(t) = (a + b\log t)\sum_{n=0}^{\infty} \frac{(-1)^{n}}{n!}t^{n+1} + b(-1 + t^{2} - \tfrac{3}{4}t^{3} + \ldots).$

(iii) $x(t) = (a + b\log t)(1 - 3t + \tfrac{3}{2}t^{2} - \tfrac{1}{6}t^{3}) +$

$b\left[7t - \tfrac{23}{4}t^{2} + \tfrac{11}{12}t^{3} - 6\sum_{n=4}^{\infty} \frac{(n-4)!}{(n!)^{2}}t^{n}\right].$

(iv) $x(t) = (a + b\log t)\sum_{n=0}^{\infty} (n!)^{-2}t^{n} - b(2t + \tfrac{3}{4}t^{2} + \tfrac{11}{108}t^{3} + \ldots).$

5 (i) $x(t) = a\left[1 + \sum_{n=1}^{\infty} \frac{(-1)^{n}2^{n}\lambda(\lambda-2)\ldots(\lambda-2n+2)}{(2n)!}t^{2n}\right] +$

$b\left[t + \sum_{n=1}^{\infty} \frac{(-1)^{n}2^{n}(\lambda-1)\ldots(\lambda-2n+1)}{(2n+1)!}t^{2n+1}\right].$

(iii) $H_{0}(t) = 1, H_{1}(t) = 2t, H_{2}(t) = 4t^{2} - 2, H_{3}(t) = 8t^{3} - 12t.$

6 $L_{0}(t) = 1, L_{1}(t) = 1 - t, L_{2}(t) = 2 - 4t + t^{2}.$

8 $\lambda = n^2$, where n is any non-negative integer.

10 $x(t) = a \cos(1/t) + b \sin(1/t)$.

11 (i) $x(t) = at + b \sum\limits_{n=0}^{\infty} (2n-1)^{-1} t^{2n}$.

(ii) $x(t) = at + c \sum\limits_{n=1}^{\infty} (2n+1)^{-1} t^{-2n}$.

13 (i) $y(x) = aF(\frac{1}{2}, 1; \frac{1}{2}; -x) + b(-x)^{1/2} F(1, 3/2; 3/2; -x)$.

(ii) $y(x) = aF(2, 2; \frac{1}{2}; \frac{1}{2}(x+1)) + b[\frac{1}{2}(x+1)]^{1/2} F(5/2, 5/2; 3/2; \frac{1}{2}(x+1))$.

14 $y(x) = F(1, 1; 14/5; (3-x)/5)$.

Chapter 8

1 (i) $\lambda_n = n^2$, $u_n(x) = \cos nx$ $(n = 0, 1, \ldots)$,

$$\int_0^{\pi} u_m(x) u_n(x) \, dx = 0 \ (m \neq n).$$

(ii) $\lambda_n = n^2 - 2$, $u_n(x) = \sin nx$ $(n = 1, 2, \ldots)$, same orthogonality relation as in (i).

(iii) $\lambda_n = -n^2$, $u_n(x) = e^{-x} \sin nx$ $(n = 1, 2, \ldots)$,

$$\int_0^{\pi} e^{2x} u_m(x) u_n(x) \, dx = 0 \ (m \neq n).$$

(iv) $\lambda_n = -n^2$, $u_n(x) = e^{-x}(\sin nx + n \cos nx)(n = 1, 2, \ldots)$, and $\lambda_0 = 1$, $u_0(x) = 1$, same orthogonality relation as in (iii).

2 (i) $\dfrac{d}{dx}\left[(1-x^2)^2 \dfrac{dy}{dx}\right] + (n^2 + n - 2)(1-x^2)y = 0$.

(ii) $\int_{-1}^{1} (1-x^2) P'_m(x) P'_n(x) \, dx = 0 \ (m \neq n)$.

3 $\int_{-\infty}^{\infty} e^{-x^2} H_m(x) H_n(x) \, dx = 0 \ (m \neq n)$.

4 $\int_{-1}^{1} (1-x^2)^{-1/2} T_m(x) T_n(x) \, dx = 0 \ (m \neq n)$.

5 $\int_{-1}^{1} (1-x^2)^{1/2} C_m(x) C_n(x)\, dx = 0 \quad (m \neq n)$.

6 (i) $G(x;x') = \begin{cases} x(x'-1), & 0 < x < x', \\ x'(x-1), & x' < x < 1. \end{cases}$

(ii) $G(x;x') = \begin{cases} -x, & 0 < x < x', \\ -x', & x' < x < 1. \end{cases}$

7 (i) $y(x) = x(x^3 - 1)/12$. (ii) $y(x) = x\cos 1 - \sin x$.

8 $G(x;x') = \begin{cases} \frac{1}{3}(x+1)(x'-2), & 0 < x < x', \\ \frac{1}{3}(x'+1)(x-2), & x' < x < 1. \end{cases}$

9 (i) $G(x;x') = -\dfrac{2}{\pi^2} \displaystyle\sum_{n=1}^{\infty} \dfrac{\sin(n\pi x)\sin(n\pi x')}{n^2}$.

(ii) $G(x;x') = -\dfrac{2}{\pi^2} \displaystyle\sum_{n=0}^{\infty} \dfrac{\sin[(n+\frac{1}{2})\pi x]\sin[(n+\frac{1}{2})\pi x']}{(n+\frac{1}{2})^2}$.

11 λ_n are the positive roots of the equation $\tan \lambda L + 2\lambda = 0$;
$u_n(x) = \sin \lambda_n x$, $\int_0^L u_m(x)u_n(x)\,dx = 0 \quad (m \neq n)$.

Chapter 9

6 $J_n(x) = [\Gamma(n+1)]^{-1}(\frac{1}{2}x)^n e^{-ix} F(n+\frac{1}{2};\ 2n+1;\ 2ix)$.

8 (i) $x^2 = 2 \displaystyle\sum_k \dfrac{J_2(\lambda_k x)}{\lambda_k J_3(\lambda_k)} \quad (0 < x < 1)$,

where λ_k are the positive zeros of $J_2(x)$.

(ii) $x^2 = 2 \displaystyle\sum_k \dfrac{\mu_k J_3(\mu_k) J_2(\mu_k x)}{(\mu_k^2 - 4)J_2^2(\mu_k)} \quad (0 < x < 1)$,

where μ_k are the positive zeros of $J_2'(x)$.

10 $U(r,t) = \displaystyle\sum_k a_k J_0(\lambda_k r)\exp(-k\lambda_k^2 t)$,

where λ_k are the positive roots of the equation $J_0(\lambda a) = 0$ and

$a_k = \dfrac{2}{a^2 J_1^2(\lambda_k a)} \displaystyle\int_0^a r f(r) J_0(\lambda_k r)\,dr$.

11 $U(x, t) = \displaystyle\sum_k [A_k \cos(\tfrac{1}{2}a\,\lambda_k t) + B_k \sin(\tfrac{1}{2}a\,\lambda_k t)] J_0(\lambda_k \sqrt{x}),$

where λ_k are the positive roots of the equation $J_0(\lambda\sqrt{L}) = 0$,

$$A_k = \frac{1}{LJ_1^2(\lambda_k\sqrt{L})} \int_0^L f(x)J_0(\lambda_k\sqrt{x})\,dx,$$

$$B_k = \frac{2}{a\lambda_k LJ_1^2(\lambda_k\sqrt{L})} \int_0^L g(x)J_0(\lambda_k\sqrt{x})\,dx.$$

15 $F(x) = \tfrac{3}{2}P_1(x) - \tfrac{7}{8}P_3(x) + \ldots\,.$

16 $a_0 = \dfrac{1}{\pi}\displaystyle\int_{-1}^{1} \dfrac{f(x)\,dx}{\sqrt{1-x^2}}\;.$

17 $a_0 = \tfrac{1}{4},\; a_1 = \tfrac{1}{2}kR/(kR+1),\; a_2 = \tfrac{5}{16}kR(kR+2).$

Index